A HISTORY OF ANALYTICAL CHEMISTRY

Editors

Herbert A. Laitinen
Galen W. Ewing

Published by
The Division of Analytical Chemistry of the
American Chemical Society

1977

NOTICE

The original contributions to this History, complete
with bibliographical documentation as supplied by the
authors, have been recorded on microfiche cards.
Copies are available at cost through the Secretary of
the Division of Analytical Chemistry, ACS.

Copyright © 1977 by
The Division of Analytical Chemistry
of the American Chemical Society

Printed in the United States of America
by The Maple Press Company, York, Pa.

TABLE OF CONTENTS

PREFACE

In 1975 the American Chemical Society launched a
project to prepare a history of the Society and of the
various branches of chemistry, to be published in its
centennial year, 1976. The executive committee of the
Division of Analytical Chemistry decided that in addition to providing information for the ACS volume "A Century of Chemistry," it would undertake a centennial history project of its own.

There is no shortage of historical treatments of
chemistry, but the analytical aspects are at best buried
within more general treatments and at worst are omitted
entirely. In the fourth volume of Partington's monumental "History of Chemistry," covering the 19th and
20th centuries, no section is explicitly devoted to analytical chemistry. Only five entries to analysis appear
in the index, the longest being to a five-page account
of organic analysis.

The outstanding historical work in the analytical
field is the "History of Analytical Chemistry," by
Ferenc Szabadváry (Pergamon Press, 1966). This excellent work is largely devoted to classical methods, with
only one chapter of 15 pages on "Electrometric Analysis"
and another of 12 pages on "Other Methods of Analysis"
in a book of 401 pages.

Modern analytical chemistry is so diverse in its
activities and in its origins that very few, if any,
can profess to be expert in all of its current branches,
let alone its historical background. It was therefore
decided to call upon a wide variety of sources to
assemble the first draft material and to use a two-step
editorial process to integrate it into the final version.

Four major sections were identified to deal with
the chemical, spectrochemical, electrochemical, and

separations aspects of analysis. A fifth section, on
instrumentation, was later prepared, incorporating portions of these, supplemented by additional material.
Each section was handled by a topical editor, and the
final integration was achieved by the two co-editors.
Individual contributors are acknowledged by topic rather
than by distinct pages because in the process of eliminating gaps and overlaps the editors were obliged to
omit and to rearrange many sections of the original contributions. The original papers, which contain many
bibliographical references omitted from the final text,
have been placed in microfilm storage and are available
for purchase at a modest cost through the American Chemical Society.

For brevity we have chosen to de-emphasize those
aspects of early work that have been repeatedly covered
in general histories of chemistry. The topical editors
were instructed to stress the American scene but to
follow early developments to their origins, wherever
they may have occurred. In the subject areas the treatment varies considerably, not only because of inherent
differences in the historical development but also
because some contributors chose to adhere more closely
than others to the American viewpoint.

One of the difficulties inherent in historical
research, at least as undertaken by amateurs with
limited time and budget, is exemplified by the following
comment. This was written by Professor R. A. Osteryoung
of Colorado State University, who served as topical
editor for electroanalytical chemistry, but its implications extend to all areas:

It will not be possible to be complete or
completely accurate; information has been sought
from those with the most knowledge in a given
area, and from some original sources, but it
has proved impossible to check everything. An
example of the problem--albeit a personal one--
may put things in perspective. Even as a non-
historian attempting to put together material
that would represent historical developments,
it was realized that original records would
help. For instance, in trying to trace the
development of methods and schools, a genealogy
appeared to be a reasonable approach. I wrote
to Princeton University asking if they could
supply a list of students who had received
their Ph.D.s with the late Professor N. Howell
Furman. A reply was received which stated,
"Attached please find a list of Dr. Furman's
Ph.D. students. We checked his publication
list for names and then checked them out in the

Princeton University Alumni Directory (1974).
I think this will be quite accurate." A number
of distinguished names were included on that
list, but one name, that of Professor C. N.
Reilley of the University of North Carolina,
did not appear, and yet I was certain that he
had received his degree with Professor Furman.
The list also noted that Professor L. B. Rogers,
now at the University of Georgia but formerly
at Purdue and MIT, had received his Ph.D. with
Furman in 1942. This did not surprise me. However, a letter from Rogers did. It contained
the following material: "When I visited Purdue
last Monday for a final oral exam for one of my
students, Harry Pardue commented about the fact
that I had worked for Furman at Princeton. In
case you happen to believe that also, I can set
the record straight by stating that I worked for
Earl R. Caley, who later went to Ohio State University." This incident is included simply to
indicate the problem involved in an explicit
view of who did what and where and when.

Professor Osteryoung chose to present the material
of the electrochemistry chapter in the form of extensive
quotations from the many contributors, tied together
with his own comments. The spectrochemistry chapter,
assembled by Professor J. D. Winefordner of the University of Florida, consists of a series of presenta-
tions from his contributors, some of which have been
integrated for the sake of logical presentation without
undue duplication. A similar format was adopted by
Professor Bruno Jaselskis of Loyola University (Chicago)
for the chapter on non-instrumental methods and by Dr.
Donald Macnaughtan of Mobay Chemical Corp. for separations. The material on instrumentation was prepared by
the editors.

The individuals invited to contribute were selected
by the topical editors from contemporary practitioners
in the various specialties. Some writers reflected a
strongly European flavor, whereas others adopted a
purely American viewpoint. To complicate matters, the
development of a particular field did not follow a single path, even if a specific origin could be identified.
Especially during times of war, normal channels of scientific communication were interrupted, and important
developments followed parallel paths in different countries.

Rather than attempting to fill all of the gaps that
could be recognized, the editors have chosen to compromise, in the interests of economy of length and of
effort, permitting some omissions of foreign discoveries

and some differences in approach in the various sections. We hope that we may stimulate historians at home and abroad to explore this complex subject more fully.

Finally, it is hoped that this volume will not only provide historical perspective to students and practitioners of analytical chemistry but will also dramatize the wide scope of the modern day science of chemical characterization and measurement.

CONTRIBUTORS

Ralph N. Adams	Solid-electrode voltammetry
Herbert K. Alber	Microanalysis
Roger G. Bates	Potentiometry
L. S. Birks	X-ray analysis
David F. Boltz*	Molecular spectroscopy
Edward G. Brame, Jr.	Nuclear quadrupole resonance
Clark E. Bricker	Electroanalytical chemistry
Stanley Bruckenstein	Ring-disk electrode
Maurice M. Bursey	Mass spectroscopy
Earle R. Caley	Gravimetric analysis
Donald G. Davis	Chronopotentiometry
Paul Delahay	Electroanalytical chemistry
Louis J. DeHayes	Nuclear magnetic resonance
James R. DeVoe	Radiochemical analysis
Philip J. Elving	Polarography
Leslie S. Ettre	Gas chromatography
Jud B. Flato	Electroanalytical instrumentation
James S. Fritz	Nonaqueous titrimetry
Ivo Hais	Paper chromatography
Albert W. Herlinger	Chelometric and complexometric methods
Gary M. Hieftje	Signal processing
James A. Howell	Molecular spectroscopy
E. G. Janzen	Electron spin resonance
Joseph Jordan	Thermometric titration and enthalpimetric analysis
Justus G. Kirchner	Thin-layer chromatography
S. Roy Koirtyohann	Atomic spectroscopy
Bruce R. Kowalski	Pattern recognition techniques
Hradec Kralove	Paper chromatography
Peter F. Lott	Molecular spectroscopy
Victor G. Mossotti	Instrumentation
Alfred O. C. Nier	Mass spectroscopy
Harry L. Pardue	Kinetic analysis
Karl H. Pearson	Molecular spectroscopy
E. E. Pickett	Atomic spectroscopy

*Deceased

Arthur Rose	Distillation analysis
Elizabeth G. Rose	Distillation analysis
Donald T. Sawyer	Nuclear magnetic resonance
Alfred A. Schilt	Dissolution of samples, and redox indicators
Joseph A. Sherma	Liquid chromatography
Sidney Siggia	Functional group analysis
A. Lee Smith	Molecular spectroscopy
Barton S. Solomon	Solvent extraction
Vernon A. Stenger	Titrimetric analysis
John T. Stock	Polarography and amperometry
Richard D. Strickland	Electrophoresis
William E. Swartz, Jr.	Photoelectron spectroscopy
Ernest H. Swift	Coulometry
Paul J. Taylor	High performance liquid chromatography
Harold F. Walton	Ion exchange
W. W. Wendlandt	Thermal methods
Gary Wheeler	Molecular spectroscopy

ACKNOWLEDGEMENTS

In addition to our great indebtedness to the topical editors and contributors, we wish to acknowledge the able assistance of the following individuals: Eleanor Crisp, who prepared the final typescript; Roland F. Hirsch, who critically reviewed portions of manuscript; Josephine Petruzzi, who provided a logistical clearinghouse and located many of the portraits; Mary W. Rakow, who provided technical copyediting for the entire manuscript; Joan Raudenbush, who did much to facilitate our editorial tasks; and Jeffrey Sturchio, assistant to the Director of the Edgar Fahs Smith Memorial Collection in the History of Chemistry, at the University of Pennsylvania, who provided a number of portraits.

Herbert A. Laitinen

The University of Florida
Gainesville, Florida

Galen W. Ewing

Seton Hall University
South Orange, New Jersey

IZAAK MAURITS KOLTHOFF, 1894-

    Educated in the Netherlands, Kolthoff has been associated with the University of Minnesota since 1927. His contributions in general and electroanalytical chemistry have been monumental.

Status of Analytical Chemistry at the End of the
19th Century. In the last quarter of the 19th century
the practice of quantitative chemical analysis was composed mainly of gravimetric and titrimetric methods and
to a minor extent of colorimetry and gasometry. The
Swede, Torbern Bergman (1735-1784), is generally considered the founder of qualitative and quantitative
inorganic analysis. Volumetric analysis was also practiced in the 18th century and became a very popular
method in the 19th century. The history of gas analysis
dates back to the 18th-century scientists, including
Priestley, Cavendish, Lavoisier, Scheele, and others,
and in the 19th century (since 1838) particularly to
Bunsen. The names of Liebig and Berzelius, and others
in the 19th century will remain connected with the
development of organic elementary analysis. The Dumas
method (1831) for nitrogen analysis, as well as the
Kjeldahl method (1883), are still finding practical
application. Although microscopy and qualitative microanalysis were practiced in the 19th century, it was not
until the beginning of this century that Fritz Pregl
published his methods of micro-elementary analysis
(1912) and Emich popularized quantitative microanalysis
in general. In this country, Benedetti-Pichler, a
student of the Austrian "microschool," has been one of
the pioneers of microanalysis. Optical methods of
analysis have been practiced for more than two centuries.
Microscopy was introduced in the 18th century by
Leeuwenhoek, a Dutchman, who characterized crystal habit
in addition to observing many other objects. The polarizing microscope entered the field early in the 19th
century. Flame reactions for detection of various ions
were generally used in the 18th century, but it was not

until the 19th century that emission and absorption spectra of colored flames were investigated (Talbot, 1834; and others). It is well known that Kirchhoff and Bunsen are to be credited for introducing qualitative and quantitative spectroscopy for analytical purposes. Colorimetry has been practiced for a few centuries in a primitive way by comparing colors visually. The laws of extinction as a function of the length of the path (Bouguer, 1729; Lambert, 1760) and of concentration (Beer, Bernard, 1845) found application mainly in visual colorimetry. At the end of the last century visual spectrophotometers were available, but they were used mainly for theoretical work. They were too laborious to use in routine analysis. Electroanalytical chemistry was born at the very beginning of the last century when Cruikshank (1800) deposited several metals on a cathode and some halogens on the anode. Electrogravimetry was introduced for quantitative determinations by the American, Wolcott Gibbs (1864), more than 100 years ago and was particularly popularized by the German, Classen (1912), and the American, Edgar Fahs Smith. The latter greatly popularized this method of gravimetric analysis by his papers and his book, "Electrochemical Analysis," the first edition of which appeared in 1894. In the Preface to the second edition he states, "Thousands of analyses are now made annually by these methods. . . ." The father of modern electroanalytical chemistry is the German, Walther Nernst (1864-1941), who is still honored as one of the great chemists and physicists of this century.

In concluding this sketchy overview of the status of analytical chemistry about 100 years ago, it may be mentioned that a great number of separation methods were practiced at that time. Of course, filtration, sedimentation, centrifugation, distillation, and extraction are time-honored methods. Rudimentary principles of more modern methods of separation were known. For example, the use of paper chromatography is found in the literature of the dye industry of the early 1800s. Capillary analysis was described in several papers by the Austrian, Goppelsroeder. His studies are closely related to modern adsorption chromatography. Columnar chromatography was discovered in 1897 by the American, J. T. Day, who applied it to fractionating petroleum by adsorption on columns of fuller's earth. Ion exchange chromatography has been utilized in soil studies since the middle of the last century. A very detailed description of the development of classical methods of analysis is found in the outstanding book by F. Szabadváry, "History of Analytical Chemistry." The names of the Americans, G. E. F. Lundell and E. B. Sandell (among others also not mentioned by Szabadváry), should be included; in the first half of this century they perfected classical gravimetry and the quantitative analysis of complex materials.

Development of Analytical Chemistry as a Scientific Discipline. The impact of analytical chemistry on the development of chemistry in general and physical chemistry in particular was well recognized by the German, Wilhelm Ostwald, in his classical book (1894) on the scientific fundamentals of analytical chemistry. It is generally recognized that Ostwald is the man who, in addition to his own original scientific contributions, has propagated in his books and papers the new discipline of physical chemistry. He is also the first chemist who recognized the great importance of the young branch of theoretical (physical) chemistry in analytical chemistry, and he may well be considered the pioneer of scientific analytical chemistry. In his book he emphasized the importance of classical analytical contributions to the development of theoretical chemistry but regrets that analytical chemists at the end of the 19th century did not take advantage of the application of fundamentals of the young field of physical chemistry. In the Preface of his book he writes:

> Analytical chemistry, or the art of recognizing different substances and determining their constituents, takes a prominent position among the applications of the science, since the questions it enables one to answer arise wherever chemical processes are employed for scientific or technical purposes. Its supreme importance has caused it to be assiduously cultivated from a very early period in the history of chemistry, and its records comprise a large part of the quantitative work which is spread over the whole domain of the science.

It is generally recognized that science is essentially the study of *quantitative relationships* and that the interpretation of the factual information demands more *quantitative* measurements. Many famous chemists from the early days have enriched chemistry with laws and other contributions which are fundamental to quantitative analysis. Boyle, Priestley, Lavoisier, Scheele, Dalton, Davy, Gay-Lussac, and Berzelius, with others, are the builders of modern chemistry and are equally the co-builders of classical analytical chemistry, together with "*bona fide*" analytical chemists like the Swede, T. Bergman. Physical chemists,

physiological chemists, and biochemists at the end of
the last and the beginning of the present century must
be credited with the development of analytical chemistry as a scientific discipline. These scientists
recognized the great importance to analytical chemistry
provided by the very young discipline of physical chemistry. It is only fitting here to mention first the
American, Josiah Willard Gibbs, who exactly 100 years
ago in publications in the obscure *Journal of the
Connecticut Academy* originated the principles of the
phase rule as well as the concept of the chemical
potential. The contributions of the Dutchman, Jacobus
Henricus van't Hoff, who, among others, originated the
osmotic law and accounted quantitatively for the effect
of temperature on reaction rates and chemical equilibria, and who simultaneously with the Frenchman,
Le Bel, 100 years ago published the theory of the asymmetric carbon atom (analytically applied in polarimetry), are fundamental to analytical chemistry. The
same is true of the classical theory of electrolytic
dissociation which originated with the Swedish genius,
Svante Arrhenius.

The contributions of these three giants, together
with those of Walther Nernst, have had a great impact
on the development of analytical chemistry, especially
of solution analysis. Although the contributions by
Nernst and his school are treated in more detail in a
later chapter; it should be mentioned here that it was
in 1889 that Nernst published the very fundamental
Nernst equation and, as mentioned earlier, can thus be
considered the father of modern electroanalysis. In
those days electroanalysis was confined to electrogravimetry. In the 1890s potentiometry and potentiometric titrations (precipitations, Behrend, 1893;
redox, Crotogino, 1900; acid-base with the hydrogen
electrode, Böttger, 1899; amperometric titrations,
Salomon, 1897, Nernst and Merrium, 1905) all originated
in Nernst's laboratory.

Applications of these fundamental studies to
chemical analysis were made early this century by
physical chemists, physiological chemists and biochemists. No exhaustive treatment can be given here.
Singled out are a few basic contributions. First we
refer to a very fundamental paper by the American,
A. A. Noyes, in 1910 entitled "Quantitative Application of the Theory of Indicators to Volumetric Analysis."
It is the forerunner of the 1914 monograph by the
Danish physical chemist, Niels Bjerrum, who presented
an exhaustive and still up-to-date treatment of acid-
base titrations in water as solvent. Of classical
value is the very fundamental paper published both in

French and German by the Danish physiological chemist,
S. P. L. Sørensen (1909), who introduced the concept of
pH and a set of buffer solutions covering the pH range
1 to 12. Also, of fundamental analytical importance
are the two monographs by the German biochemist, L.
Michaelis (1914 and 1916), and the book by the American
biochemist, William Mansfield Clark (1920), which has
remained a standard work ever since. Clark not only
originated a set of buffer solutions which are still
used the world over but also the sulfonephthaleins and
many oxidation-reduction indicators of low reduction
potential. Michaelis is still often referred to for
his pioneer work on semiquinones. Greatly inspired by
these fundamental analytical contributions, a Dutch
(later American) analytical chemist started his work on
acid-base indicators and electrometric titrations.[*]

In the early days of this century a generation of
analytical chemists grew up who became impressed with
the application of physical and general chemistry to
the improvement of classical methods of analysis and
techniques and to the development of new ones. To
understand sources of error in gravimetric analysis and
their (partial) elimination, studies were made of rates
of formation of precipitates, the growth of crystalline
precipitates, the effects of adsorption and occlusion
of impurities, of adsorption of foreign materials, and
of aging of precipitates. The method of homogeneous
precipitation, originated by the American analytical
chemist, H. H. Willard, was not an empirical discovery,
but its development was based on an understanding of
the effect of supersaturation on the rate of formation
and growth of crystalline precipitates. At the end of
the first quarter of this century and soon thereafter,
quantitative analysis was no longer taught solely as a
laboratory course, but the importance of the theory
underlying these methods and techniques was emphasized
for an understanding and future development of quantitative analysis.

In conclusion, the time-honored definition, "Qualitative (chemical) analysis deals with the detection
and identification of the constituents of a sample,
quantitative chemical analysis with the determination
of their amounts," is essentially still valid today.
What has changed are the explosive development of
instrumentation, the addition of many physical and
chemical techniques which are applied to modern qualitative and quantitative analysis, together with the

---

[*]Editor's note: This is Professor Kolthoff's
modest reference to his own monumental contributions.

increasing demands made by other scientific disciplines
and by society, in the fields of medical, environmental,
and conservation chemistry, among others. The development of modern methods and techniques, leading to a
fusion of chemical and physical analysis, is the subject of this text.

I. M. Kolthoff

CHAPTER I

INTRODUCTION

Although the practice of analytical chemistry is as old as chemistry itself, the scientific discipline as we know it today is a relatively recent development. I. M. Kolthoff, in the Foreword, describes the status of analytical chemistry at the end of the 19th century and the contributions of scientists in many areas such as physics, physical chemistry, and biochemistry, who began its development as a scientific discipline in its own right. Early analytical methodology, whether based on chemical or physical principles, was highly empirical. Measurements made for the purpose of understanding basic phenomena fell in the domain of physics, physical chemistry, or some other branch of science, and what was left for analytical chemistry was the *use* of the measurements for the determination of the composition of matter. Small wonder that analytical chemistry could correctly be termed the "handmaiden of the sciences" (Ostwald, 1894). What quality distinguishes present-day analytical research from that of the 19th or early 20th centuries? Surely it is not the use of physical measurements or instrumentation per se--although great strides have been made in these aspects--for spectroscopy has been used analytically for over a century. Rather it is the recognition that the scientific development of analytical methodology, whether chemical or physical, must be based upon fundamental understanding. Research need not lead directly to analytical applications to qualify as research in analytical chemistry.

In this introductory chapter we first examine the evolution of a leading research journal, *Analytical Chemistry*, as indicative of the evolution of the field it represents. In 1974 R. C. Chirnside and J. H. Hamence described the history of the Society for

1

Analytical Chemistry (London) and its publication, *The Analyst*, on the occasion of its centenary celebration in a book entitled "The Practising Chemists." Similar developments occurred in many other countries, but to trace them all would merely repeat the same essential story with different examples.

Apparently the earliest American journal in the field of analytical chemistry was privately published on a quarterly basis during the period 1887-1890 as volumes 1-4 of the *Journal of Analytical Chemistry*. The editor was Edward Hart, Ph.D., professor of analytical chemistry at Lafayette College, Easton, Penna. Evidently the time was not ripe for a purely scientific publication in this field, for in 1891 the title was changed to the *Journal of Analytical and Applied Chemistry*, which appeared monthly as volumes 5-7 during the period 1891-3, with the same editor. At that time, the journal was absorbed by the *Journal of the American Chemical Society* which had begun publication in 1879. The dominance of the latter journal over privately published journals during this period was to be illustrated by another notable example in 1913, when the *American Chemical Journal*, founded by Ira Remsen in 1879 was absorbed.

Early in the 20th century American analytical chemists had no specific outlet for their publications. Kolthoff found that in the September and October 1903 issues of the *Journal of the American Chemistry Society (JACS)* 22 out of 33 articles were analytical in nature, ranging from a classic paper by Edgar Fahs Smith, "The Use of the Mercury Cathode in Electrochemical Analysis," to "The Estimation of Formaldehyde in Milk," by Bernard H. Smith.

In 1909 the *Journal of Industrial and Engineering Chemistry (JI&EC)* was established, and in that same year *JACS* began to organize its papers into two classes, General, Physical, and Inorganic, on the one hand, and Organic and Biological, on the other. Fundamental analytical papers usually fell into the first class while those of applied nature were published in *JI&EC* (after 1923, simply *I&EC*).

It was not until 1929 that a separate Analytical Edition of the journal *Industrial and Engineering Chemistry* emerged as a quarterly publication. In 1933 the Analytical Edition became a bimonthly, and in 1935 a monthly publication. That same year the appointment of a special Board of Associate Editors consisting of six prominent analytical chemists was announced. The following Statement of Policy appeared in January 15, 1935:

> The Analytical Edition is primarily a
> journal for chemists specializing in analysis.

EDWARD HART, 1854-1931

A long time Professor of Chemistry at Lafayette College, Hart was a founder of Baker and Adamson Chemical Company, and of the Chemical Publishing Company, predecessor of Mack Printing Company. He was editor of *The Journal of Analytical Chemistry* and of *The Journal of the American Chemical Society*.

In it will appear articles dealing with applications of methods of chemical analysis to
problems primarily in industrial and engineering chemistry, though worthy papers in
other fields may be accepted. Such articles
will properly include apparatus and physical
tests that are employed by the analytical
chemist--for example x-ray, colorimetry, chemical spectroscopy, calorimetry and the like.
Articles dealing with the fundamental or theoretical considerations of no immediate application to chemical analysis belong more properly in the *Journal of the American Chemical
Society*.

The same group of six analytical chemists (B. L.
Clarke of Bell Telephone, T. R. Cunningham of Union
Carbide, N. H. Furman of Princeton University, I. M.
Kolthoff of the University of Minnesota, G. E. F. Lundell
of the National Bureau of Standards, and H. H. Willard
of the University of Michigan) served as Advisory Board
members from 1935 through 1942.

In 1943 Walter J. Murphy succeeded Harrison E. Howe
as editor of the parent *Industrial and Engineering Chemistry* and of its Analytical Edition. Of the original
group, Professors Furman and Kolthoff were replaced by
M. G. Mellon of Purdue University and Ralph H. Müller,
then of New York University. In 1944 the Advisory Board
was enlarged to nine members by the addition of R. P.
Chapman, J. R. Churchill, and B. L. Oser. They served
through 1948, the year the name of the journal was
changed to *Analytical Chemistry*. At the same time, a
systematic rotation of Advisory Board members was begun,
and in 1954 the Board was enlarged to its present size
of 15 members.

The period of 1943-45 was described by Walter J.
Murphy (in his December 1946 editorial):

We recall with genuine pleasure and a deep
sense of satisfaction the meetings of the original board in the years 1943-45 [the policy of
rotation was not adopted until 1948]. Three
of the meetings were held in Woods Hole, Mass.,
at the summer headquarters of the editorial
staff. The *Analytical Edition* of *Industrial
and Engineering Chemistry* was faced with many
serious problems. A more positive and dynamic
editorial program was an obvious must if the
journal was to serve the analytical chemists
adequately. The field of analytical chemistry
was expanding rapidly and it was clear that
appropriate steps must be taken quickly to
meet the needs of a fast-growing, fast-moving

field of scientific and technical endeavor.

It is interesting to recall now the discussions of what the role of *Analytical Edition* should be. Happily it was decided that the journal should expand its interest in instrumentation. Many hours were spent in discussing ways and means of completely divorcing the publication from *Industrial and Engineering Chemistry*.

The appointment, in 1944, of Lawrence T. Hallett (1900-   ) as Associate Editor proved to be a landmark in the development of the journal. With a Ph.D. in analytical chemistry (Wisconsin, 1928), some teaching experience at Oregon State College, and industrial experience at Eastman Kodak and General Aniline and Film, he had both the scientific background and the contacts with instrument makers and users to bring the journal in line with contemporary practice. In 1943 he had joined General Aniline and Film, a former German firm confiscated during World War II, as head of the analytical section, to build an analytical and service group. In 1944 he hired Sidney Siggia, now at the University of Massachusetts, who recently wrote, in part:

Larry was very progressive in his philosophy, and instruments were acquired as fast as they appeared on the market. When I arrived on the scene, the lab already had a Beckman DU and some filter photometers, a polarograph, and a single beam IR. Larry foresaw the potential in instrumental methods and hired Dr. Ralph Müller as consultant to lead us into new instrumental directions.

In answer to a question about this period, Dr. Hallett wrote to H. A. Laitinen on August 8, 1974:

In the beginning analytical papers were accepted in *Industrial and Engineering Chemistry*. Later because analytical papers were numerous enough and really out of place there, it was decided to publish analytical papers quarterly and later monthly.

Walter Murphy was brought in to head *Chemical and Engineering News* and *Industrial and Engineering Chemistry*. He decided that someone more knowledgeable than he in analytical should read and handle the analytical papers. I was asked if I would undertake this assignment. I accepted provided he would agree to a much expanded role for analytical and the possibility of a separate journal. At that time there was a small Advisory Board, but it needed to be enlarged to meet the growing

BEVERLY LEONIDAS CLARKE, 1900–

  Following graduate work at Columbia, Clarke spent a decade at
Bell Telephone Laboratories followed by 16 years with Merck & Co.
He was a member of the first advisory board of *The Analytical
Edition of Industrial and Engineering Chemistry*.

needs of analytical chemistry.

The subject matter in the analytical papers after World War II changed greatly because many instruments which had been developed from electronic research were found to apply to analysis. For this reason advertisers of instruments were attracted to the journal pages. We felt that an analytical journal should encourage new approaches in analysis and be an accepted medium for publication of analytical research.

Dr. Hallett served as Associate Editor until 1953 when he was named Science Editor. In 1956 he became Editor, a post he held until 1966 when he was succeeded by the present incumbent, H. A. Laitinen.

In the meantime Dr. R. H. Müller, who served on the editorial board through 1950, initiated in January 1946 a new monthly series, "Instrumentation in Analysis," which he contributed through 1968. Beginning in 1969 this feature has been handled by an Instrumentation Panel with rotating membership working in conjunction with the editorial staff.

The evolution of the scope of the journal over a period of four decades is dramatized by quoting from the most recent (December 1976) Manuscript Requirements:

The journal is devoted to the dissemination of knowledge concerning all branches of analytical chemistry. Articles are either entirely theoretical with regard to analysis or are reports of laboratory experiments that support, argue, refute, or extend established theory. Articles may contribute to any of the phases of analytical operations, such as sampling, preliminary chemical reactions, separations, instrumentation and data processing. They need not refer to existing or even potential analytical methods in themselves, but may be confined to the principles and methodology underlying such methods . . . Papers involving experimental data should offer a new or modified approach to analysis in a particular field, not just extend the existing library of data.

Another indication of the evolution of the discipline of analytical chemistry in America is the history of the ACS Division of Analytical Chemistry. Until the late 1930s analytical chemists had no separate identity within the ACS but were members of a section of the Division of Physical and Inorganic Chemistry. Microchemists took the lead in organizing professionally through the formation of a nation-wide Microchemical Society in 1934, with local groups in New York, Boston, and Washington. The most active group in New York City eventually evolved into the American Microchemical Society in 1963. In the meantime, largely due to the leadership of A. A. Benedetti-Pichler, the ACS held Microchemical Symposia in 1935 and 1936. These led to the formation of a Division of Microchemistry in 1938 with Walter R. Kirner as chairman and L. T. Hallett as Secretary-Treasurer. In 1940 the Division of Microchemistry merged with the Analytical Section of the Division of Physical and Inorganic Chemistry to form the Division of Analytical and Microchemistry, which finally in 1949 adopted its present name, the Division of Analytical Chemistry. The January 1949 issue of *Analytical Chemistry* carried an editorial announcing a goal for a division membership of 1000 by the end of that year. This goal was not to be reached for several years, until the exceptional efforts by G. F. Smith during his chairmanship in 1954 brought membership well above the 1000 mark. Recent divisional membership hovers around 4000. Professional activities of the Division have kept pace with increased membership. The traditional role of an ACS division in organizing sessions at national ACS meetings has been expanded to include the sponsorship of symposia in recognition of award recipients as well as special symposia on selected topics. Beginning in 1948 the Division, jointly with the *Analytical Chemistry* journal, has sponsored a Summer Symposium. A divisional fellowship program was initiated in 1966 to support analytical graduate students either for a summer or a full year with funds from outside sources supplemented by divisional support. These fellowships are nationally competitive and are regarded as a distinct honor. Beginning in 1968 the Division has sponsored undergraduate awards, consisting of a subscription to *Analytical Chemistry*, to students who have excellent scholastic records and have an interest in the field selected locally in several hundred institutions. Various divisional committees are active in areas of concern to the profession.

Parallel developments in professional journals and societies have occurred in many countries throughout the world. It is beyond the scope of this treatment to trace all of these events, but two main trends should be pointed out. The first trend is towards the establishment of many, increasingly specialized journals, usually handled by a commercial publisher rather than a professional society. Their circulation is generally limited, sometimes less than 1000, mainly to technical libraries. The growth of these specialized journals has kept the expansion of broadscope publications within reasonable bounds even with the spectacular growth of the field as a whole. The other trend has been towards

LAWRENCE TRENERY HALLETT, 1900–

   A native of Canada, Hallett took his doctorate at the University of Wisconsin.   His professional career was spent at the Eastman Kodak Company and at General Aniline and Film Corporation. He was editor of *Analytical Chemistry* from 1957 to 1965.

the establishment of regional analytical societies, as
for example in several industrial regions of the United
States, as well as of world-wide professional societies
in analytical specialties. Many analytical chemists
find their loyalties divided between their specialties
and the larger analytical profession.

On the international scene a brief mention should
be made of the development of the Analytical Chemistry
Section of the International Union of Pure and Applied
Chemistry (IUPAC). To quote from a talk by Professor
I. M. Kolthoff,

> [In 1949], there was only one Commission on
> Reactions and Reagents in Quantitative Analysis
> which represented analytical chemistry. I wrote
> a stiff letter to Dr. M. T. Bogert, then Presi-
> dent of IUPAC and Professor of Organic Chemistry
> at Columbia University, explaining the poor rep-
> resentation of analytical chemistry in IUPAC. I
> was asked to act as an alternate at the IUPAC
> Conference in 1949 in London. There I had hot
> arguments, not only with colleagues in the above
> Commission, but also with W. A. Noyes and Linus
> Pauling. They told me that physical chemistry
> could take care of the Commissions in analytical
> that I wanted to have established. In short,
> under W. A. Noyes as President, the entire struc-
> ture of IUPAC was reorganized. Five Sections
> (now Divisions) were established, one of which
> was the Analytical Section. It then became pos-
> sible to establish various Commissions repre-
> senting the entire field of analytical chemistry.

Finally, a word may be added about the development
of analytical chemistry as an academic specialty in
America. In the 1930s scarcely a dozen institutions in
the United States could rightly claim to educate Ph.D.s
in analytical chemistry. Most institutions offered a
variety of advanced analytical courses, mainly in the
analysis of special materials such as rocks, alloys,
fuels, foods, water, etc., and a few stressed special
techniques such as microscopy, microanalysis, and gas
analysis. By the 1960s most of these had been displaced
by courses organized according to methodology--e.g.,
spectrochemical analysis, separations, electroanalysis,
electronics, and instrumentation.

G. A. Rechnitz [*Anal. Chem.* 43[4], 51A (1971)] in
surveying graduate education noted that 122 institutions
were listed in the 1969 ACS *Directory of Graduate Research* as offering a Ph.D. program in analytical chemistry. The thrust towards increasing vitality and
variety has intensified since that time, and this trend
seems destined to continue into the foreseeable future.

CHAPTER II

CHEMICAL METHODS OF ANALYSIS

In the past century and in the beginning of this century we have witnessed the development of the classical branch of analytical chemistry namely, gravimetric and titrimetric analysis, followed by the studies of chemical reactions, side reactions, kinetics and reactions at high temperatures during ignition and the development of sophisticated electronic instrumentation. In this chapter we follow the development of classical analytical chemistry. We dwell on some of the important names which made analytical chemistry the art it is today, and we go back to the foundations of particular disciplines. This task has been carried out with the help of many chemists who have contributed valuable material and time on various aspects.

At the center of the classical period is the analytical balance. The art and science of weighing was known in Egypt as early as 3000 B.C. The earliest written reference to an equal arm balance dates back to approximately 1300 B.C., as described in the papyrus of Hannafer. Also a reference to weights and balance is made in Proverbs 11:1: "A false balance is an abomination to the Lord, but a just weight is his delight."

It was not until the Middle Ages, however, that the balance was used to follow a chemical reaction. One of the early applications was in cupellation which was a statutory procedure for examining gold in the 14th century. Philip VI of France described the procedure, which is perhaps one of the earliest examples of a standard method of analysis, stating that "the balance used for the test should be of good construction, precise, and should not pull to either side. The test should be carried out in a place where there is neither wind nor cold, and whoever carries out the test

Reilley   Bates   Laitinen   Lingane   Meinke   Mitchell
Smith   Craig   Elving   Morrison   Kolthoff

A group of Prominent American Analytical Chemists, winners of the ACS Award in Analytical Chemistry, sponsored by the Fisher Scientific Company.   The complete list of awardees is the following:

1948 N. H. Furman	1958 J. J. Lingane	1968 L. B. Rogers
1949 G. E. F. Lundell	1959 J. I. Hoffman	1969 R. G. Bates
1950 I. M. Kolthoff	1960 P. J. Elving	1970 C. V. Banks
1951 H. H. Willard	1961 H. A. Laitinen	1971 G. H. Morrison
1952 M. G. Mellon	1962 H. A. Liebhafsky	1972 W. W. Meinke
1953 D. D. Van Slyke	1963 D. N. Hume	1973 J. D. Winefordner
1954 G. F. Smith	1964 J. Mitchell, Jr.	1974 P. W. West
1955 E. H. Swift	1965 C. N. Reilley	1975 Sidney Siggia
1956 Harvey Diehl	1966 L. C. Craig	1976 H. V. Malmstadt
1957 John H. Yoe	1967 L. T. Hallett	1977 G. G. Guilbault

must take care not to burden the balance by breathing upon it."

Analytical balances before the first quarter of the 19th century were custom made by craftsmen who specialized in the construction of scientific instruments. The first balances of standardized design were made by a London instrument maker named Robinson shortly before 1825. In the United States such balances were first manufactured and sold about 1855 by Christopher Becker, a Dutch instrument maker who had settled in New York city.

The analytical balance in use in the first half of the 19th century had a long solid, hollow, or open-work, brass or bronze beam with a central knife edge of steel or agate resting on a polished flat piece of the same material placed on the top of a supporting pillar. A pointer attached to the center of the beam moved over a graduated scale placed low on the pillar. The pans were suspended by thin metal wires or silk threads from hooks at the ends of the beam. The beam was controlled by a simple arresting mechanism, but there were no pan arrests. None of these early balances was very sensitive, about 0.5 mg at best. With such balances weighing was tedious, not only because of the slow movement of the long beam and lack of pan arrests but because all weights, even the smallest, had to be added and removed from the weight pan by forceps.

The improvements made in balances in the second half of the century were mostly directed to increasing sensitivity and reducing the time required for weighing. The graduated beam with rider was introduced shortly after 1850 by L. Oertling. Becker's balances of the third quarter of the 19th century, though still of the long-beam type, had pan arrests and agate knife edges for supporting the pans. Paul Bunge of Hamburg, Germany, constructed the first rapid, short beam balance in 1866. In the last quarter of the century the Sartorius company of Göttingen, Germany, began to manufacture balances with short, triangular, aluminum beams and with a synchronized system of beam and pan arrests. Although the chain weight device was invented as early as 1890, the first successful Chainomatic balance was not developed until 1915 when Christopher A. Becker received a patent for a balance of this type.

Microanalytical balances were developed at the end of the 19th century. E. Warburg and T. Ihmori described in 1886 a microbalance; this development was followed by E. Salvioni with a spring balance around 1900 and the first quartz fiber balance by Walther Nernst in 1903. Nernst and E. H. Riesenfeld used this type balance for atomic weight determination of rare earths

shortly thereafter. Modified Nernst balances served
F. Emich and J. Donau for the weighing of precipitates
in milligram amounts. Emich also had ordered from the
balance manufacturer, Wilhelm H. F. Kuhlmann in Hamburg,
a special assay balance with a sensitivity of $\pm 1 \times 10^{-5}$ g
and a load capacity of 20 g, which he used sometimes
when the load overstepped the capacity of the Nernst-
type balances. F. Pregl used an improved Kuhlmann balance with a reproducible sensitivity of $\pm 1 \times 10^{-6}$ and a
load capacity of 20-30 g in his development of quantitative organic microanalysis. These balances came to
be known as microchemical balances of the Kuhlmann type.

F. Emich constructed still more sensitive weighing
instruments (described in 1915 and 1921); one had a
solid quartz beam, a quartz fiber suspension, and weight
compensation by electromagnetic power, reaching a reproducible sensitivity of $\pm 5 \times 10^{-9}$ g. The electromagnetic
microbalance was used by E. Wiesenberger (1931) for
residue determinations with amounts of sample down to
10 µg.

Julius Donau improved the Nernst balance again in
1933 to provide easier weighing, making the suspension
more stable and long lasting.

Precision balances of the suspension type, as well
as weighing instruments based on other principles, have
been described on several occasions by F. Emich in 1915,
by Georg Gorbach in 1938, and in numerous publications
by A. A. Benedetti-Pichler. An important advance in
balance construction was made by Erhard Mettler in 1945
by deviating from the equal arm construction and introducing the substitution principle. Mettler, in 1951,
developed an ultramicrobalance having a sensitivity of
10^{-7} g. Smaller weights are preferably handled on
quartz fiber balances, based on the torsion principle.
These have been described by H. El Badry and C. L.
Wilson, Garner, Korenman, Carmichael, Rodden, Belcher,
and others.

GRAVIMETRIC ANALYSIS

The earliest form of gravimetric analysis, and
indeed the earliest form of any kind of quantitative
chemical analysis, was the fire assay procedure for
gold and silver ores invented in Germany in the 15th
century by some person or persons now unknown. By the
early 16th century this method of quantitative determination was extended to the assay of ores of certain
base metals, particularly those of copper and lead, and
to the determination of the fineness of alloys containing precious metals.

Information about these assay methods was first
made public in the early 16th century by a succession
of small printed booklets, usually called "Probier-
büchlein" from the short title of the earliest one
issued about 1510. These booklets outlined assay procedures, and miscellaneous notes were set down as dis-
connected recipes with no particular arrangement.
Nevertheless, these booklets are of unusual interest
because they are the earliest publications that deal
with any form of gravimetric analysis. The first systematic account of the assay methods of the 16th century
appears in Chapter VII of the famous "De Re Metallica"
of Georgius Agricola first published in 1556. The first
book solely devoted to a detailed description of these
methods is that by Lazarus Ercker published in 1574.

Some minor improvements in the methods of fire
assaying were made in the 17th and 18th centuries, but
the method remained essentially the same in principle
and practice. These dry methods were the only ones
available for the quantitative determination of metals
until the last quarter of the 18th century. They were
necessarily limited in their application to metals that
could be isolated from samples in the form of beads or
buttons suitable for weighing, and they were of course
not applicable at all to the determination of non-
metals.

Origin and Early Development of Wet Methods.
Torbern Bergman (1735-1784), a Swedish chemist, first
suggested that metals need not be isolated as such for
their quantitative determination but could be isolated
for weighing in the form of suitable compounds, especially in the form of compounds obtained by precipitation. Bergman showed that the weights of metals present in given weights of dried precipitates could be
found by the use of suitable conversion factors, which
he obtained by direct experiment. He could not obtain
his gravimetric factors by calculating them from the
formulas of the compounds and atomic weights because
neither was then available. Bergman determined the
composition of various minerals and ores, but the
results of his analyses are generally far from accurate.

Martin Heinrich Klaproth (1743-1817), first professor of chemistry in the University of Berlin, not
only greatly improved the gravimetric procedures of
Bergman but devised a great many more and extended the
general method to the determination of non-metals. In
fact, Klaproth's life was largely devoted to devising
procedures for wet separation and gravimetric determination. Prior to the work of Klaproth the composition
of very few minerals was known with any degree of

accuracy, but Klaproth established the quantitative composition of nearly 200 minerals by his own analyses. He was the first to apply and to devise many quantitative procedures for finding the composition of various manufactured products such as glasses and non-ferrous alloys. Klaproth published the results of his analyses in a multitude of papers that finally appeared in collected form in 1815.

Many of Klaproth's contemporaries and immediate successors also devoted a great deal of attention to improving the methods of gravimetric analysis and determining the composition of minerals. Prominent among these were Louis Nicolas Vauquelin (1763-1829) and Friedrich Stromeyer (1766-1835), but the most famous was Jöns Jakob Berzelius (1779-1848), who made so many other contributions to chemistry. Berzelius devised many new procedures and introduced some new reagents such as hydrofluoric acid for the decomposition of silicates and the determination of silica. He also greatly improved the technique of gravimetric analysis--e.g., by the use of filter paper of low ash content and the handling of precipitates by a convenient wash bottle. This improvement of technique was so great that he was the first able to determine atomic weights that had any claim to accuracy. Berzelius was especially interested in determining the composition of the many inorganic compounds which he and his contemporaries were preparing for the first time, but he also did some of the pioneer work on methods for determining the ultimate composition of organic compounds. He was the first chemist to use the metric system in weighing.

Elementary Organic Analysis. The composition of minerals and other inorganic compounds received by far the greater share of attention in the last quarter of the 18th century and the first quarter of the 19th, but some attention was paid by a few chemists to the problem of determining the composition of organic compounds. Most of the early procedures for elementary organic analysis involved gravimetric methods.

After Lavoisier (1743-1794) realized from the qualitative experiments of Priestley and Scheele that organic compounds contained carbon and hydrogen, he proceeded to make quantitative analyses of a few compounds, the first being ethyl alcohol. He burned the alcohol in a lamp in air to which oxygen was fed as needed. From the weight of alcohol and oxygen that was consumed and from the weight of carbon dioxide formed he was able to estimate the elementary composition of ethyl alcohol. The composition of a few other readily combustible liquids was estimated in the same way. In

later experiments, in which he analyzed some difficultly
combustible solids such as cane sugar, the oxygen was
supplied from certain metal oxides such as red lead.
This method of supplying oxygen became the basis of
nearly all later methods for determining carbon and
hydrogen. However, Lavoisier's experimental procedure
was too slow and cumbersome for practical analysis, and
his results were not accurate.

The first convenient procedure for analyzing
organic compounds was devised in 1811 by Joseph Louis
Gay-Lussac (1778-1850) and Louis Jacques Thénard (1777-
1857), but it depended on the volumetric measurement of
the gases evolved from the combustion of the sample with
potassium chlorate. In 1814 Berzelius published a
better method in which the evolved water vapor and carbon dioxide were trapped and weighed. In this method
the sample was mixed with potassium chlorate and sodium
chloride. The sodium chloride reduced the violence of
the combustion, which was one of the disadvantages of
the method of Gay-Lussac and Thénard. The evolved water
was trapped in a calcium chloride tube, and carbon dioxide and other gases were collected over mercury. Thomas
Thomson (1773-1852) improved the method of Berzelius by
using cupric oxide as the oxidizing agent. In 1831
Justus von Liebig (1803-1873) devised a more convenient
method, using cupric oxide in which carbon dioxide was
absorbed in a special weighing bulb charged with concentrated potassium hydroxide solution. Liebig's apparatus and procedure for the determination of carbon and
hydrogen were so satisfactory that they remained, with
various slight modifications, standard for many years.
At about the same time, Jean-Baptiste Dumas (1800-1884)
devised his method for nitrogen determination, and this
also was generally adopted as the standard procedure.
Thus by 1831 reliable methods were available for the
ultimate analysis of many types of organic compounds,
and as a consequence the development of organic chemistry as an important branch of the science became
possible.

Expansion of Inorganic Gravimetric Analysis. As
is shown by the first edition of the "Handbuch der analytischen Chemie" of Heinrich Rose (1795-1864) published
in 1829, at least one more-or-less satisfactory method
for the separation and gravimetric determination of each
of the known elements was available at the beginning of
the second quarter of the 19th century. During the
remainder of that century hundreds of additional gravimetric procedures were devised. Many of the new procedures arose out of the discovery of new minerals,
elements, and compounds. Still others arose from the

application of chemistry to problems of agriculture and industry.

Among the many important new procedures were, for example, the molybdate method for phosphorus, introduced by Franz Leopold Sonnenschein (1819-1879), and the method for the determination of alkalies in silicate minerals and rocks, devised by J. Lawrence Smith (1818-1883). Elaborate schemes were also devised for the analysis of complex materials, a notable example being that of William Francis Hillebrand (1853-1925) for the complete analysis of silicate and carbonate rocks.

Karl Remigius Fresenius (1818-1897) is generally recognized as the leader in the development of chemical analysis in general and gravimetric analysis in particular during the second half of the 19th century. Fresenius was a student under Liebig at Giessen, received his doctorate there in 1842, and became a Privatdocent at Giessen in 1843. He left in 1845 to become the professor of chemistry, physics, and technology at the small Nassau Agricultural Institute near Wiesbaden. Even though this was a scientific and technical school, it had no chemical laboratory--a circumstance that was understandably a source of considerable dissatisfaction to Fresenius. Furthermore, there seemed to be little hope that the governing body of this school would establish one very soon. Thus, Fresenius prevailed on his prosperous father to provide funds to purchase a building at Wiesbaden and to convert it into a suitable laboratory. This laboratory, which opened in 1848, became a center for training analytical chemists, for research on methods of analysis, and for commercial analytical work done for individuals, government bodies, and industry.

As a writer and editor in analytical chemistry Fresenius occupied a commanding position. His textbook on quantitative analysis, published in 1846, was immediately recognized as a work of unusual merit. A second edition was issued in the next year, a third in 1854, a fourth in 1858, a fifth in 1862, and a sixth and greatly enlarged edition in two volumes in 1873-1877. This edition was no longer a textbook suitable for university instruction but a comprehensive reference work describing all the best methods known at the time. A final and further amplified printing of the sixth edition appeared in 1898, a year after Fresenius' death. In all these editions the methods described are mainly gravimetric, and although their number increases from edition to edition, their proportion falls somewhat because titrimetric methods were increasingly added. Various editions were translated into Chinese, Dutch, English, French, Russian, and Spanish. The final English

WILLIAM FRANCIS HILLEBRAND, 1853-1925

Hillebrand was educated at Cornell University and at Heidelberg, where he studied under Bunsen and Kirchhoff. He was for 28 years a chemist with the U. S. Geological Survey, joining the National Bureau of Standards as Chief Chemist in 1908, where he remained until his death. He is known for his practical methods for the analysis of silicate and carbonate rocks. He was President of the ACS in 1906.

translation, by Alfred I. Cohn, was from the final revised German edition of 1898. It was published in New
York in 1904 in two large volumes totalling over 2,000
pages and was reprinted in 1915. Other textbooks, trea-
tises, and reference works dealing with gravimetric
analysis were published in the second half of the 19th
century; some were quite notable, such as the "Select
Methods in Chemical Analysis" by Sir William Crookes
(1822-1919) first published in 1871 with enlarged editions in 1886 and 1888, but none of these other works
had the wide use and high reputation of those of
Fresenius.

In 1862 Fresenius founded the *Zeitschrift für ana-
lytische Chemie* as a medium for publishing the increasing
amount of research on chemical analysis being done in
his laboratory and elsewhere. Many of the papers published in this journal in its early years were written
by Fresenius himself or in collaboration with his co-
workers. This first journal exclusively devoted to analytical chemistry had and continues to have an important
influence in furthering the advance of this branch of
chemistry. The editorship remains in the fifth generation of the Fresenius family.

Improvements in Materials and Apparatus. Prior to
the last quarter of the 19th century analytical chemists
had to prepare or to purify most of their own reagents
because sufficiently pure chemicals were not available
commercially. Most of the textbooks on analysis published up to that time, such as those of Fresenius,
contain detailed directions for preparing analytical
reagents. The first reagents of guaranteed purity were
placed on sale by the Kahlbaum Co. in Germany.

Quantitative filter papers washed with both hydrochloric and hydrofluoric acids to remove mineral matter
were introduced by Schleicher and Schüll of Düren, Germany, in 1883. Hardened filter paper was introduced at
about the same time.

The kinds of apparatus available in the first half
of the 19th century for heating and evaporating solutions, and especially for drying and igniting precipitates, were neither convenient nor very efficient.
Charcoal was often used as the fuel for furnaces and
ovens and alcohol or whale oil for laboratory burners.
The invention in 1855 by Robert Wilhelm Bunsen (1811-
1899) of a clean and convenient laboratory gas burner
was a great improvement that led to the development of
a wide variety of gas ovens, furnaces, and muffles in
the second half of the 19th century. Although electric
resistance heaters for laboratory use were introduced
shortly before 1900, the early ones were not very

successful. Those that had platinum heating elements
were too expensive, and those that had other kinds of
elements burned out too fast. The general use of electric ovens, crucibles, furnaces, and muffles for gravimetric analysis beginning about 1910 was made possible
by the discovery by Albert Leroy Marsh of the remarkable
properties of certain nickel-chromium alloys, in which
high electrical resistance is coupled with a very slow
rate of oxidation at high temperatures.

The invention of the filter crucible in 1878 at
Yale University by Frank Austin Gooch (1852-1929) radi-
cally improved the handling of many kinds of precipitates. It was especially suitable for precipitates that
could not be ignited without decomposition and for those
which were reduced by the carbon of filter paper on
being ignited. The original Gooch crucible was made by
drilling a number of fine holes in the bottom of an
ordinary platinum crucible and covering the inside of
the bottom with a mat of asbestos fibers formed by
pouring a suspension of the fibers in water into the
crucible while it was attached to a suction flask by a
special holder. Gooch prepared his asbestos by scraping
fibers from a piece of amphibole asbestos with a knife
and boiling these fibers for some time in hydrochloric
acid to remove iron and other impurities. However, the
asbestos prepared in this way was not entirely satisfactory because it lost weight in varying degrees at
different elevated temperatures. In 1888 Charles Edward
Munroe (1849-1938) remedied this drawback by substituting a filter mat of spongy platinum for the asbestos.
Neither the original Gooch crucible nor Munroe's modification was used widely because of the high cost and
the time and trouble required to prepare the asbestos
or spongy platinum. After specially prepared asbestos
fibers and glazed porcelain crucibles of the Gooch type
became available shortly after 1900, the filter crucible
began to be used widely. About 1925 two superior types
of filter crucibles were introduced, one being the
glazed porcelain crucible with a plate of unglazed porcelain fused into the bottom and the other being the
glass crucible with a plate of fritted glass fused to
the body near the bottom; both were available in different degrees of porosity.

Electrodeposition Methods. Analytical methods that
depend on the application of electricity are generally
classed as instrumental, but an exception should be made
for those based on the measurement of the weights of
elements deposited on metal electrodes by electrolysis
for these are actually gravimetric methods in which
electrons act as the reagent. The fact that metals

could be separated from solution and plated on electrodes became known in the first few years of the 19th century, but chemists were slow to apply this knowledge to chemical analysis; apparently because no convenient and reliable source of electricity was available until well into the second half of the century. The first account of a quantitative application--the determination of copper and of nickel--was published in 1864 by Wolcott Gibbs (1822-1908), professor of chemistry at Harvard. His priority was disputed by C. Luckow, a chemist at the Mansfeld copper works in Germany, who stated that for over two years he had been regularly using the electrolytic method for determining copper and that as far back as 1860 he had used electrolysis to separate copper from solutions of samples of the crude metal to obtain for analysis solutions containing the metals present as impurities. Many investigations on this method were published by various chemists between 1870 and 1900.

Atomic Weight Determinations. The determination of atomic weights is a special form of gravimetric measurement in which sample weights of very pure substances are analyzed or are synthesized with extreme care. Berzelius, the pioneer in this field, determined the atomic weights of the elements known in his day and summarized his results in a series of atomic weight tables published in 1814, 1818, and 1826. These results were largely unchallenged in the first half of the 19th century, but the need for more accurate values for certain elements was realized early in the second half. Beginning about 1860 Jean Servais Stas (1813-1891), a professor in Brussels, re-determined with meticulous care the atomic weights of bromine, carbon, chlorine, iodine, lead, lithium, nitrogen, oxygen, potassium, sodium, and sulfur, using silver as the standard of reference.

Despite its fundamental importance, the weight ratio of oxygen to hydrogen in water had not been accurately established by Berzelius and a few later chemists who worked on this problem. The first very careful measurements of this ratio were made by Edward Williams Morley (1836-1923) at Western Reserve University. He allowed known weights of pure hydrogen to burn in known weights of pure oxygen in a special apparatus, which was weighed before and after the combustion. In most of his experiments the weight of water produced was around 34 g. Palladium containing adsorbed hydrogen was weighed before and after heating to determine the weight of hydrogen supplied for the combustion, and the oxygen supplied to the special apparatus was weighed in a large glass globe. His painstaking experiments

extending over several years yielded 7.9396 as his final
result for this ratio, which he announced in 1895.

Beginning about 1895 and extending through the
first quarter of the 20th century, Theodore William
Richards (1868-1928) of Harvard University and his students determined with great care the atomic weight of
28 elements. During their work various special analytical techniques and procedures were developed, as
well as many methods for the preparation of extremely
pure compounds. Some of Richards' students went on to
do important independent work on atomic weights, notably
Gregory Paul Baxter (1876-1953) at Harvard University
and Otto Hönigschmidt (1878-1945) at the University of
Munich.

Organic Precipitants and Solvents in Inorganic
Gravimetric Analysis. Oxalic acid, usually as ammonium
oxalate, began to be used early in the 19th century for
the determination of calcium and its separation from
magnesium. The calcium oxalate precipitate was always
ignited to its carbonate or oxide for weighing. At
nearly the same time ammonium succinate came to be used
for separating ferric iron from divalent metal ions.
When the iron was to be determined, the precipitated
iron succinate on the filter was always treated with
ammonium hydroxide solution to form hydrated ferric
oxide before ignition and weighing. These two were the
only organic precipitants used in inorganic gravimetric
analysis until 1885, when M. A. Ilinski and G. von
Knorre found that α-nitroso-β-naphthol could be used to
determine cobalt in the presence of nickel. This reagent oxidizes cobalt to its trivalent state, which then
reacts with unreduced reagent to form an insoluble
cobalt compound. Ilinski and von Knorre found that the
precipitated cobalt compound varied so much in composition, probably because of the presence of reduced reagent, that results calculated from the weight of the
dried precipitate were unsatisfactory. They recommended
that the precipitate be reduced with hydrogen to cobalt
metal for weighing. It was later shown that simple
ignition in air to Co_3O_4 was simpler and almost as
accurate.

Two organic precipitants for inorganic anions were
introduced very early in the 20th century. In 1902
Wolf Müller (1874-1941) devised a procedure that depends
on the precipitation of slightly soluble benzidine sulfate when a solution of benzidine hydrochloride is
added to a neutral sulfate solution. The precipitated
benzidine sulfate can be weighed for the sulfate determination, but the preferred method is to titrate a suspension of the precipitate or the excess of precipitant

with standard base. In 1905 Max Busch (1865-1941) introduced 4,5-dihydro-1,4-diphenyl-3,5-phenylimino-1,2,
4-triazole (nitron) as a precipitant for the gravimetric
determination of nitrate. The precipitated "nitron
nitrate" is simply dried at 105°C and weighed. Nitron
was later (1930) found to be a good reagent for the
determination of rhenium since it also forms an insoluble precipitate with perrhenate ion.

In 1905 Lev Tschugaeff (1873-1922) synthesized
dimethylglyoxime and observed that a solution of it
forms an insoluble red precipitate when added to a
nickel solution. Two years later Otto Eduard Brunck
(1866-1946) applied this reaction to the gravimetric
determination of nickel in steel. He found the precipitate to be stable to heat and of very definite composition. No one seems to have realized then that dimethylglyoxime was the prototype of a class of selective
reagents that form special kinds of complex compounds
with metals.

In 1909 Oskar Baudisch (1881-1950) introduced the
ammonium salt of nitrosophenylhydroxylamine (cupferron)
as a versatile reagent for separating and determining
various metals. The special merit of this reagent is
that, unlike most organic precipitants, it is applicable
when solutions are strongly acidic. Unfortunately,
because of contamination with the reagent, metal "cup-
ferrates" cannot be weighed as such but must be ignited
to oxides for weighing.

Alan Richard Powell and Walter Raymond Schoeller
observed in 1920 that tannin (gallotannic acid) could
be used to separate tantalum from niobium, but they did
not publish the results of their investigation until
1925. This reagent was later found to be useful for
other difficult separations. As with cupferron, the
precipitates produced with tannin must be ignited and
weighed as oxides.

Towards the end of the first quarter of the 20th
century Fritz Feigl introduced two organic reagents for
metals which form precipitates that need only to be
dried and weighed to obtain accurate results. One is
α-benzoinoxime, recommended by him in 1923 for the
determination of copper, and found in 1932 by Howard B.
Knowles to be even more useful for the determination of
molybdenum. The other is pyrogallol, recommended in
1924 for the determination of antimony.

Many new organic reagents for the determination of
metals were discovered in the second quarter of the
20th century. Only a few of the more important can be
mentioned here, all of which form precipitates that need
only to be dried and weighed. Fredrich L. Hahn in 1926
and Richard H. Berg in 1927 independently advocated

8-hydroxyquinoline as a reagent suitable for a number
of separations and determinations. The compound is
especially convenient for determining aluminum and magnesium. In 1927 G. Spacu and J. Dick introduced the
use of a combination of pyridine and thiocyanate, which
forms slightly soluble complex compounds with various
divalent metals such as cadmium. Salicylaldoxime, introduced in 1930 by Fritz Ephraim, is particularly good
for the determination of copper. Picrolonic acid as a
reagent for determining calcium was recommended in 1931
by R. Dworzak and W. Reich-Rohrwig. It was later found
to be useful also for determining lead and thorium.
Dipicrylamine as a reagent for the determination of
potassium was introduced in 1939 by I. M. Kolthoff and
G. H. Bendix. Schemes were devised by several analysts
for making a series of separations and determinations
solely by means of organic precipitants.

At the beginning of the 19th century ethyl alcohol
was the only organic solvent used in inorganic gravimetric analysis, and later in the century it was the
principal solvent used. It was often added to aqueous
solutions to reduce the normal solubility of slightly
soluble precipitates. For example, in the determination
of strontium as sulfate, Fresenius recommended that at
least an equal volume of 95% alcohol be added to the
solution after adding the sulfuric acid for precipitation. Ethyl alcohol of various concentrations was
used to separate the components of mixtures of dried
salts. For example, in the determination of potassium
as chloroplatinate the mixture of potassium and sodium
chloroplatinates was leached with 80% alcohol to dissolve out the sodium salt. Again, in the original procedure of T. Schlösing for the determination of potassium as perchlorate published in 1871, the mixture of
potassium and other perchlorates was treated with absolute alcohol to isolate the potassium salt for weighing.
Alcohol was also used for washing certain precipitates
and for washing platinum electrodes before and after
the deposition of metals. Amyl alcohol was the only
higher alcohol used in the 19th century for quantitative
purposes. It was first recommended in 1886 by Gooch
for separating potassium and sodium from lithium by
heating the chloride solutions with this alcohol to
drive off the water and to dissolve the lithium chloride. Philip E. Browning used it in an analogous way
to separate barium or strontium from calcium in nitrate
solution since calcium nitrate is freely soluble in
this alcohol.

Ethyl ether was also much used for separations and
determinations in the last quarter of the 19th century.
It was widely used, for example, for the gravimetric

determination of fats in foods and other agricultural
products by means of procedures devised by Franz Soxhlet
(1848-1926) and others. In 1892 J. W. Rothe introduced
the ether extraction method to separate large amounts
of iron from commonly associated elements such as aluminum, the iron being present in the ferric state in
hydrochloric acid solution. Mixtures of ethyl alcohol
and ethyl ether were also used. For example, W. Wenze
in 1891 published a procedure for separating and determining potassium as perchlorate using a solvent composed of two volumes of 97% ethanol and one volume of
anhydrous ethyl ether.

A number of additional organic solvents and mixed
solvents were used for the same or similar purposes in
the first half of the 20th century. For example,
n-butyl alcohol was recommended by H. H. Willard and
G. Frederick Smith in 1922 for the separation and determination of potassium as perchlorate, and Smith and
John F. Ross showed in 1925 that a mixture of equal
parts of n-butyl alcohol and ethyl acetate gave even
better results when used for this purpose. To separate
potassium and sodium chlorides from lithium chloride,
pyridine was recommended by Louis Kahlenberg and F. C.
Krauskopf in 1908, acetone by M. H. Brown and J. H.
Reedy in 1930, dioxane by Alexander Sinka also in 1930,
and 2-ethylhexanol by Earle R. Caley and Herbert D.
Axilrod in 1942.

Precipitation from Homogeneous Solution. The technique of progressively generating a precipitant uniformly within a solution was used in the 19th century
in a few special procedures, for example in the thiosulfate method for precipitating aluminum as the hydroxide, but its systematic development as a general technique began with the work of Willard and Ning Kang Tang
at the University of Michigan shortly before 1930.
These investigators found that by adding urea to a
slightly acid solution and heating near the boiling
point, the hydrogen-ion concentration throughout the
solution was gradually reduced due to the slow hydrolysis of the urea to ammonia and carbon dioxide, and that
when aluminum was present in such a solution it was
slowly precipitated either as the hydroxide or as a
basic salt, depending on the particular anion in the
solution. The physical properties of the basic sulfate
or basic succinate were far superior from an analytical
standpoint to those of aluminum hydroxide precipitated
in the ordinary way with ammonium hydroxide since both
salts formed in this way are much less bulky and much
more easily filtered and washed. The details of the
analytical procedure for the separation and determination

of aluminum by this technique were not published by
these investigators until 1937. The precipitate of
basic sulfate or succinate is not weighed as such but
is ignited to oxide. In the same year Willard and H. C.
Fogg published a method for the determination of gallium
in the presence of zinc using the same technique except
that precipitation as the basic sulfate rather than
basic succinate is necessary for quantitative results.
In 1950 Willard and J. L. Sheldon published a procedure
for the precipitation of ferric iron as basic formate
by the urea method. From the standpoint of good separation from other metal ions they found that a single
precipitation by this method yielded results almost as
good as those obtained by a double precipitation with
ammonium hydroxide.

Another general technique of precipitation from
homogeneous solution depends on the slow hydrolysis of
esters for the release of a desired precipitating ion.
For example, in 1949 Willard and R. B. Hahn recommended
the use of trimethyl phosphate for the separation of
zirconium and its determination as the pyrophosphate,
and in 1950 P. J. Elving and R. D. Van Atta published
a procedure for the precipitation of barium in 20%
methanol by the use of dimethyl sulfate. In general,
the use of esters in precipitation from homogeneous
solution yields more accurate determinations and sharper
separations than precipitations done in the ordinary way.

Advances in the First Half of the 20th Century.
Because organic reagents made such striking contributions to the improvement of inorganic gravimetric analysis in the first half of the 19th century, relatively
little attention was paid during this period to the
possibility of improvements based on the use of inorganic reagents. Nevertheless, some new uses were found
for a few more or less familiar inorganic reagents such
as perchloric acid. The development of this acid as an
analytical reagent is recounted in some detail below.
New uses were also found for hydriodic acid. In 1936
Earle R. Caley and M. Gilbert Burford showed that this
acid could be advantageously used to make certain determinations and separations involving difficultly soluble
substances--i.e., substances that are insoluble in
hydrochloric acid, nitric acid, and aqua regia--since
hydriodic acid was found to dissolve readily many of
these substances, some at room temperature and others
at elevated temperatures. For example, when a mixture
of silver iodide and quartz is treated with cold concentrated hydriodic acid, the silver iodide dissolves
immediately leaving the quartz unaffected, so that the
quantitative composition of the mixture is easily found.

These investigators also showed that this acid can be used to correct the weights of certain precipitates of residues by dissolving out the main component and leaving the impurity or impurities behind for weighing. For example, mercuric sulfide precipitated with hydrogen sulfide always contains admixed sulfur. Upon treatment of the weighed precipitate contained in a filter crucible with cold concentrated hydriodic acid the mercuric sulfide is dissolved at once, leaving the sulfur behind for weighing. A few familiar salts came to be used as reagents in new ways. For example, fusion with ammonium fluoride was recommended by A. C. Shead and G. Frederick Smith in 1931 for the decomposition of refractory silicates and for the determination of silica by difference in glass sands.

The problem of finding a satisfactory selective reagent for the determination of sodium was not solved until the third decade of the 20th century. Of the few qualitative reagents for sodium discovered in the 19th century that of Johann August Streng (1830-1897) showed the most promise. He reported in 1886 that a sparingly soluble triple acetate of uranium, magnesium, and sodium is formed when a solution containing uranyl acetate, magnesium acetate, and acetic acid is added to one containing sodium. Streng employed this reagent solely for the microscopic detection of sodium but suggested that it might be used in ordinary analysis. S. S. Miholic reported in 1920 that he had met with failure when he tried to use Streng's reagent to determine sodium because the precipitate was not of constant composition. On the other hand, in 1923 A. Blanchetière published a quantitative micromethod using this type of reagent and claimed that it yielded excellent results. A. Kling and A. Lassieur tested Blanchetière's procedure in 1924, introduced some minor modifications, and pronounced it satisfactory although their test results show rather high relative percentage errors. E. Crepaz reported in 1926 that he had tried this procedure and found it to be entirely unsatisfactory. In 1927 Earle R. Caley and C. W. Foulk began a critical study of Blanchetière's procedure, located the several sources of error, and modified it accordingly. They published their own procedure in 1929. In 1927 H. H. Barber and I. M. Kolthoff introduced a solution containing uranyl acetate, zinc acetate, and acetic acid as a reagent for the detection of sodium, and then used it to determine sodium according to a procedure published in 1928. Both procedures have been widely adopted for the direct determination of sodium in a wide variety of materials. The converse problem of selective precipitation of potassium was not solved until 1951, when P. Raff and

W. Brotz published the use of sodium tetraphenyl borate for this purpose.

Important work on methods for the analysis of industrial materials was done at the U. S. Bureau of Standards during much of this period, especially under the leadership of Gustav Ernst Frederick Lundell (1881-1950). Much of this work arose out of the preparation and analysis of a long series of standard samples. Although most of the analytical work of the Bureau dealt with the critical testing and improvement of methods already known, some new methods were introduced, and elaborate schemes were devised for the complete analysis of complex materials. These methods and schemes are largely gravimetric.

This concludes a brief sketch dealing with history of practical gravimetric analysis in the second half of the 19th and the first half of the 20th centuries. In this period gravimetric analysis reached its height, incorporating not only better understanding of chemical reactions but also greatly improved balances, burners, glassware and above all, improved quality of reagent grade chemicals. The art of analysis also progressed from macro- to micro- and even to ultra-microtechniques.

DEVELOPMENT OF MICROCHEMISTRY AND MICROANALYSIS

The development of the microanalysis as a special branch of analytical chemistry is presented by Herbert K. Alber, who studied under the founders of microanalytical chemistry at the Technical University of Graz, Austria, and who recently received the "golden Ingenieur Diploma" with five other graduates of 1926.

Microchemical analysis, although similar in principle to macroanalysis differs distinctly in the requirements of skill, equipment, and temperament of the operators. It is no surprise that this discipline has its beginnings in Austria. The primary goal of microanalysis rests on the ability to analyze small amounts of samples, particularly where the amount of the sample is very limited, such as in forensic, physiological, toxicological, and other areas. The sample may range from a few milligrams or milliliters to lower limits of micro- to picograms or micro- to picoliters. The history of microanalysis is closely connected with that of general microchemistry, and it would be rather difficult to separate the two fields.

The Early Microchemical Period. Some historians mention an iron sulfate test by C. S. Plinius (23-79 A.D.) as the first microchemical analysis, but it is

GUSTAVE ERNST FREDERICK LUNDELL, 1881-1950

Lundell received his formal education at Cornell University.
Following ten years on the Cornell faculty, he joined the National
Bureau of Standards in 1917, to retire in 1948. Lundell was en-
dowed with an unusual ability to spot the heart of a tough analytical problem and then to solve it. He was co-author of a number of important texts, and was the acknowledged dean of applied
analysis in America.

very doubtful that the test was carried out with small amounts. Herbert Harms in his careful historic studies selects Johann Wolfgang Döbereiner (1780-1849) as the first to define microchemistry with the understanding of working with small amounts of material and obtaining a rather high degree of precision without using a microscope in his wet analytical methods, including also previously described blowpipe tests and flame reactions. Döbereiner published his pamphlet "Zur mikrochemischen Experimentirkunst, 1. Theil, Jena 1921," emphasizing pneumatic (i.e., gasometric) techniques.

The observation of small particles, moving objects, crystals, and precipitates, etc., was performed with crude magnifying glasses, giving very low magnifications. Robert Hooke of the Royal Society in London was one of the first to publish "Micrographia" in 1667. Over a century later Sigismund Andreas Marggraf (1709-1782) used a microscope for chemical investigations.

From the beginning of the 1800s microscopes of improved construction became available for scientific work. Using a simple compound microscope, the Frenchman François-Vincent Raspail (1794-1878) made chemical tests with small amounts of materials, a technique that can be considered to belong to microanalysis. He applied iodine tincture to individual kernels of grain or to sections, sometimes by using for the first time a freeze technique, to identify starch and its location in different parts of plants. In numerous pamphlets from 1825 to 1835 he established himself as the founder of chemical microscopy, and he probably can be recognized as the first microchemist. His life and work was studied by many historians; the detailed study by Dora B. Weiner (1968) is especially valuable.

All branches of science, such as botany, histochemistry, geology, mineralogy, etc., profited from improved microscopes. Without detailing this part of history between 1830 and 1870 we come to the significant contributions of Theodor Heinrich Behrens (1843-1905). He came to the Polytechnic Institute in Delft, Holland, in 1874 and there established probably the first microscopy laboratory, teaching inorganic crystal tests under the microscope but turning soon to the classification of organic compounds by means of crystallization tests. P. D. C. Kley, his student, co-worker, and later successor, published with Behrens "Organische Mikrochemische Analyse" early in the 20th century, including some of Behrens' later work posthumously. The 1922 German edition was translated into English by Richard E. Stevens under the title "Microscopic Identification of Organic Compounds" (1969). Emile M. Chamot, who met Behrens in 1897 during a visit in Europe, became the

foremost propagator of chemical microscopy in the
United States.

   The Classical Period of Microanalysis from 1900 to
about 1945. During the first years of this period
microchemistry emerged as a new branch of science. Most
of the microtechniques with milligram samples were
developed during the intensive search for refined microanalytical procedures.
   It is generally agreed that Friedrich Emich (1860-
1940) at the Technical University in Graz, Austria, was
the founder of classical microchemistry. In his rec-
toral address in 1899 he described his philosophy of
working with minute amounts of material, and he defined
limits of identification, using as examples, spectroscopic identification of sodium and recognition of
minute amounts of mercaptan through smelling. He
attempted the experimentation with chemical and physical
procedures, starting first with qualitative techniques
both for inorganic and organic microanalysis. He developed methods for crystal precipitates on slides, fiber
tests for nanogram amounts of acid, alkali, boron, and
sulfide, working in a capillary not only for identification but also for preparation of organic compounds.
He improved the same techniques for working in centrifuge cones, elementary tests in organic compounds,
fractional distillation and boiling point determination,
Schlieren experiments, critical solution temperatures,
observation of colors in capillaries, polarimetry, etc.
Some of these contributions go under the name of his
co-workers only, but Emich had a leading hand in all.
   Quantitative microanalysis, however, was his main
field of interest, and here he opened completely new
vistas since little was known in this field at the time.
Emich and his co-worker Julius F. Donau (1877-1960)
showed conclusively that working with milligram amounts
of sample permits gravimetric determinations with the
same precision and accuracy as with the regular (macro)
procedures. Various procedures for handling, weighing,
precipitation, filtration, drying, and weighing on modified Nernst and Kuhlmann microbalances were published
around 1909. Titrimetric methods, such as the determinations of ammonia after Kjeldahl digestion, acid and
alkali titrations, iodometric titration of halogens,
etc., were described by his co-worker, F. Pilch, in 1910.
   Emich had shown convincingly that quantitative
organic microanalysis is possible with milligram amounts
of material and deserves recognition as the founder of
quantitative microanalysis in both inorganic and organic
chemistry. However, the Nobel prize was awarded to
F. Pregl, who adopted Emich's techniques.

<u>Quantitative Organic Microanalysis</u>. Another Austrian scientist sparked interest in this important practical application, which has become the most widely used technique in microanalysis. Fritz Pregl (1869-1930) had isolated a degradation product from bile acids in such a small yield that it would be lost in regular combustion analyses for carbon and hydrogen. Together with most organic chemists of his time he was familiar with the Liebig combustion procedure and he described in 1905 an automatic, gas-heated furnace so that "the organic chemist does not have to stay continuously with the furnace when performing a combustion." Influenced by Emich's success in quantitative microanalysis (through a lecture in 1909 Salzburg and by visiting Emich's laboratory), he decided to reduce the amounts of material in the macroprocedures to several milligrams, using a Kuhlmann-type balance.

Pregl proceeded promptly to develop microprocedures for carbon and hydrogen as well as nitrogen by the Dumas method in his laboratories in Innsbruck, Austria. His assistant, Max De Crinis, demonstrated a complete carbon and hydrogen analysis during a one-hour lecture given by Pregl before the German Chemical Society on February 11, 1911. Pregl described the methods developed at this time in "Abderhalden's Handbuch der biochemischen Arbeitsmethoden" (1912), and later as a professor in Graz in 1917 he published "Die quantitative organische Mikroanalyse," which had many revised editions with H. Roth and translations into other languages. An excellent staff of co-workers and the many international visitors spread the success story throughout the world, so that Pregl was awarded the Nobel prize in chemistry in 1923.

After Pregl's death in 1930 Hans Lieb succeeded as director of the Pregl Laboratories, and he continued work in organic chemistry, physiology, clinical chemistry, and toxicology and guided the affairs of the Austrian Microchemical and Analytical Society.

In the 1930s microanalysis was well established by continuous work in the area and by publications of Alfred Friedrich in Vienna (1933), Josef Lindner in Innsbruck (1935), Bötius in Berlin(1931), and C. Weygand in Leipzig (1931).

Following the Nobel prize award to Pregl, his methods found followers in the United States. Joseph B. Niederl started with teaching quantitative organic microanalysis at the Washington Square College, New York University in 1925, after he had taken courses in the laboratories of Pregl and Emich, on the advice of John A. Mandel, to increase his industrial experience in microchemistry. Since the American industry preferred

at that time to employ laboratory technicians for the
day-to-day analytical work, the above classwork included
simplifications of the procedure whenever possible. As
a result, the first American manual, "Micromethods of
Quantitative Organic Elementary Analysis," was published
by J. B. Niederl in 1938 followed by a second edition
with his brother Victor Niederl in 1942.

Working the hard way, by following the descriptions
in Pregl's book, the Hungarian scientist Adalbert Elek
(1887-1964) established probably the first American
microanalytical laboratory in 1923 at the Rockefeller
Institute in New York City. He described several variations of microanalytical procedures for halogens and
other elements, and for acetyl groups, methods which
are still used today. After retirement, he moved to
Los Angeles, where he established a well-known commercial microlaboratory.

Oskar Wintersteiner (1899-1971), a former co-worker
of Pregl, established microanalytical laboratories
wherever his research on natural products gave him an
opportunity to stay for a long enough time, such as the
Johns Hopkins University, Columbia University, and
finally the Squibb Institute for Medical Research.
Pregl personally instructed some of the foreign visitors
in the courses given at the University in Graz, provided he had acquired a personal interest in the individual, a development which did not occur very frequently. Pregl invited Karl Paul Link to the evening
assembly at the Heirichshof, where many of the unusual
names for microtools such as Dachhundbrenner, Hohl-
granate, etc., were created. He also invited Link to
the famous "Herringsalat" on Ash Wednesday, a special
ceremony to which only Pregl's closest friends could
come. The herring was shipped from Stockholm by H. von
Euler by special arrangement between these two Nobel
prize winners. Pregl remained a bachelor, and restaurant visits were of great importance.

Karl Paul Link repaid the favors received by establishing one of the finest microchemical laboratories at
the University of Wisconsin, Madison, about 1928. Together with Eugene W. Schueffel he later enlarged the
laboratories during the period to 1935. Link also per-
suaded the American manufacturers of laboratory apparatus to import equipment from Europe and then to manufacture it here, so that analysts became independent of
imports before World War II. Recognizing the importance
of carefully maintained dimensions in microapparatus,
Link used his influence to establish the first committee for recommended Specifications on Microchemical
Apparatus in the ACS Division of Microchemistry, with
George L. Royer as the first chairman and H. K. Alber

FRITZ PREGL, 1860-1930

    Pregl earned an MD degree at the University of Graz in 1894.
He worked for a time under Ostwald at Leipzig. His greatest
contributions were in the area of microchemistry, for which he was
awarded the 1923 Nobel Prize in Chemistry.

as a representative from industry. Another committee
to study performance of microchemical balances came a
little later, with C. J. Rodden as first chairman (followed by A. Corwin). These committees found their work
incorporated into international standardization under
the aegis of the American Society for Testing Materials
(ASTM) and by individuals in the Microchemical Commission of IUPAC.

W. R. Kirner, an early chairman of the Section of
Microchemistry, ACS, published several papers from the
Coal Research Laboratory of the Carnegie Institute of
Technology in 1935 and 1937 and also started American
reviews of developments in quantitative organic microanalysis. In a paper in 1939 he listed most of the U.S.
research institutes and industrial laboratories employing
microprocedures. These important reviews were continued
by Lawrence T. Hallett from the Eastman Kodak laboratories, where he established one of the first microanalytical laboratories in the nation. In his papers
he compared electric furnaces as described by G. L.
Royer (1940), J. A. Kuck (1940), and those obtainable
from American laboratory supply houses. The success of
organic chemistry is closely intertwined with the progress in the delicate procedures of elementary analysis
with even less than milligram amounts of natural products available for analysis. Especially in biochemical
and clinical research some of the methods had to be
adapted to special requirements. Paul L. Kirk (1902-
1970) faced this problem since he was self-taught in
microchemistry, when he started the first microcourses
at the University of California in Berkeley around 1920.
Needing fine pipets, burets, and other precision instruments for his biochemical research, he made them himself
at first and then supervised their manufacture with
strict controls, so that at least this line could soon
be used universally (1920-1934). He had to work in the
microgram and even down to the nanogram range. This
work led to the publication of the first book on "Ultra-
microanalysis" in 1950. At the same time at the Copenhagen research laboratories of the Carlsberg Brewery,
where Kjeldahl and Sørensen had conducted their investigations, K. U. Linderstrøm-Lang (1896-1959) with Heinz
Holter was more or less forced to develop ultra-deli-
cate procedures and instruments for enzyme studies in
cell material and in individual cells. They developed
burets and stirred vessels of a few microliters capacity.
Later advances into the nanogram range were also made
by David Glick around 1934 and used for clinical investigations by Samuel Natelson.

The first micro gas analytical procedures were
originated by August Krogh (1874-1949) in Scandinavia

in 1907. He measured gas volumes directly in micro gas
burets over mercury in the range of a few microliters
or less. Similar experiments were carried out by F. E.
Blacet and co-workers (1940) in their analyses of combustible compounds.

A different approach was taken by Donald D. Van
Slyke (1883-1971) with his manometric gas analysis tech-
niques--i.e., by measuring the pressure exerted on a
constant volume at room temperature. His methods, which
were designed for blood gas analysis, were published
with John P. Peters in 1932. As in other gas analytical
procedures--e.g., hydrogenation of unsaturated com-
pounds--internal stirring with magnetic elements eliminated the need for vigorous shaking of the large gas
buret setup. Magnetic stirring apparatus was originally
developed in the laboratories of the Arthur H. Thomas
Co., Philadelphia (1941).

Qualitative Organic Microanalysis. Emich advised
one of his former co-workers in 1933 by saying: "A
very much neglected field but very promising and badly
needed for synthetic work in natural products is the
systematic approach to qualitative *organic* microanalysis." In response to this challenge, H. K. Alber first
studied physical methods for establishing the necessary
physical constants and semi-quantitative estimation of
elements after decomposition. Frank Schneider and his
co-workers continued their investigation on a systematic
course of instruction in the identification of pure
organic compounds and published their results in the
manual "Qualitative Organic Microanalysis" (1946).

Micropreparative methods had become indispensable
with the increased research into the structure of
natural products, vitamins, biological entities, and
other chemical compounds obtained in small yields. From
the many approaches in this field the one by Hans Lieb
gained widest acclaim. He covered preparative methods
in organic chemistry with small amounts of material in
several publications with A. Soltys and then in book
form with W. Schöniger in 1950 and 1961.

A new and independent approach to the identification of organic compounds was offered by Fritz Feigl
(1891-1970) at the University of Vienna, in his spot
test analysis, which permitted the identification of
inorganic and organic compounds down to the microgram,
nanogram, and even picogram range. Color formation in
drops of liquids either on solid spot test plates or on
paper was considered by Feigl "not only a technique,
but experimental chemistry on a reduced scale." Feigl
is credited with a new systematic approach to the identification of organic structures in the microgram range,

FRIEDRICH EMICH, 1860–1940

Professor at the Technical University of Graz, Emich is considered the founder of classical microchemistry.

especially by applying the basic concepts of coordination chemistry to chemical reactions which result in color changes. He clearly defined the lower limits of identification and the elimination of disturbing groups by masking. His methods found immediate acceptance in teaching, even on the undergraduate level, and in industrial laboratories for controlling chemical processes. Recognition by other microchemists was rapid. For example, already in 1930, F. Emich invited Feigl to write a chapter on his work for the second edition of "Mikrochemisches Praktikum" (1931).

Other new approaches to the identification of organic compounds came from the fields of plant analysis and histochemistry. The botanist, Hans Molisch (1856-1937) enlarged the analysis of plants with his book, "Mikrochemie der Pflanzen" (1913), including methods which find frequent application in the analysis of drugs. Theodor Georg Wormley (1826-1897), at the University of Pennsylvania in 1867 and in 1885, published the book, "Microchemistry of Poisons," containing microscopic observations and methods. Also A. Mayrhofer in Vienna (1928), studied sublimation procedures to obtain well-formed crystals for the further identification of poisons.

Based on Otto Lehmann's experiments on thermo-microscopy (1891) and his crystallization microscope (1910), both unfortunately not widely known, two investigators in Innsbruck opened a new field of qualitative organic microanalysis intended primarily for pharmaceutical purposes but generally applicable to identification purposes in organic chemistry. Ludwig Kofler (1891-1951) and his wife, Adelheid Kofler, developed two hot stages, one with thermocouple and the other with thermometer indication of temperature. They heated drugs or other organic crystals to the melting point and observed their behavior under the microscope. Thus they made available added physical constants and crystallographic data for the pharmaceutical field and combined them into many tables, which help in the quick identification of organic compounds. Since only one crystal suffices for determination of characteristic constants, the micro hot stage has become an important tool in the day-to-day work of the analyst in special fields such as criminal investigations. Maria Kuhnert-Brandstätter, successor to Kofler, published many papers and an English book in 1971 (Pergamon Press). Another co-worker, Robert Fischer, specialized in determining critical solution temperatures using the hot stage microscope. Hot stage investigations during World War II resulted in a book by Walter C. McCrone on "Fusion Methods" (1957), as the thermo-micromethods are called here.

Qualitative and Quantitative Inorganic Microanalysis. The teaching of chemical microscopy at Cornell University and further developments center around the personality of Emile M. Chamot (1868-1950). The chemical microscopy laboratory was established on the advice of H. Behrens, even though Chamot was interested at the time in water research. Since comparatively few publications appeared from the laboratory prior to the so-called bible, "Chemical Microscopy" with Clyde M. Mason in 1918, the effective spirit of this institution can only be judged by the rapid advance of their students into leading positions in Universities and industrial management. Chamot and Mason trained many students: Julius A. Kuck, T. G. Rochow and George L. Royer (at American Cyanamid Co.), John Mitchell (at DuPont Co.), Walter C. McCrone (founder of W. C. McCrone Associates), and Mary L. Willard (at Pennsylvania State University), who have imprinted their names on the development of microchemistry in the United States.

It was very fortunate that Anton A. Benedetti-Pichler (1894-1934), assistant to F. Emich, was so impressed by the beauty of the National Park System during a visit in the United States because he made a prompt decision to accept an invitation from Washington Square College, New York University, where a center for microchemical research was established (1931) under William C. MacTavish. At the beginning he promoted qualitative procedures, developed a qualitative system of analysis, and emphasized the teaching of microchemistry even in undergraduate courses.

Co-workers and visitors to microchemical courses at New York University and those who joined Benedetti-Pichler at lunch in a Japanese restaurant in Greenwich Village were impressed by his preaching of accuracy, precision, and honesty in reporting data. Thus he became a great influence in the establishment of microchemical and analytical groups, but he never liked to take an official position.

One of the first micro quantitative analyses and separations was reported by the Swedish mineralogist Robert Mauselius in 1880, who analyzed the mineral kainosite from Nordmarken for SiO_2, Y_2O_3, Fe, Ca, Mg, alkali metals, and H_2O using only 67 mg of sample. Certainly this was an astonishing accomplishment even at the centigram level. V. Goldschmidt of Heidelberg published in 1877 a quantitative procedure for determining silver and gold in the form of spheres (after cupellation) by measuring their diameters under the microscope. This method is considered to be one of the first quantitative microprocedures.

Quantitative Separations. F. Emich with J. Donau published the first quantitative separation procedures, using mostly gravimetric methods, in 1909 and the following years. F. Pilch described the first titrimetric procedures, using a special microburet permitting measurements of 20 nl. Mercury-driven dispensing burets were designed by Linderstrøm-Lang and H. Holter and by Paul L. Kirk for titration of extremely small quantities of material.

Donau continued the development of improved separation procedures and published, with Friedrich Hecht, many gravimetric procedures in "Anorganische Gewichtsanalyse" in 1940.

A. A. Benedetti-Pichler was interested in extending the limits of all his microchemical work beyond their current range. After establishing with B. Baule (1928) the possible limits of a uniform sample size, which is the first prerequisite for obtaining accurate and reproducible results, he calculated the necessary reduction in the size of working tools, vessels, pipets and burets. First he studied the qualitative processes, and then he showed with his co-workers M. Cefola, A. Loscalzo, J. R. Rachele and S. Siggia that working techniques with nanograms are comparable in accuracy with those used for micrograms. The nanogram procedures proved not to be as difficult as expected, and they could be demonstrated to larger audiences. Together with the methods developed by Paul L. Kirk these methods formed the foundation for the separation of the uranium elements in the Manhattan Project during World War II.

The Instrumental Period from 1945 to 1970s. After the end of World War II the secrecy surrounding several major advances was lifted, and free communication between all countries was possible again. The post-classical approaches are either continuations and perfections of prior analytical work or offer new viewpoints through the use of physical methods and instrumentation improved by electronic discoveries. Wider use of the microgram procedures developed from the atomic energy research in the Manhattan Project enabled identification of new elements available only in the amounts of a few micrograms and having unknown radiation effects.

Under the guidance of Glenn T. Seaborg, who was familiar with radiochemistry and tracer techniques, several scientists combined their knowledge from various fields (microgram and nanogram chemistry, entomology, biochemistry) and isolated 2.77 µg of plutonium dioxide. Burris B. Cunningham constructed a modified Salviono balance to weigh such small amounts with his co-workers M. Cefola, R. Patton, I. Perlman, and others. Kirk

with Craig, Gullberg, and Boyer, at the University of
California, improved this instrument in 1947 to give a
sensitivity of 0.02 µg with a load capacity of 25 mg.

Studies of the chemistry of the transuranium elements included more and more quantitative aspects and
were extended to handling and measuring accurately solutions in the microliter range. The micrometer buret
of P. F. Scholander (Swarthmore College), the modified
Rehberg universal-type capillary buret of Paul L. Kirk
(1941), and the self-filling horizontal buret of Benedetti-Pichler (1942) gave the necessary accuracy. These
burets, together with several types of self-filling and
full-displacement pipets, allowed quantitative titrimetric procedures to be carried out; the dimensions
were found to be satisfactory for the microgram procedures and have been recommended by the Standardization
Committees of ACS, ASTM, and AOAC.

Introduction of fluorescence, x-ray, atomic absorption, neutron activation, microradiography, electron
probe, and other methods made possible the analysis of
substances at lower levels than previously possible.
This revolutionized identification of counterfeits and
overpaintings and enabled analysis of ultra-small
amounts.

An excellent review of Russian contributions to
the nanogram techniques was presented by I. A. Alimarin
and M. N. Petrikova in their book, "Anorganische Ultra-
mikroanalyse," (Berlin, 1962), with reference to the
contributions by I. M. Korenman, K. Komarek, E. N.
Vinogradov, and others. Only in the latest International Microchemical Congresses in 1970 in Graz were
personal contacts permitted with the scientists from
communist countries.

Maria Kuhnert-Brandstätter combined thermomicroscopic methods with UV spectroscopy, especially for substances that decomposed upon heating (1965-1973). Walter
C. McCrone and his co-workers popularized the field,
first by emphasizing the "fusion methods," which are
similar to the thermomicroscopic techniques (1957); then
they showed in many publications the usefulness of the
ordinary microscope and of the most elaborate optical
instruments with the highest magnifications in research
and industrial applications. Especially in the biological sciences the electron microscope has gained a
dominant position. Ernst Wiesenberger combined electrolytic microtechniques with observations in the electron microscope in 1961, mostly on inorganic compounds.
The temperatures of the hot stages have been raised
considerably over the years, from 360°C in the original
Kofler stage to ca. 1800°C in high temperature models,
and the low temperature range has been reduced to -80°C.

WALTER C. McCRONE, 1916-

    Educated at Cornell University, McCrone worked for 12 years at the Armour Research Institute prior to founding his own company to provide services in microscopical chemistry. He has done much to further the interests of this branch of analytical chemistry.

The thesis that teaching of organic chemistry to large classes could be improved by a greater number of experiments in a shorter time motivated Nicholas D. Cheronis (1896-1962) to compose numerous manuals and textbooks together with John B. Entrikin, T. S. Ma, Herman Stein, and others on macro-, semimicro-, and micromethods for organic chemistry and qualitative organic analysis. He promoted also the extension of microtechniques to the lowest possible limits and chaired the symposium on "Submicrogram Experimentation" in 1960. He edited the papers of the International Symposium on Microchemical Techniques in 1961, which appeared in Volume 2 of the *Microchemical Journal Symposium Series* (1962).

F. Feigl's spot test analysis and chemistry of specific, selective, and sensitive reactions found many interesting applications to research and industrial problems. Especially original was the new ring-oven technique of Herbert Weisz, in which microgram amounts of ions were eluted from a spot and were deposited by evaporation in rings. In the most recent work biological complexes are formed as adsorption rings without heat, samples and reagents are added into the center, and fluorescent segments appear in time sequence according to the quantities of enzymes present (1975). The sensitive and adaptable ring-oven techniques have been used successfully in trace analysis, air pollution studies, chromatographic separations, etc.

Communications in the progress of quantitative organic microanalysis techniques were hindered during World War II, especially with Germany. In a report by R. Belcher and D. F. Phillips (*B.I.O.S.* No. 3315) for the British Department of Scientific and Industrial Research on visits to leading German microchemical laboratories in 1947, the surprising statement was made that most laboratories used atleast semi-automatic combustion trains with electric furnaces, which were not used much in England at the time. The generally accepted method for organic oxygen was the direct determination, based on the oxidation of the formed CO by iodine pentoxide, introduced by Josef Unterzaucher (1901-1973) and based on the semi-micromethod of M. Schütze (1939). A group at Hercules Powder Co., V. A. Aluise, R. T. Hall, F. C. Staats, and W. W. Becker, introduced the method after the war into the United States (1947). Wolfgang Kirsten promoted it in Sweden, and A. Steyermark described it in detail, with available references on applications, in his manual and reference book, "Quantitative Organic Microanalysis" (1951, 1961).

A novel decomposition procedure for organic compounds was successfully introduced by Wolfgang Schöniger

(1920-1971) in 1955 for microdetermination of halogens
in organic compounds, by igniting the sample, which is
held in a platinum gauze in an atmosphere of oxygen.
The oxygen flask procedure had its origin in the macro-
procedure of W. Hempel (1892), which was modified to a
semi-microtechnique by O. Mikl and J. Pech (1952-53)
but was overlooked until Schöniger re-introduced the
technique.

The fundamental combustion step in the basic Pregl
technique was studied by numerous microchemists in order
to obtain a rapid and complete combustion of the organic
material and eliminate interference by certain elements.

In the post-World War II period the sample weight
of substances difficult to obtain was reduced in time
from milligram to microgram, as demonstrated by R.
Belcher in England (1966), Wolfgang Kirsten in Sweden
(1962), K. Hozumi in Japan, and Unterzaucher and Günther
Tölg in Germany. Tölg in a book, "Chemische Elementar-
analyse mit kleinsten Proben" (1968), discussed the
difficulties in handling, weighing, and decomposing the
organic matter at the lowest levels. Advances in micro-
titrimetry were reviewed and published by J. Mika (1958).

The rapid developments in electronics are closely
connected with and largely responsible for analytical
progress independent of the amounts of material involved.
The analytical service laboratories of industry require
rapid answers on numerical values for their products.
The necessary speed-up independent of costs was eventually reached through complete automation and use of
instruments of highest quality.

Since the end of the war, instruments have essentially replaced human labor in quantitative organic
microanalysis. In succession, improved electrical furnaces with temperature ranges from 100° to 1200°C,
movable heating elements, the programming of all phases
to become automatic, and determination of the end products by physical means took hold in the microchemical
laboratory and led to the construction of elemental
analyzers for C, H, N, O. Several workshop meetings
were held at the International Symposium at Pennsylvania
State University 1965, 1968, and 1973 and in 1970 at
Graz, where the new equipment and its use were demonstrated.

Several automatic analyzers have been developed
for carbon, hydrogen, nitrogen, and/or oxygen determinations with a capability of interfacing with a computer. The efforts of Wolfgang Merz at the microchemical analysis laboratories of the BASF in Ludwigshafen am Rhein were directed toward completely automated individual analyzers for carbon, for hydrogen,
for nitrogen, and for oxygen, which were coupled with

digital display, balances, an automatic sample feeder,
pulse counter, and printer.

Thus microanalysis has indeed reached its heights
in the past 100 years. With humble beginnings in Austria its influence was extended to Germany, the United
States, Britain, and Sweden and nurtured the leading
microchemists of today. However it is interesting that
many American universities have dropped formal courses
in microchemistry while on the other hand the industrial
need of these specialities has greatly increased.

Decomposition and Dissolution of Samples for Analysis. The success of classical macro- and microanalysis
of substances--animal or mineral--depended upon suitable
methods of decomposition and dissolution of samples to
liberate or to simplify subsequent separation of individual, simpler components of the samples. Development
of such methods and suitable reagents began, not surprisingly, with the ancient alchemists. Certainly the
earliest method utilized was thermal decomposition,
serving at the time to liberate noble metals and mercury
from rocks and minerals. In the 1st century A.D., Greek
alchemists greatly refined the thermal decomposition
technique by inventing stills and crude distillation
apparatus. In the hands of Arabic alchemists in the
10th century, the distillation apparatus of the Greeks
was further improved and used for destructive distillation and crude analysis of animal substances. During
this same period Arabic alchemists first prepared
caustic alkalis and sal ammoniac, reagents that later
proved useful for sample dissolution. An extremely
significant advance, which made possible tremendous
progress in chemical analysis, was the introduction and
preparation of nitric and sulfuric acids, described in
an early 13th century Byzantine manuscript. Later contributions, described by Geber in the 14th century,
provided methods for preparation of nitric acid and
aqua regia by distillation of mixtures of vitriol and
saltpeter or sal ammoniac. The discovery and availability of strong mineral acids greatly enhanced the
ability of chemists to dissolve and to decompose substances for analysis. Nitric acid and aqua regia soon
became common reagents and were produced on a large
scale. A further achievement was the preparation of
free hydrochloric acid, first described in the 16th
century.

With the advent of the scientific method in chemistry and the need for accurate quantitative methods,
it soon became imperative to develop methods and reagents that would enable efficient, effective dissolution and decomposition of a great variety of substances.

The requirements were strict. Methods had to be reasonably rapid, could not result in loss of sought-for substances or contamination by interfering substances from
vessels or added reagents, should not introduce exces-
sive amounts of salts even if relatively inert, must
liberate or convert sought-for substances completely
into readily measurable forms, and ideally should not
require unusual or elaborate equipment. Obviously no
single method could possibly serve all purposes let
alone completely satisfy all the ideal requirements.
Considerable ingenuity and much tedious investigation
were frequently necessary to achieve the best compromise
for each sample type. The history of further developments in the art and science of sample preparation for
analysis consists of innumerable contributions, often
small but rarely insignificant, by countless and even
unknown chemists. Thanks to the work of such forbears,
modern analytical chemists have the equipment, methods,
and reagents available from which to select or to devise
the most appropriate means of dissolving or decomposing
a remarkable array of different substances. The following paragraphs present some historical perspectives
of certain selected and important advances in this area,
with particular attention to the individuals involved.

Wet Combustion Methods. Certainly the most successful and famous of the earliest wet combustion
methods is that of the Danish chemist Johan Gustaf
Kjeldahl, reported in 1883 for the determination of
nitrogen content of proteins. The key to the success
of Kjeldahl's method was the use of concentrated sulfuric acid, a mild oxidizing agent, as digestion medium.
Numerous modifications in apparatus and auxillary reagents have been made since 1883, but the essential
method remains fundamentally the same to this day. Its
use is widespread and of great value to industry, nutrition, biology, and medicine.
Although sulfuric acid proved an excellent medium
for digesting many samples for determination of nitrogen, it was not satisfactory for certain types of samples or for the complete destruction of organic matter.
Stronger oxidizing agents were needed. Among the oxidants investigated in early 1900s for this purpose were
persulfate, permanganate, peroxide, and perchloric acid.
A remarkable renaissance in methodology of sample
treatment began with the introduction of perchloric
acid and recognition of its potential in chemical analysis. With the availability of perchloric acid, a new
technique was to come forth which would largely replace
dry ashing of organic substances--i.e., wet chemical
oxidation utilizing the strong oxidizing action of

perchloric acid when concentrated and hot.

Typical of many important discoveries in chemistry, a long interval (over a century) elapsed between the synthesis and the eventual popular analytical utilization of perchloric acid. First prepared in 1816 by F. von Studion, who referred to it as oxygenated chloric acid, perchloric acid was first obtained as an aqueous solution containing about 70% $HClO_4$, approximating the dihydrate. Following procedures similar to those of von Studion, involving preparation of pure potassium perchlorate from the chlorate and distillation of mixtures of potassium perchlorate and concentrated sulfuric acid, the French chemist G. S. Sérrulas obtained the crystalline monohydrate ($HClO_4 \cdot H_2O$) in 1831, the English chemist H. E. Roscoe prepared the anhydrous acid ($HClO_4$) in 1862, and the Americans A. Michael and W. T. Conn isolated the anhydride (Cl_2O_7) in 1900. The various hydrates and forms of perchloric acid displayed remarkable differences in properties, especially in explosive tendencies, considering the minor differences in compositions. Difficulty and cost of preparation, coupled with the uncertainty and risk of explosion, discouraged all but the most brave from further investigations on the possible analytical utility of perchloric acid. By 1900 it had become obvious that only the monohydrate, dihydrate, or aqueous solutions less than 72% $HClO_4$ might be employed with impunity. Perchloric anhydride preparation had proved very dangerous. In the words of Michael and Conn "the apparatus may be virtually pulverized by violent explosion, and personal precautions must be taken accordingly." Chlorine heptoxide explodes on contact with flame or by percussion and decomposes spontaneously on standing for a few days. According to Roscoe, anhydrous perchloric acid also decomposes spontaneously within a few weeks, even in the dark, and eventually explodes. If added to water, it produces a hissing sound, and in contact with bare skin it causes serious and painful wounds. Surely it was with some trepidation that subsequent investigators of perchloric acid approached their subject. Among those who persevered to brave the risks were Hobart H. Willard at the University of Michigan and his doctoral students, one of whom was destined to become the leading advocate, innovator, and manufacturer of perchloric acid. The individual, whose name was to become synonomous with perchloric acid in the minds of generations of analytical chemists, was G. Frederick Smith (1891-1976).

G. F. Smith pursued his long and productive studies of perchloric acid chemistry, first as a doctoral student of Willard at the University of Michigan and later as a faculty member at the University of Illinois, where until recently, although officially retired since 1956,* he maintained an active interest by encouraging others in their investigation on uses of perchloric acid. When Smith began graduate work in 1918, Willard assigned him the problem of preparing the alkali and alkaline earth metal perchlorates and determining their solubilities in water and various organic solvents. First Smith had to prepare and distill 200 lbs of 70% $HClO_4$, following a procedure that Willard had devised in 1912 based upon the treatment of ammonium perchlorate with nitric acid. Experiencing no mishap or difficulty, except for the usual rigors of research, Smith succeeded in preparing the 200 lbs of acid and then the metal perchlorates. It was during the solubility measurements that he met with mishap. While heating a mixture of approximately 50 ml of ethyl acetate and solid magnesium perchlorate to effect saturation, a violent explosion occurred. In his words, "the glass fragments from the exploding vessel perforated windows, reagent bottles, light bulbs and myself like sieves, causing part of our contents to flow forth in small streams." Taken to the University Hospital and anesthetized for removal of glass fragments, Smith regained consciousness to behold a vision of an angel which gradually assumed the form of his nurse, later to become his wife, Mary Ellen Sweeney. According to Smith, this one fateful explosion was his first and only serious accidental one in all his many years of studying perchloric acid chemistry. He had learned his first lesson well: always begin with very small samples in testing new mixtures of perchlorate chemicals. Moreover, he was not deterred but more determined than ever to continue his research and to develop safe, practical methods for the utilization and study of perchloric acid chemistry.

One of the first important applications of perchloric acid in analysis was in the determination of silica in steel, metals, alloys, limestone, and soluble silicates, as described by Willard and Cake in 1920. Samples treated with perchloric acid and concentrated by heating to the azeotrope (68-70% $HClO_4$) yielded silica quantitatively and rapidly in easily filtered form. Moreover, the silica was efficiently dehydrated by the constant boiling acid mixture and could be readily washed free of metal perchlorate salts, most of which are highly soluble. Perchloric acid thus provided exceptional advantages over hydrochloric or

---

*Professor Smith died in 1976, while this History was being prepared.

GEORGE FREDERICK SMITH, 1891-1976

Following graduate studies at the University of Michigan,
where he worked under the mentorship of H. H. Willard, Smith
joined the faculty of the University of Illinois, where he rose
through the ranks to become Emeritus Professor in 1956.   He was
founder of two companies, the G. Frederick Smith Chemical Co. and
Aeration Processes, Inc., and ran them with the help of his two
brothers.   He is especially known for his work with compounds related to 1,10-phenanthrolene, and for his enthusiastic championing
of perchloric acid as an analytical reagent.

sulfuric acids. In view of the importance and frequency
of silica determinations in commercial analysis the
prospects for popular acceptance of perchloric acid
seemed bright indeed. Cost and commercial availability,
however, remained as deterrents to widespread use. By
1925 other analytical uses for the acid and its salts
had been reported, increasing the interest and demand
for perchlorate chemicals. Smith and Willard (1922)
had demonstrated magnesium perchlorate to be an excellent desiccant and Smith (1925) had reported on the use
of perchloric acid in the separation and determination
of alkali metals. To supply the needs of a growing
number of requests for perchlorates, Smith undertook
the commercial preparation of perchloric acid and magnesium perchlorate on a part-time basis in 1925, working
in his garage in Urbana with equipment purchased with a
loan from his first customer. By 1928 the business had
grown to the stage where Smith could no longer spare
time from his very active research and teaching at the
University of Illinois. Demand for perchlorates however was too small to attract any of the larger chemical
manufacturers to purchase his business, but Smith did
manage to find two very able and optimistic partners
(his brothers C. M. and A. H. Smith) to relieve him and
his wife of the day-to-day operations. Thus the G.
Frederick Smith Chemical Co. was moved to Columbus,
Ohio, in 1928, and with time, patience and much effort
it prospered. So also, by the same measure, did perchloric acid and analytical chemistry prosper from the
availability of chemicals and technical literature provided by the company. Numerous new applications of
perchloric acid in analysis were soon forthcoming.

   The next and even more important historical development was the introduction of perchloric acid dihydrate
for use in wet oxidation and destruction of organic
matter prior to elemental analysis. Pioneers in this
development, with their earliest contribution and location noted in parentheses, included E. Kahane (1920,
France), B. Means and R. E. Hussey (1921, Williams College), E. Wolesensky (1928, U. S. Bureau of Standards),
and G. F. Smith (1932, University of Illinois). Through
the years 1930-1960 Smith and Kahane proved to be the
most prolific contributors, publishing with their students and associates numerous procedures for the destruction of a great many different substances with
perchloric acid or its mixtures with other strong mineral acids. The various methods found wide acceptance
over dry ashing techniques because of their simplicity,
lower risk of loss of volatile elements, and greatly
diminished tendency for retention by the vessel of
sought-for elements. Interest in perchloric acid

oxidations continued to grow and remains strong to this day as evidenced by frequent citations and new contributions in the recent literature.

Combustion Methods. The development of combustion methods for elemental analysis of organic compounds has been traced above. Similar methods for inorganic samples are not as commonplace, but some notable examples exist. J. C. Warf and co-workers, during the Manhattan Project (1942-45) developed pyrohydrolysis methods for fluoride and other halides, based on the passage of steam at elevated temperatures over refractory samples to evolve hydrogen halides. A somewhat opposite type of high temperature reaction is that developed by Sievers et al. (1966); he converted titanium oxide to $TiCl_4$ by reaction with CCl_4 in a sealed tube and determined titanium by gas chromatography.

A room temperature combustion method using excited oxygen activated by radiofrequencies was introduced only a few years ago. This new method, even though very slow, has achieved wide use in the determination of trace amounts of elements which could be easily lost.

A remarkably effective wet combustion method was devised by Donald D. Van Slyke in 1940 for determining carbon in biological and other samples for which dry combustion methods are either impractical or require extensive modifications. Van Slyke and his co-worker J. Folch demonstrated that a mixture of iodic and chromic acids in sulfuric and phosphoric acids effected complete conversion of the carbon content of samples to carbon dioxide within one or two minutes, giving results comparable in accuracy with conventional dry combustion methods. The Van Slyke-Folch method and apparatus were widely accepted and are commonly used to this day. Van Slyke made many important contributions to biochemistry and clinical chemistry by devising reliable methods and efficient instrumentation suitable for rapid routine applications. Trained as an organic chemist under Moses Gomberg at the University of Michigan (B.A. 1905, Ph.D. 1907), Van Slyke was destined to become as well known among analytical chemists as two other University of Michigan graduates of his era--namely, H. H. Willard (B.A. 1903) and G. Frederick Smith (B.A. 1917). All three won analytical chemistry's highest recognition, the Fisher Award; all three made notable contributions to methods for wet oxidation; all three received early inspiration and motivation from Professor Gomberg.

Although Fenton's Reagent (hydrogen peroxide in the presence of Fe(II)) had long been known in organic chemistry, it was not until 1968 that B. Sansoni, in Munich, used this reagent for decomposition of kilogram quantities of meat at room temperature to determine traces of radioactive contaminants.

Fusion Methods. The technique of fusing intractable samples with potassium or sodium carbonate in silver or platinum crucibles, originated by the German chemist M. H. Klaproth in the early 1800s, greatly facilitated analysis of minerals, especially silicates. Numerous other fluxes, acidic and basic, oxidizing and non-oxidizing, have been investigated since the time of Klaproth for use in decomposing organic as well as inorganic materials. Two fusion methods of special historical interest and importance are the J. Lawrence Smith fusion and the S. W. Parr peroxide bomb methods.

In the 1850s J. Lawrence Smith, a pioneer American analyst, developed the first satisfactory method for the determination of sodium and potassium in silicate minerals. The method which now bears his name involves ignition of a mixture of the sample with ammonium chloride and calcium carbonate in a tall-form crucible to produce a fusion product from which sodium and potassium combined can be obtained as water soluble chlorides free of other metal ions by suitable subsequent steps. During his researches on fusion methods, the Bunsen burner was introduced, and Smith was delighted with its advantages over the charcoal furnace he had been obliged to use previously. Smith's method for the determination of sodium and potassium was widely used for over 60 years, before flame photometry became popular. Even now, Smith's fusion method is frequently used to obtain suitable aqueous solutions for photometric determination of the alkali metals. The lessons from history are convincingly clear. So-called instrumental methods tend to augment more than supplant classical methods, and seemingly simple innovations can have far-reaching consequences. Witness the role of the Bunsen burner on the enhancement of ignition fusion and combustion efficiencies as well as of flame emission sensitivities of atoms in flame photometry.

S. W. Parr of the University of Illinois introduced in 1899 a new type of calorimeter for determining heats of combustion of fuels based upon the use of sodium peroxide as oxidant in a sealed vessel. Parr soon recognized that his peroxide bomb technique could also be used advantageously for elemental analysis of organic substances. Loss of volatile elements could be avoided completely. To accelerate the combustion reaction and to provide high decomposition temperatures without recourse to unusually high ignition temperatures, Parr added a small amount of potassium perchlorate to the sample as an "accelerator." Samples low in oxidizable matter required addition of sucrose, benzoic acid, or other combustible matter to facilitate ignition and to moderate combustion rates. In 1919 Parr described the use of his bomb technique for the determination of sulfur in coal. With minor modifications both macro- and microsize Parr peroxide bombs are in popular use today, not only for sulfur determinations but also for boron, silicon, selenium, phosphorous, fluorine, and other halogens in petroleum, coke, coal, ash residues, rubber, etc. Recently, Teflon-lined bombs of the Parr type were introduced for use with hydrofluoric acid or fluoroboric acid systems to decompose samples prior to flame photometric analysis, thereby eliminating serious interferences from alkali metal ions present in previously used fluxes.

R. S. Juvet and R. L. Fisher (1966) used the direct reaction of refractory alloys and compounds with elemental fluorine to produce volatile fluorides and oxyfluorides that could be determined by gas chromatography.

Future Prospects. In certain respects the past can indeed reveal the future, at least with regard to further progress in sample treatment prior to analysis. Future developments leading to improvements certainly must involve new reagents, energy sources, and apparatus. Perhaps new oxidizing agents will be generated in situ by thermal or electromagnetic energy applied to a stable intermediate that is intimately mixed with the sample.

It is clearly only a matter of time before lasers will be commonly used for thermal decomposition of certain analytical samples. It is highly probable that new materials of construction will lead to improved combustion tubes, bombs, and crucibles. The future of analytical chemistry is indeed inextricably linked with the past.

THERMAL ANALYSIS

Theophrastrus, ca. 300 B.C., recorded the effect of heat on various rocks and minerals as well as on other materials. The early analytical chemists developed methods based on the judicious application of heat, such as the assay of gold and silver metals, the use of the blow pipe for analysis of rocks and minerals, and so on. The latter technique is now only of historical interest, but at one time it was very widely used, especially for the analysis of minerals.

In the 18th century, fairly accurate temperature measuring devices were developed which placed the

application of heat to a chemical reaction on a more
quantitative basis. Guillaume Amontons demonstrated an
early air thermometer in Paris as early as 1700, but
its development into a more accurate temperature measuring device had to wait until the 19th century. The
most widely used temperature measuring technique during
this period, according to Mackenzie, was the Wedgewood
pyrometer, which was described in 1782. It consisted
of a piece of china clay, which after firing at a dull
red heat, was cut into a triangular shaped fragment.
From the change in dimensions of the fragment, the temperature of the furnace could be calculated in "degrees
Wedgewood," In an attempt to correlate this temperature
scale with the Fahrenheit scale it was found that one
degree Wedgewood corresponded to 130°F at temperatures
above 1077°F, the beginning of the scale. The results
obtained were highly erroneous because clay shrinkage
is not linear with temperature; thus, the melting point
of cast iron was calculated to be about 10,000°C.

Most of the methods of temperature measurement were
developed in the 19th century. In 1821 T. J. Seebeck
observed the thermoelectric effect which was applied to
high temperature measurements by A. C. Becquerel in
1826. Many difficulties were experienced by this new
method due to the uncertainty of the composition of the
alloys employed. However, as a result of the efforts
of Henry LeChatelier and others, the thermocouple was
eventually developed into an accurate temperature measuring device by the 1880s. Other high temperature
measuring devices--the resistance thermometer and the
optical pyrometer--were developed by W. Siemens (1871)
and LeChatelier (1892), respectively.

Once accurate temperature measuring techniques
were developed, it was inevitable that they would soon
be applied to chemical systems at elevated temperatures.
Thus, Hannay in 1877 studied the isothermal mass change
of "amorphous" materials although he did not heat them
above 100°C. LeChatelier, who was interested in both
clays and pyrometry, among other things, introduced the
identification of clays by heating rate change curves,
dT_s/dt, in 1887. Many thermal analysts today honor him
as the father of differential thermal analysis (DTA)
although others give the English metallurgist, W. C.
Roberts-Austen, credit because of his development of
the *differential* measurement technique in 1899. One
year earlier than the work in clays by LeChatelier, E.
Lovejoy published mass-loss data on clays and reported
that kaolin decomposed near the melting point of antimony, 624°C. This work, as well as that of Nernst and
Riesenfeld in 1903, probably foreshadowed the advent of
thermogravimetry (TG).

Development of DTA. Differential thermal analysis originated either in France or England. LeChatelier, who published the heating curves of several clays, used the photographic recording of the reflection from a galvanometer mirror of a spark generated by an induction coil. The curve consisted of a series of vertical lines whose spacing on the photographic paper indicated the relative temperature of the clay. As the clays decomposed, they absorbed heat, thus yielding a characteristic pattern of lines. In modern practice, these curves would correspond to the first derivative of the sample temperature, T_s, or dT_s/dt, rather than the differential temperature (T_s-T_r).

The differential temperature method, in which the temperature of the sample is compared with that of an inert reference material, was conceived by Roberts-Austen in 1899. His apparatus eliminated the effect of heating rate and other outside disturbances that could change the temperature of the sample. The difference in temperature, (T_s-T_r), was observed directly from galvanometer G_2 while the sample temperature would be obtained from galvanometer G_1. Saladin carried this method one step further in 1904 when he developed a photographic recorder that could plot (T_s-T_r) vs. T_s directly. A more versatile photographic recorder, which used a rotating drum rather than a flat plate photographic paper holder, was developed by Kurnakov in 1904. This instrument was extensively used by Russian workers in DTA for 50 or 60 years and was influential in starting the Russian school of DTA.

Development of DTA in the United States. The development of the technique of DTA in the United States can be related to the number of publications. A remarkable compilation of 4,248 references by Smothers and Chiang covers the period from 1877 to 1964 and includes practically all of the published DTA papers. There was an induction period of about 60 years before the 100 papers-per-year level was attained. However, after 1950 the number of papers increased sharply, 10-20% per year, a trend which continued to about 1969, at least in analytical chemistry. Thus, the modern era of DTA appears to have begun in about 1950.

Who were the early American workers in DTA, and what did they do? The first American to use or to mention DTA in a paper was G. K. Burgess of the National Bureau of Standards, who published a classic paper on cooling curves in 1908. He discussed the various methods of recording cooling curves, including the use of differential curves, derivative curves, and so on. This article is an excellent review of the state of the art up to 1908. Clays and silicate minerals were the subject of other early DTA papers, such as those by H. E. Ashley (1911), C. N. Fenner, and Brown and Montgomery (1912). It should be noted that these materials would be the subject of numerous future DTA studies and would constitute the major use of this technique for the next 40 years. Thus, because of its predominant geological application, DTA was developed by geologists, clay mineralogists, ceramicists, soil scientists, and others who worked in this area. Very few chemists used the technique until the late 1940s and early 1950s although there are notable exceptions such as F. C. Kracek.

Some of the early American workers in DTA, up to 1950 are shown in Table I. Most of their research subjects were in clays, minerals, and inorganic systems. After 1950, it is more difficult to select the prominent investigators due to the much greater number of authors and publications. Also, to evaluate the importance of some of these investigations, we will have to await the judgment of history. It is possible, however, to identify several prominent American workers. R. L. Stone was one. He developed a dynamic gas DTA system in 1951 which permitted the flow of a gas or vapor through a sample during the heating or cooling cycle. This gave precise, reproducible control of the furnace

Table I.   Some Early American Workers in DTA up to 1950

Year	Name	Subject of Research
1908	G. K. Burgess	Cooling curves
1911	H. E. Ashley	Clays
1925	J. W. Greig	Clays
1929	F. C. Kracek	Inorganic compounds
1936	I. Barshad	Soils
1936	H. P. Klug	$CuSO_4 \cdot 5H_2O$
1937	F. H. Norton	Clays, minerals
1939	S. B. Hendricks	Clays, soils
1940	R. E. Grim	Clays
1941	E. S. Newman	$CaSO_4 \cdot 2H_2O$
1941	R. D. Vold, M. J. Vold	Soaps
1942	R. A. Rowland	Clays
1943	J. A. Pask	Clays
1943	S. Speil	Clays, theory
1944	L. H. Berkelhamer	Clays, theory
1947	P. F. Kerr, J. L. Kulp	Clays, minerals

atmosphere. Indeed, Stone had developed the first precision DTA system, which was to change the entire
approach to this technique. He was enough of an inven-
tor and businessman to start his own company to manufacture and to sell thermal analysis equipment. For many
years his instruments were widely used in all phases of
DTA work and were considered to be the standard system
in the field. Most of the studies from 1900-1960 were
carried out using home-built instruments. Naturally,
when a precision instrument such as that described by
Stone became commercially available, it generally stimulated work in the field. However, his instruments were
not available until the middle 1950s so until the 1960s
many investigations were carried out using equipment
assembled by the various investigators themselves.

Besides the many workers mentioned in Table I,
numerous studies were carried out by Gruver, Stross,
Abrams, Whitehead, Breger, Smothers, Wittels, Borchardt,
Roy, Campbell, Gordon, Haendler, Garn, Morita, Kissinger,
Lodding, Murphy, and Wendlandt to name only a few. Most
of the investigations were still done on clays, minerals, ceramics, and coal, but numerous inorganic and
organic compounds were also being studied. DTA was
gradually being accepted by chemists as a research and
analytical technique.

The 1960s saw the introduction of elaborate DTA
instruments including the development of differential
scanning calorimetry (DSC) by O'Neill in 1964. Other
notable systems were developed by DuPont, Deltaherm,
and Mettler, to name only a few. Perhaps the greatest
impetus to the development of new instruments and thermal techniques was the interest shown by polymer chemists. DTA is an ideal tool for use in polymer charac-
terization--such parameters as melting point, glass
transition temperatures, polymerization, thermal degra-
dation, and oxidation reactions can be studied in minutes as compared with hours or days by other methods.
Not only were elevated temperatures required but low
temperature DTA was necessary for the determination of
glass transition temperatures and other data. Also,
since small sample sizes were permissible, new furnace
and sample holder designs were developed as well as
better amplifiers and linear temperature programmers.
After 1960, DTA had indeed become an important technique
in most branches of chemistry.

Development of Thermogravimetry. The effect of
heat on analytical precipitates was initially studied
to improve the accuracy of analytical procedures. To
do this conveniently, a balance had to be constructed
which permitted simultaneous heating and weighing of

the precipitate. Perhaps the first such instrument was
described by W. Nernst and E. H. Riesenfeld in 1903 and
was used to study the mass-loss on heating of Iceland
spar, opal, and zirconia. Two years later, Brill recorded what was probably the first TG curve--the mass-
loss curve of $CaCO_3$ up to 1200°C. Using a method which
resembled present-day TG, Truchot studied the effect of
heat on pyrite and pyrrhotite in 1907. In 1912 Urbain
and Boulanger constructed an electromagnetic compensation balance which was used to study the dehydration of
metal salt hydrates. Urbain, in 1922, remarked to
Duval, then a young research worker in his laboratory,
"the results depend too much on the heating conditions."
The first instrument to be called a thermobalance
was described by Kotaro Honda in 1915. He used this
balance to determine the TG curves on $MnSO_4 \cdot H_2O$, $CaCO_3$,
and CrO_3. Honda was apparently a very modest worker
because he concluded his paper by stating:

> All of the results given are not altogether
> original; the present investigation with the
> thermobalance has however revealed the exact
> positions of the change in structure and also
> the velocity of the change in respect to tem-
> peratures. The investigation also shows the
> great convenience of using such a balance in
> similar investigations in chemistry.

Honda, along with his student H. Saito, started the
Japanese school of thermogravimetry.
The French school of thermogravimetry was started
by Guichard, who in 1923 began a series "directed principally to the realization of a linear elevation of
temperature with respect to time." His pioneering
efforts in this field are summarized by this statement:

> The method of studying chemical systems through
> their changes in weight when subjected to tem-
> peratures varied in a regular fashion may be
> widely employed, provided certain precautions
> are taken. It will be usefully applied to
> certain operations of quantitative analysis.

Although a number of thermobalances were described
after the pioneering efforts of Guichard, the thermobalance developed by Chevenard and his co-workers in
1936 had the greatest influence. Chevenard was a metallurgist who was interested in the oxidation behavior of
stainless steels, which had just been developed in the
factory where he worked. To withstand the constant
vibrations present in steel mills, he adopted a bifunic-
ular suspension for the balance beam which was similar
to that found in the Kelvin electrodynamometer. Also,
to avoid air convection currents, he used an inverted
furnace geometry. Because of the impending World War II,

publication of his paper was delayed for six years,
finally appearing in print in 1941. The photographically recording model of the thermobalance became commercially available in France in 1945.

The man who had the greatest impact on modern analytical thermogravimetry was Clement Duval, who with
the recently developed Chevenard thermobalance, studied
the thermal properties of over 1000 analytical precipitates as well as the development of an automatic method
of analysis based on this technique. He recalls that
on a visit to Ludwigshafen am Rhine in 1946, he was impressed by the automatic execution of organic combustion
analyses based on the method developed by Zimmerman.
From that time on he was never free of the idea of developing rapid, automatic inorganic methods of analyses
which would require no preliminary separation and whose
results would be given in graphical form as is done with
an infrared spectrum. He also was concerned with
writers who were meticulous in specifying precipitation
conditions but who stated little if nothing about the
subsequent treatment of the precipitate beyond the simple direction of "heat and bring to constant weight."
Other loose phrases such as "heat without exceeding dull
red"; "ignite in such a fashion that the bottom of the
crucible becomes red"; and so on, were entirely inex-
cusable.

Development of Thermogravimetry in the United
States. Thermogravimetry was formally adopted as an
analytical technique in the United States much later
than DTA. R. H. Müller, who commented on Duval's book
in 1953, considered the technique to be of French
origin. Concerning the book he states:

> It is a monumental piece of work. Not only
> does it introduce a new and revealing tech-
> nique, but it furnishes critical, definitive
> information on almost 1000 gravimetric pro-
> cedures. This is the sort of book which is
> ordinarily written after a lifetime of
> achievement. The author (Duval), with a
> dozen or more students and collaborators,
> has accomplished as much in *less than five
> years* . . . When we consider how much val-
> uable information has been obtained in other
> fields by thermal analysis of one form or
> another, it seems all the more strange that
> comparable effort has not been exerted by
> the analyst. The use of cooling curves has
> been an indispensable part of the metallur-
> gist's approach to the study of alloys; and
> in a study of clays, minerals, and ceramics,

CLEMENT DUVAL, 1902–

    Professor of Microanalysis at the Sorbonne, Paris, Duval is a Director of the National Research Center. He and his coworkers have examined the thermogravimetric properties of many hundreds of analytical precipitates.

differential thermal analysis has often furnished clues about the existence of formation
of new compounds. . . . For nearly 25 years,
I had the honor of being a colleague of J. B.
Niederl and A. A. Benedetti-Pichler, who introduced the microchemical techniques of
Pregl and Emich in the United States. It is
to be hoped that some other disciple will
bring the essentially French science of thermogravimetry to its rightful place in this
country. The story of its accomplishments
have been told, and equipment is available
for all who wish to try it themselves.

Fortunately, a number of disciples, including W. W.
Wendlandt, did begin work in thermogravimetry. Professor Duval commented to Wendlandt during their first
meeting in London in 1965 that on his first lecture
tour of the United States (Washington, D.C., and Baton
Rouge, La.), not many chemists listened to what he had
to say. He said that Wendlandt was one of the few who
did. This, of course, is perhaps an understatement by
Duval because there was some interest in TG by Americans in the 1950s if not before. Mention should be
made of the studies by Newkirk, Simons, Gordon, Campbell,
Garn, Kissinger, Freeman, Carroll, and others.

An early thermobalance built by Wendlandt consisted
of a simple tube furnace attached to a precision torque
balance. Data were collected manually, of course, first
a mass reading and then a temperature measurement (as
detected by a thermocouple in the furnace chamber).

Most of the thermobalances at that time were in-
vestigator-assembled instruments, with few being available commercially (besides the Chevenard balance). The
recording balance as described by Mauer was available
from the Niagara Electron Laboratories (Andover, N.Y.)
in 1957. Apparently, this company had been making automatic recording analytical balances since 1949. The
following statement appeared at the bottom of the specifications sheet for the balance: "Deliveries will be
somewhat dependent on the ability of our expansion program to meet the yet unknown demand." At that time
there were 18 commercially available thermobalances--
six were manufactured in the United States, one each in
England and Switzerland, three in France, and seven in
Western Germany. Many of the commercial thermobalances
were built around the readily available microbalance,
the Cahn Electrobalance. This automatic recording
vacuum ultra-microbalance was first described by Cahn
and Schultz in 1962, had a sensitivity of 0.1 μg, and
permitted a precision of one part in 10,000. Since it
could be enclosed in a glass system, TG curves could

easily be obtained in controlled atmospheres or at low pressures.

Most of the pre-Cahn balances could not be operated at reduced pressures, which hindered the use of TG for many interesting investigations such as reaction kinetics, heats of sublimation determination, etc. In 1960 such a thermobalance was introduced at the Eastern Analytical Symposium and Instrument Exhibit in New York. It was called the Thermo-Grav and was built by the American Instrument Co. (Silver Spring, Md.). The balance, which was based on a tungsten or quartz helix weighing mechanism, became an instant success. TG curves could be obtained in vacuum or controlled atmospheres at temperatures of up to 1000°C. Other commercial instruments were developed in the 1960s, such as the DuPont balance, which was first described by Sarasohn and Tabeling. In Switzerland, Wiedemann developed the Mettler thermal analysis system (TG, DTG, and DTA) while Erdey, Paulik, and Paulik in Hungary developed the most widely used thermal analysis system in the world, the Derivatograph (TG, DTG, and DTA plus others).

One cannot discuss thermogravimetry in the United States without mentioning the many contributions of A. E. Newkirk and E. L. Simons of the General Electric Co. (Schenectady, N.Y.). In systematic investigations, they pointed out errors that were frequently overlooked in thermogravimetry, such as changing air buoyancy and convection, temperature measurement, and the effects of furnace atmosphere, heating rate, and other parameters. They stated that these limitations seem to indicate that the principal value of TG is in the determination of the approximate quantitative behavior of a system and not, by itself, in the determination of precise constants. In a later paper, they pointed out that the behavior of $CaC_2O_4 \cdot H_2O$ under controlled conditions in a thermobalance could provide an unusually versatile reference substance to guide the interpretation of TG measurements.

Although non-isothermal kinetics methods had been known since the 1920s, attention was refocused on this branch of kinetics by E. S. Freeman and B. Carroll in 1958. This was one year later than the application of DTA to kinetics by H. J. Borchardt and F. Daniels, who had described a non-isothermal method consisting of a simple graphical evaluation of the activation energy and order of reaction from a single TG curve.

TITRIMETRIC ANALYSIS

The Early Period. According to H. Beckurts, the establishment of titrimetric analysis as an exact

analytical technique should be credited to Joseph Louis
Gay-Lussac (1778-1850). However, the beginnings were
much earlier. As early as 1663 Robert Boyle had published a description of the actual use of an acid-base
indicator. He observed that the fluorescent blue of
Lignum Nephriticum extract in hard water would disappear
upon addition of acid but could be restored by addition
of potash solution; he further noted that he could guess
at the strength of an acid or alkaline liquor by the
quantity required to destroy or restore the blue color.
He also noted the acid-base changes of other plant
juices or dyes--e.g., syrup of violets.

In 1729 C. J. Geoffroy compared the strengths of
vinegar samples by adding a weighed amount of solid
potassium carbonate to each, a little at a time, until
no further effervescence took place. In 1756 pearl ash
(refined potash) was assayed by counting the number of
teaspoons of dilute nitric acid that could be added before effervescence stopped. Subsequently the added solution might be measured by counting drops or by weighing
a container before and after titration. L. B. Guyton
de Morveau used litmus, curcuma, and brazilin as indicators rather than observing the effervescence. He also
introduced the use of a glass cylinder for measurements
in 1782, and in 1786 F. C. Achard devised a transfer
pipet.

The foundations of stoichiometry were laid by J. B.
Richter in Germany, (1762-1807), who determined the
amounts of various bases required to neutralize 1000
parts of sulfuric, hydrochloric, or nitric acid. E. G.
Fischer (1754-1831) recalculated Richter's data and combined them in a table. This table was included in his
German translation of a paper by Berthollet in 1802 and
subsequently became widely known.

Any significant advances in oxidation-reduction
titrations were preceded by J. L. Proust's postulates
regarding the invariable proportions of elements in a
given compound and by the preparation of chlorine in
1774 by the Swedish chemist, C. W. Scheele. Chlorine
was believed to be a "dephlogisticated" or oxygenated
muriatic acid until Sir Humphry Davy in 1810 showed it
to be an element. The isolation of iodine in the following year by Bernard Courtois and the subsequent
study of this element and its compounds contributed
much to knowledge about oxidation-reduction reactions.

In 1789 a method for determining the concentration
of chlorine water using indigo solution was described
by Claude-Louis Berthollet as previously demonstrated
by Henri Descroizilles. Descroizilles used calibrated
glass tubes for his measurements, and in 1806 he made
titrations more practical by introducing the buret.

H. Dalton reported on the titration of chlorine and hypochlorite with ferrous sulfate in 1814.

Gay-Lussac's first paper on titrimetric analysis in 1824 dealt with the determination of active chlorine in bleaching powder by its destruction of sulfonated indigo. A few years later he published the determination of potash with sulfuric acid, of silver with sodium chloride solution, and he improved hypochlorite determinations by the use of arsenious oxide, potassium ferrocyanide, or mercurous nitrate as reductants and indigo as indicator. Thus he covered three major kinds of titrations: acid-base, oxidation-reduction, and precipitation.

Gay-Lussac had studied at the École Polytechnique in Paris, where he also became a friend and protegé of Berthollet and for a time worked in a linen-bleaching establishment with Berthollet's son at Arcueil. He joined the faculty at the École Polytechnique after studying with von Humboldt in Italy. In 1808 he and L. J. Thénard, his collaborator, reduced boric acid with potassium and discovered the element boron. Later they studied the properties of the recently isolated element iodine. Another of Gay-Lussac's contributions was his formulation of the law of combining volumes. Among students who learned laboratory skills from him were Liebig and Dumas.

The Period of Development and Applications. Titrimetric methods were not very popular by 1850 despite the pioneer work of Gay-Lussac and others. Recognition of equivalence points was often uncertain, there was no agreement on how to express concentrations, and the available apparatus was crude. One man who did much to advance the art was Karl Friedrich Mohr (1806-1879). A manufacturer of pharmaceutical chemicals, he had a keen interest in chemical research. He devised the system of a pinch clamp on a short section of rubber tubing, with a buret tip. Even after well-ground glass cocks became available, this was the best device to use with strongly alkaline titrants until self-lubricating plastic cocks were introduced.

Mohr proposed primary standards, oxalic acid for alkalimetry, and ferrous ammonium sulfate for oxidimetry. He also improved Gay-Lussac's chloride titration by using potassium chromate to reveal the endpoint when a slight excess of silver nitrate had been added. This eliminated time-consuming observations of disappearance of turbidity on the addition of silver nitrate.

Through Mohr's efforts, the liter was defined as the volume occupied by 1000 g of water, weighed in air with brass weights, at 17.5°C. This made calibration

very easy in central European laboratories at the time,
which were poorly heated. Later, of course, the standard temperature was taken as 3.98°C, where water has
its maximum density, and the weighing was referred to
the *in vacuo* basis.

In 1855 Mohr published his "Lehrbuch der chemisch-
analytischen Titriermethode," which did much to popularize volumetric methods. In it he recommended the use of
normal solutions and also introduced the idea of back-
titrating when direct titration was not satisfactory.

Mohr's book was preceded by the publication "Prak-
tische Anleitung zu Massanalyzen" by H. Schwarz (1850).
This appears to have been the first use of the German expression "Massanalyze" in the sense of our term "titrimetric analysis."

Almost contemporary with Mohr was Karl Remigius
Fresenius (1818-1897) who was called "the father of
modern analytical chemistry." At the Agricultural
Institute near Weisbaden, in his laboratories, he
trained many students. One of these was Emil Erlenmeyer,
designer of the flask bearing his name. Fresenius in
one of his numerous publications described the titration
of ferric chloride in acid solution with stannous chloride to the disappearance of the yellow color.

Fresenius also collated various separation methods
for use in qualitative analysis and used hydrogen sulfide, as pioneered by Torbern Bergman, to precipitate
many metal ions. Also he recognized the advantages of
controlling acidity or alkalinity in order to precipitate certain metals as sulfides while keeping others in
solution.

To appreciate the problems, consider operating a
chemical plant at the beginning of the 19th century,
with no means of chemical control except a crude assay
of the product. Clow and Clow tell of a factory carrying out the LeBlanc process for soda manufacture in
Liverpool around 1830. Raw materials were sodium chloride, sulfuric acid, coal, and limestone. Most of the
by-products, hydrogen chloride, sulfur dioxide, and
smoke, escaped to the atmosphere, while calcium sulfide
might be dumped in a river where hydrolysis would release hydrogen sulfide. Within a very few years the
ire of the inhabitants forced them to move to St.
Helens. It is not recorded why the operation was permitted to remain there, but Parliament in 1863 passed
an act requiring the conservation of hydrogen chloride.

Acid-Base Indicators and Titrations in the 19th
Century. At mid-century litmus, also called lacmus or
lakmus, an extract of various species of blue-green
lichens, was practically the only acid-base indicator

in common use.   In 1861 C. Luckow recommended cochineal.
This dye, extracted from females of the insect species
Coccus cacti L., which live on cactus plants in Central
America, had been used earlier as the coloring material
for British army uniforms.

The synthesis and probable structure of phenolphthalein (the acid form) were described by Adolf Baeyer
in 1871, and its first application as an indicator was
reported by E. Luck of Höchst, Germany, in 1877.

Methyl orange, the sodium salt of *p*-dimethylamino-
azobenzenesulfonic acid, was recommended in 1878 by
G. Lunge,.following the introduction of its diphenyl
analog, Tropaolin OO, by von Miller earlier the same
year.   Methyl red, the *o*-carboxylic acid derivative corresponding to methyl orange, was not prepared until 1908.

In 1884 M. C. Traube and C. Hock, of Bern, Switzerland, and independently R. Benedict and P. Julius of
Vienna, described a compound which they named lacmoid
(litmus-like) or resorcin blue.   Chromate ion reacts as
strongly alkaline to this indicator, while bichromate
appears neutral.

Following these early discoveries, progress in dye
synthesis was rapid, and many compounds were proposed
as indicators; many have found uses in areas such as
spot testing, precipitation and redox titrimetry, or
functional group analysis, or as intermediates to other
reagents such as fluorescein, alizarin, and phenanthro-
line.

Most of the acid-base titrations described during
the first half of the 19th century were intended for
determining the effective strengths of solutions of the
common acids and bases and the assays of alkali car-
bonates and alkaline earth oxides, and alkalinity of
borax (Gay-Lussac).

As alkaline titrants, standard solutions of soda
ash or potash were used at first.   J. Otto introduced a
dilute solution of ammonia for titrating acetic acid in
1832.   Lime water had been suggested as early as 1823
but did not find favor.

Apparently A. Bineau, a French agricultural chemist,
was the first to use sodium hydroxide solution as a
titrant in 1846.   The determination of nitrogen for
elemental analysis of organic compounds was a problem
solved only by the gas volumetric method of J. B. A.
Dumas until about 1841.   During that year Heinrich Will
and Franz Varrentrapp, working in Liebig's laboratory,
were able to evolve ammonia from organic nitrogen compounds (other than nitro) by heating with soda-lime.
The ammonia was collected in acid solution and was determined gravimetrically as ammonium chloroplatinate.
Bineau replaced this inconvenient method by collecting

the ammonia in standardized dilute hydrochloric acid
and back-titrating the excess with sodium hydroxide.
E. M. Péligot independently worked out a similar procedure within a year but used sulfuric acid and the
lime water-sugar reagent. John Mitchell in England
used sodium hydroxide for the same titration in 1847,
with logwood as indicator.

Bineau's method remained important for the determination of nitrogen in proteins and natural fertilizers
until 1883 when J. G. Kjeldahl, as mentioned previously,
was able to decompose grain and other materials by digestion in sulfuric acid, with conversion of the nitrogen into ammonium sulfate. He then made the mixture
alkaline and distilled the ammonia into standard acid,
determining the excess acid by adding a surplus of
iodate and iodide and titrating the liberated iodine
with thiosulfate. Kjeldahl's procedure has undergone
numerous modifications as to catalysts. O. Forster in
1889 made it more applicable to nitrates by adding
salicylic acid to serve as a reducing agent during the
acid digestion. Perhaps a better method for nitrates
was developed by A. Devarda in 1892 when he proposed to
reduce oxidized forms of nitrogen in alkaline solution
with an alloy of aluminum, copper, and zinc.

Although weak organic acids such as acetic were
titrated early in the century, the determinations were
only approximate because of lack of understanding about
the proper hydrogen-ion concentration at the equivalence
point as well as the lack of suitable indicators. Nevertheless applications were made, including the determination of esters by hydrolysis and back-titration.
These were the earliest examples of functional group
determinations in organic analysis by acid-base titrimetry. The saponification-number procedure for fatty
esters was brought more nearly into its present form by
J. Koettstorfer in 1882.

Hydroxyl groups were determined by acetylation followed by hydrolysis of the resulting ester and titration
of the released acetic acid in a method pioneered by
R. Benedikt and F. Ulzer (Vienna) in 1887 and modified
by J. Lewkowitsch in 1897.

The condensation reaction of ammonia with formaldehyde to form nearly neutral hexamethylenetetramine
was used by L. Legler in Germany for the alkalimetric
assay of formalin solutions in 1883. Determination of
aldehydes or ketones by reaction with a hydroxylamine
salt and titration of the liberated acid was proposed
in 1895 by the French chemists A. Brochet and R.
Cambrier.

R. T. Thomson (Scotland) in 1893 introduced the
addition of glycerin to boric acid to increase its

acidity and to improve the titration with alkali. Thomson's paper and the discussion following its presentation clearly reveal the difficulties of indicator selection and interpretation of acid-base behavior before the development and acceptance of Arrhenius' theory of electrolytic dissociation.

Oxidation-Reduction Indicators and Titrations. At the beginning of the 19th century practically the only known redox titrations were intended for analyzing bleaching powder or solutions, and they depended upon indigo as both reductant and indicator. In 1814 H. Dalton used ferrous sulfate as the reductant and judged nearness to the endpoint by whether a portion of the mixture would turn black ferrous hydroxide red or by the odor of free chlorine.

Starch (amidon) was first used as an indicator for iodine by Labillardière, who in 1826 determined hypochlorite by titrating it with a solution of iodide, starch, sodium chloride, and sodium bicarbonate. Iodine itself was first used as a titrant in 1840 by A. Du Pasquier; in his procedure for determining sulfides the titration was done with an alcoholic solution of iodine; again starch served as the indicator. Three years later M. J. Fordos and A. Gélis titrated thiosulfate and sulfite with iodine. A. F. Duflos extended iodometric titrations for determination of ferric iron. Iodine was used for titrating stannous tin by H. F. Gaultier de Claubry in 1846.

The name of Robert Bunsen is generally associated with spectroscopic analysis and the discoveries of cesium and rubidium. He also stimulated iodometry, however, with an 1853 paper on determinations of about a dozen substances, including iodate, chlorate, chromate, arsenate, and the dioxides of cerium and manganese. Further impetus was given in the same year when H. Schwarz recommended that free iodine be titrated with thiosulfate solution. The practically important direct iodometric titration of cupric copper was described in 1854 by E. de Haen.

Whereas determinations of bleach (calcium hypochlorite) by titration with arsenious acid were carried out in acid solution by Gay-Lussac in 1835, the fact that the titration could be done in an alkaline medium was not known until disclosed by Penot, also in France, in 1852.

Potassium permanganate, serving as its own color indicator and called "chamaeleon" by the French, was first used as a titrant in 1846 by F. Margueritte to determine ferrous iron in very dilute hydrochloric acid solution. Because of an error caused by oxidation of

some acid to chlorine, Lowenthal and Lenssen proposed
in 1862 that the titration be done in sulfuric acid
solution. In 1863 F. Kessler reported the inhibitory
effect of manganous sulfate on chlorine formation, but
his work escaped notice until C. Zimmermann in 1882
recommended the addition of a manganous salt and the
use of "preventive solution" (1889).

In 1847 permanganate was used by A. B. Bussy of
Paris for the titration of arsenious acid, and by T. J.
Pelouze, also in France, for a nitric acid determination
based upon reaction with excess ferrous iron. Two years
later the Danish chemist J. G. Forchhammer used permanganate to determine oxidizable impurities in drinking
water. Forchhammer also became noted for his analyses
of ocean waters. His permanganate method was the pre-
cursor of various "oxygen demand" methods which have
been widely used as measures of water quality.

Permanganate was used to determine oxalic acid,
oxalate salts (Mohr, 1855), and other reducing acids
(L. Péant de St. Gilles). A. Guyard proposed a permanganate titration of divalent manganese in 1864, and
J. Volhard refined it in 1874.

The use of potassium dichromate solution as a
titrant for ferrous iron was proposed separately by
Frederick Penny, professor of chemistry at the Ander-
sonian University of Glasgow, and by J. Schabus of
Vienna, in 1850 and 1851. Both located the endpoint by
spottesting with potassium ferricyanide solution. In
1862 Mohr recommended potassium dichromate as a standard
substance for iodometric titrations.

Berthet in France described in 1846 the use of
potassium iodate as a standard titrant for assaying
iodides. In 1874 Mohr first used a mixture of iodate
and iodide (in excess) to determine acids.

The use and preparation of ceric sulfate as an oxidizing reagent was suggested by Th. Lange in 1861.
Scarcely any applications were made of his suggestion
during the remainder of the century.

Determination of unsaturated groups in fats or oils
by the addition of bromine was first described by A. W.
Knop in 1854. Not much use was made of Knop's procedure
until it was adapted by A. H. Allen in England (1881)
for the determination of olefins in petroleum products.
Meanwhile W. F. Koppeschaar in Germany developed, in
1876, the now well-established method for determining
phenol with excess bromate-bromide reagent in acid solution. A. F. von Hübl in 1884 disclosed his method for
determining the iodine number of fats and oils. This
method was improved by J. J. Wijs in 1898 by introducing
a reagent consisting of iodine monochloride in acetic
acid.

Stefan Györy (1893) used methyl orange as an irreversible indicator, its red color being bleached by a slight excess of bromate. This appears to have been the earliest distinct use of a synthetic organic compound (other than sulfonated indigo, a modified natural product) as an indicator whose color is destroyed by oxidation.

Potassium ferricyanide was proposed as an oxidizing titrant, for determining reducing sugars, by J. G. Gentele in Germany in 1859. Although further uses of this reagent were reported by Lenssen (1860), extended applications had to await the 20th century, when its properties became better understood.

Mercurous nitrate was first used as a reducing titrant not only for permanganate by A. LeClerc (1872) but also for hypochlorite by Balland and by Marozeau. Apparently no other applications for mercurous nitrate as a titrant were proposed for nearly 70 years.

The development and widespread use of redox indicators did not evolve significantly until the early 1920s, much later than acid-base indicators. The first reversible redox indicator of definite composition--diphenylamine--was introduced in 1925 by Josef Knop. Prior to this a number of irreversible indicators, some of indefinite composition, had been used for redox titrations, but because of the need for their external application or difficulty of preparation they did not find general acceptance. One such external indicator, a solution of indigo dye, was used as early as 1835 by Gay-Lussac to titrate arsenious acid with hypochlorite to a colorless endpoint. Other irreversible indicators employed at early dates were phenosaphranine (described by M. G. Linossier in 1891) and diphenylcarbazide (introduced in 1906 by L. Brandt). Much of the needed impetus for effective development of a variety of redox indicators was lacking, primarily because of the availability and common usage of permanganate and iodine as oxidimetric titrants, the former being self-indicating and the latter readily detectable with starch.

One of the first to undertake a systematic investigation of colored redox systems in quest of suitable redox indicators was William Mansfield Clark. Clark and his co-workers were especially interested in following redox processes in biological systems. In the period 1928-1931 they published extensively on electrochemical and optical studies of a great many dyes and derivatives including indophenols, amine dyes, indamines, thiazines, orazines, and indigo sulfonic acids. Many new redox indicators were found. Ten suitable indicators, for example, were found just among the 34 indophenols studied. Clark's impressive array of indicators possess formal potentials in the range -0.2 to +0.8 volt, dependent on pH, and thus by proper selection enable colorimetric determination of redox potential and titration endpoint detection in the same range.

One of the best known and most prolific scientists in the history of analytical chemistry was also active in the development of redox indicators. Professor I. M. Kolthoff, with his colleague L. A. Sarver, elucidated the mechanism of oxidation of diphenylamine and diphenyl-benzidine in 1930 and introduced diphenylamine p-sulfonic acid as a readily soluble redox indicator in 1931.

The need for high potential, reversible, redox indicators that could be used internally became most apparent and acute in connection with exploiting the promising capabilities of cerium(IV) compounds as oxidimetric titrants. Although suitable potentiometric endpoint methods were available for carrying out cerate titrations, they lacked wide acceptance because they were slow and needed special instrumentation. Among the first to recognize and to help fill this need were G. H. Walden Jr., L. P. Hammett, and R. P. Chapman of Columbia University who introduced in 1931 the use of tris(1,10-phenanthroline)iron(II) as the first high potential, reversible, redox indicator. This indicator proved to be the forerunner of many related complexes that would provide coverage over a broad range of redox potentials. Acclaimed as the "phenolphthalein of oxidimetry," it was given the name ferroin by Karl Gleu in 1933.

The introduction of ferroin began one of the most interesting and extensive sagas in the history of indicators. In 1934, following in the footsteps of Chapman as a graduate student of Walden and Hammett, S. M. Edmonds discovered that the redox potential of ferroin could be significantly increased by nitration of the 1,10-phenanthroline groups. Recognizing the analytical possibilities of this discovery, Professor G. Frederick Smith initiated an extensive investigation of substituted ferroins with the invaluable assistance of Professor Francis H. Case of Temple University, whose ingenuity in organic synthesis would provide the necessary derivatives. Over a period of about 20 years Smith and Case with their graduate students prepared and studied more than 150 different substituted phenanthrolines and related compounds. Their systematic studies, in addition to characterizing the influences of different substituent groups on the various properties of the ligands and complexes, produced a number of outstanding colorimetric reagents for iron and copper as well as an extensive series of reversible redox indicators. The latter cover the potential range 0.87 to

1.33 volts and by proper selection make possible rapid
and accurate titrations of a great variety of oxidants
and reductants, especially those involving cerate oxidimetry. In addition to his own direct contributions,
G. F. Smith, through his warm personality and enthusiasm,
influenced many of his friends and associates to pursue
researches on ferroin-type redox indicators. For example, Harvey Diehl of Iowa State University contributed
sulfonated and hydroxy substituted ferroin indicators
in 1961 and 1975; Byron Kratochvil of the University of
Alberta developed ruthenium analogs of ferroin as reversible fluorescent redox indicators in 1964; A. A.
Schilt of Northern Illinois University devised a number
of mixed ligand complexes of iron, ruthenium, and osmium
as both nonaqueous acid-base and aqueous redox indicators
in 1962-1963.

The present-day availability of a diverse and versatile series of redox indicators is obviously the
result of the combined efforts of many chemists too
numerous to name here, but certainly the series would
be sparse had it not been for the perseverance of men
such as W. M. Clark and G. F. Smith.

Precipitation Titrations. Experiments performed
by J. B. Richter in Germany around 1792 preceded the
description of any actual titration method based on a
precipitation reaction. Richter determined the weight
of pure sulfuric acid (in a diluted solution) that would
precipitate a given weight of lead acetate as lead sulfate. Apparently the first practical titration, however, was for the examination of potash described in
1799 by the French General Administrator of Explosives
and Nitrates. Potassium carbonate and sulfate were
determined together by adding calcium nitrate solution
up to the stage at which a subsequent addition would
produce no more precipitate.

In 1819 de Saint-Venant determined chlorides by
adding lime water to serve as an indicator and titrating
with silver nitrate solution until the brown coloration
of silver oxide appeared. This was probably the first
use of a precipitation indicator, but unfortunately it
was not published until 1846. Meanwhile Gay-Lussac in
1828 reported the titration of soluble sulfate salts
with barium chloride solution, again taking the endpoint
when precipitation appeared to be complete. In 1832
Gay-Lussac described his titration of silver with a
standard sodium chloride solution, relying for the endpoint upon no further appearance of turbidity. G. J.
Mulder refined this titration for the Dutch mint after
carrying out a systematic study in 1857; he used the
fact that a saturated silver chloride solution is made

turbid by addition of either chloride or silver, so
that the equivalence point is reached when equal tur-
bidities are produced by adding equal quantities of the
opposite reagents to separate portions of the supernant
liquid. This is probably the most accurate titration
ever devised. A weight buret for the chloride solution
was disclosed in 1858.

If further applications of either de Saint-Venant's
method or the reverse of Gay-Lussac's silver titration
for the determination of chloride, bromide, or iodide
were published during the first half of the 19th century, apparently the work has escaped the attention of
historians. In 1853 the French chemist A. F. Levol
introduced sodium phosphate as an indicator for titrations of chloride, a faintly yellow silver phosphate
color signalling the endpoint. Mohr found the endpoint
to appear late, and after noting some improvement by
substituting arsenate, he obtained the best results
with potassium chromate in neutral solution. A more
generally applicable method for determining halides in
acid solution was proposed by J. Volhard in 1874, using
ferric iron as the indicator in the presence of thiocyanate. It is perhaps worthy of mention that a direct
titration of silver solution with thiocyanate, with a
ferric salt as indicator, had been described by Char-
pentier in 1870.

A different kind of precipitation method--actually
the first example of a complex-formation titration--was
developed by Marozeau in 1832 for the determination of
iodide. Mercuric chloride solution was added, yielding
a temporary turbidity of HgI_2 which would redissolve in
the solution as long as enough iodide remained to form
K_2HgI_4. In 1840 Probst reversed this procedure to
determine mercuric chloride.

Two precipitation methods for organic analysis
were proposed quite early. E. Ossian Henry titrated
alkaloids with tannic acid in 1834, and L. C. Barreswil
titrated reducing sugars with an alkaline cupric tartrate solution in 1844. Both chemists were French, and
Barreswil was editor of the *Bulletin de la Société de
Chimie de Paris*. The Barreswil reagent was modified by
H. Fehling in 1848 and has since borne his name.

A. F. Duflos in 1837 published a titration in which
cyanide was first complexed and then precipitated by
silver nitrate. (Duflos, born in France in 1802, served
as professor of pharmacy and chemistry at Breslau and
lived to be 87 years old.) Liebig published a similar
method in 1851 but added sodium chloride in an attempt
to sharpen the endpoint. The titration was improved
greatly in 1893 by G. Denigès who used an ammoniacal
medium and added potassium iodide.

A precipitation titration of potassium with perchlorate was developed by Henry in 1845. In his report, a buret having a stopcock at the lower end was described for the first time. Sodium sulfide solution was used in 1846 as the precipitant for titrating copper, by T. J. Pelouze, and in 1856 by Max Schaffner for zinc. Both used ammoniacal tartrate solutions, Pelouze taking the disappearance of the blue cupric complex color as the endpoint and Schaffner adding ferric hydroxide, some of which was converted into black iron sulfide at the end.

Henry reported the titration of copper with ferrocyanide solution in 1847. The possibility of using the same reagent for zinc was pointed out by Maurice Galletti (chief assayer of the Bureau de Guarantie de Gênes) in 1856 but not published until 1864. C. Fahlberg in 1874 used uranyl nitrate as an external indicator, producing brown uranyl ferrocyanide at the endpoint.

The first precipitation titration for soluble phosphate was described by C. Leconte in 1849, with uranyl nitrate as the reagent. Neubauer and Pincus separately modified the method, using different acetate buffers but both employing potassium ferrocyanide as an external indicator for the uranium. Breed, as reported by Liebig in 1851, titrated soluble phosphates with neutral ferric chloride solution and tested the filtrate with ferrocyanide. Stoddart substituted thiocyanate for the ferrocyanide.

A procedure which included a unique indicator action and which found wide practical acceptance for a long period was the "soap hardness" determination of T. Clark of Aberdeen, developed in 1841. Calcium and magnesium were precipitated as fatty acid salts, and the end of the titration was signalled by the appearance of a stable foam when the mixture was shaken. This method was in general use until about 1960 when EDTA became available.

The Development of Scientific Principles Applicable to Titrimetry. Analytical chemists are sometimes criticized for being content to carry out determinations in a routine way while allowing others to bring about new advances in their field. It is true that until an adequate understanding of chemical principles was attained, analytical methods could be developed only empirically. However, it is also true that the quantitative formulation of a principle must be based upon accurate test data. Physical chemistry, the science which deals with chemical principles, rests upon a foundation built up over a long period by the efforts of many investigators. Most of them took great pride in the quality of their analytical work even though their performance may seem now to have been more an art than a science.

It was not until the latter part of the 19th century that physical chemistry assumed importance on its own merits. Chemists had long been interested in the idea of chemical affinity, the mysterious force which caused elements to interact or to replace one another in compounds. Much work had gone into studies of displacement, electromotive series, reaction rates, and heat absorption or evolution. A landmark was reached with the formulation of the law of mass action by C. M. Guldberg and Peter Waage. They were brothers-in-law, professors of mathematics and chemistry at Christiana University in Oslo, Norway. Their work was begun in 1864, was published in a preliminary way in 1867, and was put into final form in 1879.

During the same period Josiah Willard Gibbs, professor of mathematical physics at Yale University, was developing his classical theories about chemical equilibria. Using a thermodynamic approach, he introduced the concept of chemical potentials and derived the phase rule. Unfortunately his series of papers (1874-1878) appeared in a journal with limited circulation and did not receive much notice at first. In Holland, J. D. van der Waals, professor of physics at the University of Leyden and known for his refinement of the gas laws in 1873, called the attention of Hendrik Bakhuis-Roozeboom to Gibbs' work. Roozeboom was then studying the hydrates of sulfur dioxide; he found Gibbs' ideas to be very helpful and continued to apply them in subsequent research, especially on alloys and in solubility studies of complex systems. Through his papers the value of the phase rule was established in Europe.

Mass law expressions for equilibria were derived independently in Holland by Jacobus Henricus van't Hoff in 1877. Among many other subjects, he authored papers on osmotic phenomena, concluding that the gas laws hold for dilute solutions of non-electrolytes. For electrolytes, however, he had to include another factor, which became known as van't Hoff's i.

In Sweden, Svante Arrhenius worked as a student under P. T. Cleve (the discoverer of thulium and holmium) at Uppsala. During Arrhenius' research on the electrical conductivity of salt solutions he conceived the theory of electrolytic dissociation and incorporated it in his doctoral thesis in 1884 at the age of 25. It was too revolutionary for the examining committee, but his experimental work was good and his degree was awarded with reservations. He then worked for short periods in the laboratories of Kohlrausch, Ostwald, and van't Hoff. As the ionic theory became known, it became

clear that van't Hoff's *i* factor represented the degree
of dissociation of an electrolyte into ions. The completed theory was published in a short paper in 1887.
Later Arrhenius developed his equation for the effect
of temperature on reaction rates. He taught for a number of years in the technical high school in Stockholm,
and when the Nobel Institute of Physical Chemistry was
established, he became its director.

The theories of van't Hoff and Arrhenius encountered considerable resistance from older chemists, and
we have to thank Wilhelm Ostwald for recognizing their
importance. Born in Riga, Ostwald taught there for a
time (during which he travelled to Uppsala to visit
Arrhenius and offered him a lectureship) and later moved
to Leipzig. He had himself worked on reaction velocities as affected by acidity, was quick to see the value
of thermodynamic concepts in chemistry, and insisted
upon considering physical chemistry as a science in its
own right. With van't Hoff he founded the *Zeitschrift
für physikalische Chemie* in 1887. He was also very
cognizant that analytical chemistry depends upon physicochemical principles. In his 1894 book "Die wissen-
schaftlichen Grundlagen der analytischen Chemie" he
tried to clarify the theories of van't Hoff and Arrhenius for analytical chemists and to show how they could
be applied in understanding the behavior of acid-base
indicators, in the titration of weak or strong acids,
and in precipitation methods.

Nobel prizes in chemistry were awarded to van't
Hoff in 1901, Arrhenius in 1903, and Ostwald in 1909.
I. M. Kolthoff, who had met Arrhenius personally and
who has discussed the work of the three men, regards
van't Hoff and Arrhenius as geniuses and Ostwald as a
great scholar and prolific writer whose books and research have contributed much to chemists. On the other
hand, he feels that Ostwald failed to give suitable
recognition to the work of Hermann Walther Nernst, some
of it done in Ostwald's own laboratory at Leipzig while
Nernst was his assistant. The now well-known Nernst
equation relating emf to chemical concentration and
temperature was published in 1889. Earlier Nernst had
originated potentiometric titrimetry and had studied
the electrodeposition of metals at controlled potential.
Kolthoff considers Nernst to be the father of modern
electroanalytical chemistry. His efforts were not confined to electrochemistry, however. In 1889 he also
published a significant paper evaluating the common ion
effect on the solubility of several electrolytes. He
received the Nobel prize in 1920.

Ostwald's interest in the application of theoretical principles to analytical chemistry seems to have

been slow to bear fruit in the United States in spite
of various opportunities. A number of American chemists
obtained part of their training in Europe. T. W.
Richards, for example, after teaching analytical chemistry at Harvard for about five years, during which he
began his atomic weight work and some research on physical chemistry, spent a year's leave of absence in 1894
with Ostwald at Leipzig and Nernst at Göttingen. Louis
Kahlenberg took his doctorate with Ostwald and returned
to begin a research program on the dissociation theory
at the University of Wisconsin, but he encountered
troubling questions and became an opponent of the
theory, which actually applied only to dilute aqueous
solutions.

Two routes by which Ostwald's efforts had an effect
in America are interesting to trace. The earliest involved the well-known text, "Qualitative Chemical Analysis," by Albert B. Prescott and Otis C. Johnson of the
University of Michigan, which went through a number of
editions beginning in 1874. Prescott was one of the
founders of the American Chemical Society and was its
president in 1886. He is also reputed to have been the
analyst who arrived at the figure of 99.44% for the
purity of a common brand of soap. For the fifth edition
of the book (1901) Eugene C. Sullivan (1872-1962), then
a young instructor at Ann Arbor, was asked to prepare a
section on Solution and Ionization according to Ostwald's
ideas, which he did very well in about four pages.
Sullivan had studied at Michigan, Göttingen, and
Leipzig, receiving his Ph.D. under Ostwald in 1899 on
trivalent iodine compounds. After teaching three years
at Michigan, he was with the U.S. Geological Survey
until 1908, when he went to the Corning Glass Works.
There with W. C. Taylor he developed the low-expansion
glasses later known under the brand name Pyrex, which
did so much to simplify laboratory work.

The later route of Ostwald's influence was through
Holland. Nicolaas Schoorl (1872-1942) studied analytical chemistry and pharmacy under J. W. Gunning and
C. A. Lobry de Bruyn at the University of Amsterdam,
where he also came under the influence of van't Hoff
and Bakhuis-Roozeboom. Hence he became thoroughly
familiar with physicochemical theory. At the beginning
of the 20th century he was teaching analytical chemistry
at the University of Utrecht. Here the man who was to
become his most famous pupil, Izaak Maurits Kolthoff
first studied quantitative analysis with him in 1913.
Schoorl already in 1904 had published a series of papers
on the characteristics of acid-base indicators and how
to choose the proper one for a particular titration.
Kolthoff found these papers difficult and was forced to

study other literature. In particular he was inspired
by Sørensen's 1909 publication on pH and by Joel Hildebrand's 1913 contribution on electrometric titrations.
After carrying out a systematic study of many titrimetric methods, Kolthoff with the cooperation of H.
Menzel compiled the first German edition (1926) of a
two-volume set on (I) "Die Theorie," and (II) "Die
Praxis, der Massanalyse." These were dedicated to
Schoorl. Translated by N. H. Furman of Princeton University, the books were published in the United States
in 1928. Kolthoff himself came to this country in 1927
to teach at the University of Minnesota, where he headed
the Division of Analytical Chemistry until his "retirement" and where as emeritus professor he still maintains
an active research program with post-doctoral fellows.
Through the years he has trained his students to be
guided by scientific theory but to make decisions on
the basis of experimental evidence.

Schoorl continued to teach at Utrecht. In 1918 he
introduced the idea of using "rational" atomic and
equivalent weights, modified just enough from the
accepted values to compensate for errors of weighing in
air rather than in a vacuum. In his later years he
authored a three-volume work on organic analysis, published in Holland between 1935 and 1941. Being in the
Dutch language, the books hardly became known in the
United States though they would have filled a real need
at the time.

Returning to the theory of electrolytic dissociation, its status at the turn of the century was that
the idea of complete dissociation could be accepted for
strong electrolytes in dilute aqueous solution but that
for other conditions there were difficulties. Ostwald
had derived his dilution law, giving the relationship
between the concentration and degree of ionization of
weak acids and bases. Compounds like aluminum sulfate
did not appear to behave as normal electrolytes, and
there were many cases where the molecular conductivity
and molecular freezing point depression of strong electrolytes decreased with increasing concentration. In
1909 Niels Bjerrum, in Denmark, pointed out that the
deviations must be due to a mutual effect of the ions
upon each other. A comprehensive theory explaining
this effect was derived in 1923 at Zürich by Peter Debye
and Erich Hückel, who were able to calculate the decrease
in mobility of ions surrounded by oppositely charged
ions. The Arrhenius theory was also reinforced by the
finding of C. Tubandt and S. Eggert in 1920 that fused
salts are conductors and that therefore salts are probably already ionized in the solid state. Previously
there had been a problem about how water could cause

THEODORE WILLIAM RICHARDS, 1868-1928

Educated at Haverford College and Harvard University and in
Germany, Richards became Professor of Physical Chemistry at Harvard. His chief work was in the precise revision of atomic
weights. He was unusually skilled in discovering and eliminating
subtle sources of error. He was President of the ACS in 1914 and
was awarded the Nobel Prize in Chemistry for 1915.

ionization. Bjerrum also published a book in 1914 on the theory and practice of acid-base titrations which thoroughly explained its fundamental principles.

Acid-Base Indicators and Titrations in the 20th Century. As a result of the developments described in the previous section, considerable work was done in Europe and England to clarify the behavior of acids, bases, and indicators in aqueous solutions. Dissociation constants were determined both electrochemically and colorimetrically. A notable paper on the range of indicators was published by Edward Salm in 1907. Salm arranged columns numbered from 1 to 14, corresponding with hydrogen-ion concentrations from 10^{-1} to 10^{-14}, and in these columns he appropriately located the color shown by each indicator through its transition interval. Thus in effect he had a pH system before one was formalized by Sørensen though he did not use mantissae for defining the logarithmic values more closely. Salm included practically all of the indicators available to him. He also pointed out that for an indicator base, the dissociation constant is the same as the hydroxyl-ion concentration at which it is 50% dissociated. Salm had begun his study in H. Friedenthal's laboratory at Berlin and completed it at Aachen. Friedenthal had proposed in 1904 that the reaction of a solution, whether acid, alkaline, or neutral, should be expressed in terms of hydrogen-ion concentration, (H^+).

The classical paper on pH is that of Søren P. L. Sørensen (1868-1939). A native of Denmark, he not only formulated the pH system but furnished definite procedures for determining pH colorimetrically and potentiometrically as well as for preparing a set of buffer solutions of standard pH values. He had studied at the University of Copenhagen, majoring in analytical and inorganic chemistry. In 1901 he was appointed director of the Karlsberg Laboratory in Copenhagen, succeeding Johann Kjeldahl, and from that time he worked in physiological chemistry. The pH work, published in 1909, was done in connection with studies on enzyme activity. The formol titration method for amino acids was developed during the same period. In 1924 Sørensen was made an honorary member of the American Chemical Society.

Methyl red was introduced as an indicator in 1908 by E. Rupp and R. Loose who described both its synthesis and indicator action. It became one of the most useful indicators. During the same year Arthur Hantzsch published a study of the structural changes associated with the color shifts of indicators, showing that Ostwald's concept of an indicator was too simple. Ostwald had considered an indicator to be either a weak base or a

weak acid, the cation or anion of which (respectively)
has a different color from the undissociated form.
Hantzsch found that the azo-dye indicators change from
their yellow-orange azo forms to pink-violet quinoid
structures on acidification. A native of Dresden and
primarily an organic chemist, Hantzsch spent most of
his career at Leipzig.

Further work on the sensitivity and applications
of indicators was done in England by Henry T. Tizard at
the Davy-Faraday Laboratory of the Royal Institute. He
worked especially with methyl orange and methyl red and
studied the titration of anilinium salts, published in
1910. Later while at Oxford he and A. R. Boeree contributed a paper describing the derivation of titration
curves for dibasic acids (1921). Meanwhile a book on
indicators was published in Stuttgart in 1911 by A.
Thiel.

The first syntheses of several sulfonephthaleins
which later became popular as indicators appear to have
been carried out by M. D. Sohon, a doctoral candidate
under Ira Remsen at John Hopkins University in Balti-
more, whose work was published in 1898. Solomon F.
Acree (1875-1919) became interested in the structure of
the alkaline forms of these compounds while teaching at
Johns Hopkins from 1905-1914, and he published several
papers on this subject. From 1914 to 1917 he worked at
the Forest Products Laboratory in Madison, Wis., where
Edwin C. White was a graduate student with him at the
University. In 1915 White and Acree published a note
in *Science* about the colored quinoid forms of phenol-
sulfonephthalein and its tetrabromo and tetranitro
derivatives. The same year and in 1916 H. A. Lubs and
W. M. Clark published papers in the *Journal of the
Washington Academy of Science* on various indicators
suitable for pH determinations of biological fluids.
One indicator that they recommended highly was phenol-
sulfonephthalein, a sample of which they had received
from White and Acree.

William Mansfield Clark (1884-1964) was trained at
Williams College and Johns Hopkins University. He
worked with the Dairy Division, Bureau of Animal Industry, U.S. Department of Agriculture, from 1910 to
1920 and then with the U.S. Public Health Service for
seven years. During the earlier period he prepared his
widely used text, "The Determination of Hydrogen Ions"
(1920). From 1927 to 1952 he was professor of physiological chemistry at Johns Hopkins Medical School,
after which he served as emeritus professor until his
death. For his work on pH and oxidation-reduction indicators he received the Nichols Medal and the Borden
and Remsen awards. Herbert A. Lubs received his

education at Newberry College and at Johns Hopkins. He
worked as an organic chemist with the Public Health Service, the Dairy Division, and the Bureau of Chemistry
until 1919, then joined the duPont Co. as a research
chemist, progressing through various positions until he
retired as manager of the dyes and chemical products
section in 1955. Acree, who had studied in Texas and
Chicago Universities and also had done postdoctoral
work in Berlin, eventually went to the National Bureau
of Standards, where he was chief of the section on fiber
structure and hydrogen-ion concentration standards from
1928 until 1949. E. C. White was associated with the
hospital and medical school at Hopkins for many years.
R. T. Birge did his doctoral work at Wisconsin in
physics, then taught until 1918 at Syracuse where he
carried out the spectral studies on sulfonephthaleins
published with Acree in 1919. For the rest of his life
he taught physics at the University of California.

Kolthoff's first monograph, "Der Gebrauch von Far-
benindicatoren," published in Germany in 1920, was too
early to describe the sulfonephthaleins, but subsequent
editions, including the English translation by Charles
Rosenblum, (1937) dealt with them fully. The addition
of these compounds to those already known made such a
good assortment available for acid-base titrations that
there has been little incentive for further research on
indicators. However, several chemists have proposed
the use of mixed indicators to permit sharper endpoints.
Thus Abraham Cohen of London recommended in 1922 a mixture of bromocresol purple and bromothymol blue for a
sharp change between pH 6.0 and 6.8. K. C. D. Hickman
and R. P. Linstead at the Royal College of Science in
South Kensington the same year proposed adding xylene
cyanole FF to methyl orange to improve the endpoint;
this mixture is still sold commercially. Hickman later
joined the Eastman Kodak Co. in research at Rochester,
N.Y., and became noted for contributions to molecular
distillation.

Turbidity indicators consisting of semi-colloidal
acids or bases were introduced by Carl Naegeli of the
University of Zürich in 1925. These differ in their
action from the earlier used inorganic precipitation
indicators in that they flocculate more sharply within
narrow pH intervals and allow the titration of weak
acids like phenol. Although several compounds were
recommended by Naegeli and A. Tyabji in 1932, the
method has not become popular.

Fluorescent indicators appear to have been suggested originally by F. Krüger who used fluorescein in
titrations at Frankfurt, Germany, in 1876. R. Robl of
the University of Breslau recommended umbelliferone as

an indicator in 1926. In this country L. J. Desha at the College of Medicine of the University of Tennessee pointed out in 1920 that the fluorescence of compounds such as iodeosin and quinine is pH dependent, but he did not use them for titrations. In 1926 Desha, R. E. Sherrill, and L. M. Harrison at the Washington and Lee University in Virginia studied the relationship between pH and fluorescence for several sulfonic acids of substituted phenols and naphthols. Later E. A. Kocsis and co-workers at the University of Szeged in Hungary made use of chromotropic acid, morin, thioflavin, and other compounds.

To prepare standard hydrochloric acid solutions, F. Raschig of Germany in 1904 gave directions for adding hydrogen chloride to water, finding the amount added by the gain in weight, and diluting to volume. Further details on this method were published by workers of several countries, among them Sørensen and Acree. In 1909 G. A. Hulett and W. D. Bonner at Princeton University recommended the use of constant-boiling HCl; C. W. Foulk and Marion Hollingsworth at the Ohio State University studied this method carefully in 1923 and gave precise directions for the distillation. Bonner and co-workers at the University of Utah determined the boiling points and compositions over a wider range of pressures between 1926 and 1930. N. Schoorl in 1930 published in Holland a table of densities vs. weight normalities for various solutions of hydrochloric, sulfuric, and nitric acids and sodium hydroxide.

Today acids are most frequently standardized against primary standard grade sodium carbonate, which is available commercially with suitable purity. Formerly this was not the case. In 1894 B. Reinitzer at the Technische Hochschule in Graz gave a procedure for preparing sodium carbonate from sodium bicarbonate through a crystallization and heating process. This was studied intensively by George Lunge of Zürich as well as by Sørensen and A. C. Andersen. Sørensen had proposed in 1903 sodium oxalate as the primary standard since it could also be used to standardize permanganate solutions. The preparation, testing, and procedure for use were studied carefully by William Blum at the National Bureau of Standards in 1912, and a modified procedure was issued by the Bureau in 1930.

Potassium biphthalate is most often used today as the reference substance for standardizing alkalies. It was recommended independently by Francis D. Dodge of the Dodge & Olcott Co., Bayonne, N. J., and by W. S. Hendrixson of Grinnell College, Iowa, in 1915. Benzoic acid, originally proposed as a standard by J. Wagner of Leipzig in 1903, was studied by I. K. Phelps and

L. H. Weed at Yale University in 1908. It was also recommended by George W. Morey of the National Bureau of Standards, who published his results and purification methods in 1912. Both potassium biphthalate and benzoic acid are issued as standard substances by the Bureau.

NONAQUEOUS ACID-BASE TITRIMETRY

Before the development of gas chromatography as an analytical method in 1950-60 and the more recent development of liquid chromatography, the availability of this convenient and reasonably selective titration method for acidic and basic substances was especially helpful. Even today nonaqueous titrimetry is quite useful and provides a degree of accuracy that is unmatched by chromatography or by most other methods of organic analysis. In this account the development of methods for titration of bases is discussed first. Then the titration of acids is taken up in chronological order. Finally, a few milestones in acid-base equilibria in organic solvents are mentioned.

The best methods used today for titration of bases in nonaqueous solvents stem directly from a brilliant series of papers published in 1927-1930 by N. F. Hall, J. B. Conant, and T. H. Werner at Harvard University. They found that salts of amides and other very weak bases are often completely hydrolyzed in water but that salt formation is essentially complete in glacial acetic acid. These solutions in acetic acid were termed superacid solutions. The goal of the researchers was primarily to study the relative basicity of weak organic bases, but their experimental techniques provided the basis for the practical procedures that were published years later by other investigators.

In the first paper of their series the chloranil indicator electrode, in conjunction with a lithium chloride salt bridge (in acetic acid) and a calomel reference electrode, was used to measure hydrogen ion activities of acids and bases in glacial acetic acid. Potentiometric curves for titration of several bases with sulfuric acid in acetic acid were given. In the third paper of the series perchloric, sulfuric, and hydrochloric acids were compared as titrants in acetic acid, and perchloric acid was shown to be the strongest acid and best titrant. A pH scale for glacial acetic acid was proposed. The fourth paper dealt with the strengths of weak and pseudo bases in acetic acid and set the stage for later use of crystal violet as an indicator for titrating bases in acetic acid. The last paper from Hall (who was now at University of Wisconsin)

showed that for a large number of bases titrated potentiometrically in acetic acid, the relative base strengths
in acetic acid and water are nearly porportional. A
plot showed clearly the leveling effect of acetic acid
on bases stronger than approximately $pK_b = 9$ in water.

Although the guidelines in nonaqueous titrations
had been established, there was very little activity
for almost 20 years. In 1935 Nadeau and Branchen (University of Rochester and Eastman Kodak) published a
practical analytical method for titration of amino
acids, which are weakly basic and difficult to titrate
in water. The titration was performed in acetic acid
with perchloric acid titrant, using either a potentiometric endpoint (chloranil indicator electrode) or a
visual endpoint with crystal violet. In 1946 Palit
(Stanford University) introduced a "G-H," glycol-hydro-
carbon, solvent for titrating salts of weak acids. One
or two other papers appeared during this period but
nothing of much consequence.

Starting around 1947-1950 renewed interest in acid-
base titrations led to the development of excellent
analytical methods and their widespread use in laboratories throughout the world. At Shell Development Co.
in California C. D. Wagner, R. H. Brown, and E. D.
Peters (1947) developed the first convenient analytical
scheme for determining primary, secondary, and tertiary
amines in mixtures. This method was based on an observation published in 1941 by Blumrich and Bandel at I. G.
Farbenindustrie in Höchst, Germany. The Shell workers
were apparently the first to use the glass electrode
for potentiometric titrations in acetic acid.

The half-decade from 1950 through 1954 was perhaps
the golden age for the publication of papers on nonaqueous titration of bases. Fritz and co-workers, first
at Wayne University and then Iowa State University,
accurately titrated weak bases in dioxane, acetic acid,
chlorobenzene, nitromethane, acetonitrile, and other
solvents. Aliphatic and aromatic amines in mixtures
were differentiated by titration in acetonitrile with
perchloric acid in dioxane. Very weak bases such as
caffeine and nicotinamide were titrated successfully by
Fritz. Even lithium nitrate was titrated as a base,
nitric acid being a neutralization product.

The pharmaceutical industry was one of the first
to make extensive use of nonaqueous titrations. C. W.
Pifer and E. G. Wollish of Hoffmann-LaRoche (New Jersey)
published several papers, including a clever method for
titration of hydrohalide salts of amines. This method
was successfully applied to numerous alkaloids and
several vitamins, whether present as the free base or
as the salt. J. A. Riddick of Commercial Solvents Corp.

played a prominent role during this period. He published several papers and reported the titration of over 400 organic compounds in acetic acid.

By about 1955 most of the fundamental analytical procedures used today for nonaqueous titration of bases had been worked out, and the scope of such titrations had been fairly well delineated. However, titration of very weak bases (especially amides) in acetic anhydride and its mixtures was studied further by C. A. Streuli (American Cyanamide) and by D. C. Wimer (Abbott Laboratories) in 1958, and improvements in titration conditions for amides were suggested by D. J. Pietrzyk (University of Iowa) in 1967. Spectrophotometric titration methods for titration of very weak bases and for closely related binary base mixtures were advanced by T. Higuchi (University of Wisconsin) and by D. N. Hume (MIT) and their students. In 1964 H. J. Keiley and Hume developed a thermometric method for titrations in acetic acid that permitted the accurate titration of bases as weak as acetamide and acetanilide.

The greatly increased use of organic epoxides necessitated an improved analytical method for that functional group. In 1956 A. J. Durbetaki (FMC Corp.) found that many epoxy compounds could be titrated directly in acetic acid with anhydrous hydrogen bromide in acetic acid as the titrant. Their method was later improved by R. Dijkstra and E. A. M. F. Dahmen (Royal Dutch Shell, Netherlands) who added an excess of a quaternary ammonium bromide or iodide and then titrated with perchloric acid in acetic acid.

The outstanding early work on titration of acids in nonaqueous solvents was published by a biochemist, O. Folin, and his students working at Harvard University. A paper published in 1910 described a method for titrating fatty acids in solvents such as chloroform, carbon tetrachloride, benzene, or toluene, with a sodium alkoxide titrant and phenolphthalein as the indicator. A quotation from this paper sums up their contribution rather well:

> Our titration method represents, we believe, a new departure in alkalimetry and is not only interesting from a theoretical standpoint but practically should become applicable to a large number of organic acids which hitherto it has not been possible to determine by titration.

Unfortunately little attention was paid to their work at the time, and the development of methods for acid titrations languished for many years. Titration with alcoholic potassium hydroxide was often used, but this only permitted titration of medium strength acids and acids soluble in water or water-alcohol mixtures.

In 1944 an excellent and comprehensive paper was published by a group at Shell Development Co., headed by Louis Lykken, in which a 50-50 mixture of benzene and 2-propanol was used as the solvent for titration. Acids in petroleum products and other samples were titrated with potassium hydroxide in 2-propanol using a glass-calomel electrode pair to follow the titration potentiometrically.

In 1948 a significant breakthrough was scored by M. L. Moss, J. H. Elliott, and R. T. Hall at Hercules Powder Co. For the first time they were able to titrate accurately substances as weakly acidic as phenol and resins containing phenolic groups. The titrations were done in anhydrous ethylenediamine with sodium aminoethoxide titrant and were followed potentiometrically. Their discovery undoubtedly stimulated others to do research in this exciting area and was the forerunner of other papers on titration of acids soon to come.

From 1951 to 1957 Fritz and his students published an extensive series of papers on titration of acidic compounds in nonaqueous solution. Sodium methoxide in benzene-methanol was introduced as a titrant and dimethylformamide as a solvent for titration of acids. The classes of compounds titrated included carboxylic acids, salts of weak bases, sulfonamides and sulfa drugs, enols, imides, phenols, nitroaromatic amines, and miscellaneous compounds such as thioureas. Mixtures of phenols and other acidic compounds were titrated in acetone.

In 1956 use of tetrabutylammonium hydroxide as a titrant was suggested independently by G. A. Harlow, C. M. Noble, and G. E. A. Wyld (Shell Development Co.) and by R. H. Cundiff and P. C. Markunas (Reynolds Tobacco Co.). Both of these research groups made extensive use of pyridine as a solvent and titrated successfully a wide variety of acids and acid mixtures.

In mixtures containing substances of different acidic strength it is often possible to obtain a separate potentiometric endpoint for each acid present. However, titration of phenols and carboxylic acids often produces a titration curve with an abnormally steep slope that makes a differentiating titration of mixtures difficult. Van der Heijde (Royal Dutch Shell) and D. B. Bruss and Harlow (Shell Development Co.) found that this was caused by formation of an association complex between the free acid and the acid anion. Fritz and L. W. Marple (Iowa State University) noted that this association does not occur in *tert*-butyl alcohol, and they demonstrated this compound to be an excellent solvent for titrating mixtures containing carboxylic acids and phenols.

Indicator transition ranges in *tert*-butyl alcohol and pyridine were reported in 1963 and 1966. In 1967 D. H. Morman and Harlow suggested sulfolane as a promising solvent for titration of acids and bases. This solvent has a high dielectric constant and an unusually long potential range for acid-base titrations.

The state of the art for titration of acids now seemed rather well developed. However, the presence of weak base impurities (carbonate and tertiary amines) in tetraalkylammonium hydroxide titrants remained something of a problem. Coulometric titration of acids with electrolytic preparation of the titrant (Fritz and Gainer, 1968) gave excellent results but was limited to titration of quite small amounts of acids.

The work of Brønsted (University of Copenhagen) in explaining the fundamental nature of acid-base reactions was undoubtedly a vital aid in the development of practical acid-base titrations. As early as 1928 he determined the relative acidic strength of 24 compounds in benzene. The work of Conant and Hall also provided much information concerning acid-base behavior in acetic acid. However, the really definitive study on acid-base behavior in acetic acid was by I. M. Kolthoff and S. Bruckenstein at the University of Minnesota in 1956. They measured ionization constants of acids, bases, and salts, calculated the course of titration curves, and contributed much to our understanding of acid-base equilibria in acetic acid. However, it is interesting that their contributions came *after* many practical titration methods had been developed empirically.

Studies on acid-base equilibria in other solvents followed the acetic acid work. These solvents included dimethylformamide (Teze and Schaal, Paris, 1962), dimethylsulfoxide (Kolthoff and students, 1962-1968, and Courtot-Coupez and leDémézet, Brest, France, 1969), ethylenediamine (W. B. Schaap and students, Indiana University, 1961, and Bruckenstein and students, University of Minnesota, 1965), and acetonitrile (Kolthoff, J. F. Coetzee, M. K. Chantooni). Work of this type has provided valuable data on ionization constants of acids and bases in the solvents studied. This is likely to be an active area for future work.

NONAQUEOUS REDOX TITRIMETRY

Oxidation-reduction titrations in nonaqueous solvents have not received as much attention as their acid-base counterparts. In 1925 E. F. Armstrong and T. P. Hilditch reported on the oxidation of the olefinic linkage of oleic acid with potassium permanganate in acetone and acetic acid solutions. They found that aqueous chromic acid solutions and aqueous methanolic potassium permanganate solutions would not give complete oxidation of the olefinic linkage. However, acetic acid and acetone solutions of potassium permanganate gave much more quantitative conversion to the desired products.

The classic example of a redox reaction in a non-aqueous solvent is the Karl Fischer titration (1935). This method of water determination is one of the most widely applicable chemical methods yet developed. It can be used conveniently to determine the water content of more sample types than any other single method, and it suffers from very few interferences. Waters of hydration are easily abstracted, and even in samples containing oxidizing or reducing agents, which can react with the Karl Fischer reagent, one can correct for this type of interference if the stoichiometry is known.

The first systematic study of reactions in a non-aqueous solvent was performed by Professor Oldrich Tomiček in Prague. In 1949 the first of a series of papers appeared dealing with what might be best phrased "analytical chemistry in acetic acid." Over a five-year period he explored bromination, neutralization, reduction, oxidation, and precipitation titrations in acetic acid. Most of the titrations were done either potentiometrically or amperometrically. He also dealt with the question of pH scales in acetic acid, formic acid, pyridine, and water. During this work some new oxidizing titrants were introduced--namely, iodine monochloride, plumbic acetate, and bromine--in acetic acid, which were used for the determination of organic substances.

In 1956 O. N. Hinsvark and K. G. Stone were the first to explore the potentialities of a cerium(IV) nitrate solution in glacial acetic acid as a titrant. A carbon-14 tracer study revealed that the carbon dioxide formed during the oxidation of oxalic acid did not come from the oxalic acid but rather from the acetic acid solvent. Since 1956 few papers have appeared dealing with redox reactions in nonaqueous solvents.

In 1975 W. J. Mergens and G. W. Ewing reported a study of titration interactions between Sn(II) and the redox couples Mn(VII)-Mn(II), Fe(III)-Fe(II), I_2-I_3^-, and Cu(II)-Cu(I) in acetone, acetylacetone, acetonitrile, pyridine, and acetic acid. They showed that solvents of low dielectric constant exert a leveling effect toward ligands, whereas those with high dielectric constant tend to differentiate between ligands.

CHELOMETRIC AND COMPLEXOMETRIC METHODS

In the broadest sense, any analysis carried out in solution might be considered to involve coordination since the chemistry of solutions is the chemistry of complexation. Applications of complex-forming reactions pervade qualitative and quantitative analysis, with coordination compounds being widely used in gravimetric, titrimetric, and colorimetric determinations as well as in fluorimetry, electrochemical analysis, and separations. The foundations of coordination chemistry began in Europe before the beginning of the 19th century with the discovery of ammines by Tassaert, who observed in 1798 that cobalt salts will combine with ammonia. About the same time, Louis Jacques Thénard, a lecturer at the École Polytechnique and the University of Paris, was also involved with the preparation of slightly dissociated compounds.

The first logical attempt to explain metal ammonia compounds was made by Jöns Jakob Berzelius (1779-1848), who observed that a metal in "conjugation" with ammonia did not lose its capacity for combining with other substances. Berzelius, a Swedish chemist, became prominent among the leading chemists of the world while still quite young. Among his accomplishments were his dualistic theory, the determination of a large number of atomic weights, and the invention of chemical symbols which are still in use today. The pioneering work of Christian Wilhelm Blomstrand (1826-1897) and Sophus Mads Jörgensen (1837-1914), two Danish chemists, and their students provided a series of compounds containing either chromium(III), cobalt(III), or platinum(II) combined with ammonia for which no explanation could be given in terms of the classical valence picture. Blomstrand was the first of the two to set forth his ideas. In 1869 he published "Die Chemie der Jetztzeit," in which he proposed not only to present the then current ideas but to join them with the past. Blomstrand used the idea of a chain of ammonia molecules analogous to the chaining of methylene groups in the hydrocarbons as the basis of his theory. Jörgensen, a methodical experimentalist, tested each of Blomstrand's propositions and on the basis of his findings suggested modifications of the theory. It soon became obvious, however, that their efforts were becoming more frustrating and the theory less convincing. Ultimately, Blomstrand's formulas for the cobalt ammonia compounds became the center of a long controversy between Jörgensen and Werner.

The complete failure of the classical valence picture to explain metal complexes was first realized by

Alfred Werner, a Swiss chemist. Werner started his chemical career as an organic chemist and was awarded a Ph.D. by the University of Zürich for work done under Arthur Rudolf Hantzsch on the structure and stereochemistry of organic nitrogen compounds. Werner finished his chemical career as one of the foremost inorganic chemists, won the Nobel prize in 1913, and has been called the founder of coordination chemistry. Proceeding mostly on the basis of work performed by Jörgensen, Werner introduced two different kinds of valence forces to account for the chemistry of these compounds: the primary valence (charge) and the secondary valence (coordination number). In his paper "Contributions to the Theory of Affinity and Valence," published in 1891, Werner suggested that an atom does not have a certain number of valence bonds but that the valence force is exerted over the whole surface of the atom and can be divided into several units of varying strength, depending upon the demands of the atoms which unite with it. This thought was the forerunner of the postulate of primary and secondary valence. Pfeiffer has written of Werner:

> According to his own statement, the inspiration came to him like a flash. One morning at two o'clock he awoke with a start; the long-sought solution of this problem had lodged in his brain. He arose from his bed and by five o'clock in the afternoon the essential points of the coordination theory were achieved.

At that time Werner was 26.

The studies of Werner, followed by the ideas of G. N. Lewis and N. V. Sidgwick on electron-pair bonding, led to the ideas that ligands are groups that can in some way donate electron pairs to metal ions, thus forming a coordinate-covalent bond. This approach to bonding in complexes was extended by Linus Pauling and was developed into the valence bond theory of metal ligand bonding. This theory enjoyed great and virtually exclusive popularity among chemists through the 1930s and 1940s, and was supplemented during the 1950s by ligand field theory. Ligand field theory was developed by physicists, mainly J. H. Van Vleck and his students between 1930 and 1940, and was rediscovered in the early 1950s by several theoretical chemists. Ligand field theory evolved out of a purely electrostatic theory called crystal field theory which was based on the premise that the metal ion in a complex is subjected to an electric field originating from the ligand as originally proposed in 1929 by J. Becquerel. This was formulated into an exact mathematical theory by

H. Bethe in that same year. The foundations for all
further theoretical work in this area came from Bethe's
investigation of how the symmetry of the complex and
the strength of a crystal field affect the electronic
levels of gaseous metal ions. The first application of
crystal field theory to chemistry was made by Van Vleck
in 1932 to explain why the paramagnetism of complexes
of first-row transition elements corresponds to a spin-
only value.

The earliest analytical methods based on complex
formation appeared around 1851. The first was the
determination of cyanide by Justus Liebig, which
involves titrating with silver(I). Liebig also devised
a method for separating cobalt and nickel based on a
complexation reaction with cyanide. The reaction
between silver(I) and cyanide is also utilized indirectly
for the determination of other metals which form stable
cyanide complexes. The cyanide method was greatly
improved by George Denigès, who used potassium iodide
as the indicator and titrated in an ammonia solution.
Denigès, a French chemist, received an M.D. degree, a
doctorate of Science, and the degree Pharmacien Super-
ieur from the University of Bordeaux. He became professor of medical chemistry there in 1892, and from
1898 to 1930 he held the chair in biological chemistry.
He authored 680 papers in organic chemistry, pharmacy,
and analytical chemistry; however, the bulk of his work
dealt with analytical chemistry.

Justus Liebig, one of the outstanding chemists of
the 19th century, has been called the father of organic
chemistry. Analytical research was a minor interest
with him. Jacob Volhard (1834-1910) was Liebig's
assistant for a while in Munich and was editor of
Liebig's *Annalen* for 39 years. Volhard had originally
wanted to be an historian, but his father, a close
friend of Liebig, forced him to become a chemist.
Liebig assisted Volhard in his career by employing him
as a Privatdozent at Munich and later recommending him
for a post as director of an agricultural research
institute. Volhard's most important work which dealt
with analytical and inorganic chemistry was summarized
in papers appearing between 1875 and 1880. He is probably best known because of his method for the determination of halides. The distinctive color reaction
between iron(III) and thiocyanate used to indicate the
endpoint in Volhard's method had been recognized and
used by Berzelius nearly 50 years earlier, but the
nature of this iron-thiocyanate complex was not understood until fairly recently.

The classical complexing reactions which are analytically most useful are those of mercury(II) with

halides and of cyanide with silver(I). Mercurimetric methods for determining chloride were first proposed by Liebig who recommended urea as an indicator. The method may be reversed so that mercury(II) can be titrated with chloride ion using sodium phosphate as an indicator. This indicator had been previously used in 1853 by Alexandre François Levol for argentometric chloride determinations. Friedrich Mohr, in his text on titrimetric methods, named potassium ferricyanide as the preferred indicator. Mohr was the son of a pharmacist, and he also studied pharmacy. His university studies were carried out in Bonn, Heidelberg, and Berlin, where he came under the influence of the famous analyst, Heinrich Rose. Mohr had a vivid imagination which caused him to dabble in various sciences; however, he appears to have been irritable, critical, and generally disagreeable. He became a Privatdozent at the University of Bonn and in 1867 the deputy professor of pharmacy. Mohr's literary accomplishments were outstanding; his publications numbered more than 100 and dealt with meteorology, analytical chemistry, mechanics, beekeeping, toxicology, and geology. His book on titrimetry was published in many editions and was revised and enlarged as this subject developed.

The mercurimetric method for the determination of chloride first achieved practical importance with the introduction of sodium nitroprusside as an indicator by Emil Votoček. Votoček studied at the Technical Universities of Prague and Mulhouse and later worked in Göttingen and Prague. A particular advantage of his method is that it can be applied to quite strongly acid solutions. I. M. Kolthoff and A. Bak found that the procedure gives excellent results if the appropriate indicator blank correction is determined. Diphenylcarbazide and diphenylcarbazone have also been used as indicators in mercurimetric titrations of chloride by J. V. Dubsky and J. Trtilek. As long ago as 1832 this reaction was applied to the assay of potassium iodide by J. Marozeau. Corrections for a premature endpoint have been determined by Kolthoff, but these are so large, they make the titration of little practical value.

The complexation reaction between mercury(II) and iodide has also been used in the application of mercuric oxide as a primary standard for acids and thiocyanate solutions. In 1878, Volhard described this determination and recognized the premature endpoint. The $Hg(SCN)_4^{2-}$ complex ion has been used as a precipitating agent for zinc and other divalent metal ions. L. L. deKoninck and Grandry later introduced $K_2[Hg(SCN)_4]$ as a volumetric reagent. Various divalent metal ions may

be determined by precipitation of the double thiocyanates with pyridine and alkali thiocyanate. Spacu and
his collaborators advocated the determination of copper,
zinc, nickel, cobalt, and even pyridine in this manner.

Complexation reactions have also been used to
develop special methods of acidimetry and alkalimetry.
The direct determination of hydrocyanic acid or mercuric
salts exemplifies these methods. The method originated
with Andrews, who used p-nitrophenol as the indicator,
but this was shown to be less satisfactory than methyl
yellow. Cyanide has been used to titrate metal ions
which form neutral cyano complexes. The excess cyanide
is detected by the increase in hydroxide concentration
which occurs at the endpoint. The mercuric cyanide
complex is so stable in solution that no hydrolysis of
cyanide is apparent. E. Rupp (1908) used this behavior
in his method for determining mercuric salts. A similar
effect has been used to determine fluoride ion. Fluoride combines with aluminum(III) to form the stable
hexafluoroaluminate (III) complex ion, and this reacts
neutral to phenolphthalein in aqueous solution as
described in the early 1930s by Kurtenacker and Jurenka.

Until fairly recently, complex-formation titrations
were of relatively minor significance in analytical
chemistry. The classical methods of complexometric
analysis utilize coordinating agents that occupy only a
single coordination position. Niels J. Bjerrum showed
that complexes form in a stepwise manner. Bjerrum, one
of S. M. Jörgensen's most distinguished students, was
later to become known as the dean of Danish physical
chemists. He studied at the University of Copenhagen
and received his Ph.D. there under Jörgensen in 1908.
Bjerrum taught at the University of Copenhagen and at
the Royal Veterinary and Agricultural College of Copenhagen, where he was professor of chemistry from 1914
until retirement in 1949. Much of his work was in the
area of chemical physics. He was interested in the
relationships of thermodynamic data to spectroscopic
parameters, the dissociation of strong electrolytes,
interionic forces, activity coefficients, ionic distribution coefficients, and the theory of acid-base
titrations.

An important early quantitative study of complex
equilibria was done by Niels' son, Jannik Bjerrum, who
showed that monodentate ligands invariably added in a
succession of steps. Unless one particular step happens
to be extraordinarily stable, the complexation reaction
will not be suitable for analytical purposes. Most
reactions involving the formation of complexes with
monodentate ligands fail to fulfill one or more of the
requirements necessary for the existence of a sharp

endpoint. However, polydentate ligands, in particular chelating agents, are most satisfactory for this purpose. The term chelate was proposed by G. T. Morgan to designate those cyclic structures which arise from the union of metal ions with organic or inorganic moieties containing two or more functional groups when both functional groups occupy positions in the coordination sphere. The chelate effect was used by G. Schwarzenbach to describe the enhanced stability of a complex involving ring formation vs. a complex involving no rings. Rudolf Pribil suggested the term chelometric titrations for those volumetric methods which use chelating agents as titrants. Pribil graduated at the University of Prague and worked in the Analytical Institute at the Charles University in Prague. For a time he worked in industry, but in 1946 he returned to the university. Since 1955 he has been directing one of the research departments of the Czechoslovakian Academy of Sciences.

An early comprehensive review of chelate compounds was presented by Harvey Diehl, and the chemistry of the metal chelate compounds was discussed in length by Arthur E. Martell and Melvin Calvin in their book which was published in 1952. During the 1930s it was found that certain aminopolycarboxylic acids formed stable, soluble complexes with a large number of metal ions, most notably with the alkaline earths. The I. G. Farben Industrie prepared and marketed these compounds as metal-complexing agents. The theoretical examination and characterization of the metal complexes of some of these acids was begun in the 1940s by H. Brintzinger and Paul Pfeiffer with co-workers. These investigations ultimately led to what is probably the most outstanding reagent development of this century. In 1945 Gerold Schwarzenbach and co-workers initiated a series of fundamental studies of polyaminopolycarboxylic acids (which they designated as complexones) as analytical chelating reagents. The term Complexone, used by Schwarzenbach in a generic sense for polyaminocarboxylate chelating agents, has been registered as a trademark. Thus, the term "chelon" was proposed by Charles N. Reilley for analytically useful polyamines, polyaminocarboxylic acids, and related compounds which form stable, soluble, usually 1:1 complexes with metal ions and which may consequently be used effectively as titrants for metal ions. Of these, ethylenediaminetetraacetic acid, EDTA, has become one of the most important reagents used in titrimetry. Since Schwarzenbach's first paper on this topic appeared, approximately 3000 papers dealing with complexation analysis have been published along with a number of monographs on this subject. Schwarzenbach graduated from the Technical University in Zürich and

was appointed professor of analytical chemistry there
in 1947. In 1955 he became the director of the Institute for Analytical Chemistry at the Technical University, and he was the 1963 Talanta prize winner for analytical chemistry. Most of his papers on compleximetry
have appeared in *Helvetica Chimica Acta*.

In early 1945 Schwarzenbach, in an address before
the Swiss Chemical Society, disclosed the indirect
determination of metal ions via the pH effects displayed
on addition of an EDTA salt to solutions containing the
metal ion. This report commenced Schwarzenbach's classical work on the titrimetric determination of calcium
and magnesium which virtually revolutionized the analytical approach to metal ion analysis. The first
method involved titration of the hydrogen ion liberated
during the complexation reaction with sodium hydroxide
using an acid-base indicator. This procedure was
quickly and universally adopted for determining the
permanent hardness of water. Since then the applicability of the EDTA titration has been extended to the
determination of over 50 elements, either by direct or
back titrations with EDTA or indirectly via titration
of another element after precipitation. The spectacular success of EDTA in titrimetric applications is due
to the fact that complex formation is generally rapid,
stoichiometric, and quantitative. The stability constants of a number of these complexes have been determined by Schwarzenbach and his co-workers, mainly from
pH measurements of the liberated hydrogen ion.

The sodium salt of ethylenediaminetetraacetic acid
which is generally used as the titrant has been marketed
under various trade names, and it is often referred to
in the older literature as Versene, Sequestrene, Tri-
lon B, Complexone II, III, or IV. EDTA forms very
stable complexes with nearly all divalent, trivalent,
and quadrivalent metal ions and thus is not a very
selective titrant. In practice, however, the lack of
specificity may be made less severe or circumvented by
judicious use of pH and masking agents to mitigate the
interfering effects. D. D. Perrin has defined a masking
reagent as one that decreases the concentration of a
free metal ion or a ligand to a level where certain of
its chemical reactions are prevented. EDTA itself
functions as a versatile masking agent. Other masking
agents which have received attention include various
amines and ammonia which, although not highly selective,
are commonly used for metal ions.

The original method Schwarzenbach used to detect
the endpoint in titrations involving EDTA was based
upon estimating the acid liberated upon complex formation. When the disodium salt is used, two hydrogen

ions are liberated for each divalent or polyvalent metal ion complexed. The liberated hydrogen ions can be titrated with standard base using an acid-base indicator. This method is of considerable historical interest as it was the first to use EDTA in a titration but not as a titrant. EDTA titrations have been comprehensively reviewed by H. Flaschka, A. Ringbom, and others.

The introduction of metallochromic indicators by Schwarzenbach and his co-workers, which permit EDTA titrations to be carried out visually, led to the development of many methods involving the direct titration of metal ions. The first metal indicator to be used in the EDTA titration by Schwarzenbach was murexide. Although murexide forms complexes with many metal ions, only those with calcium, nickel, cobalt, zinc, cadmium, and copper are sufficiently stable to be of analytical interest.

Early in 1946 Schwarzenbach noted without details that the endpoint in a titration with EDTA might be ascertained by using metal-sensitive indicators. Patents relating to these discoveries were filed in Switzerland in 1945 and were issued in 1947. The use of murexide as a metal-sensitive indicator was disclosed in 1946, and in 1948 Schwarzenbach and Biedermann reported the color changes, ionization constants, and stability constants of the calcium and magnesium complexes of four o,o'-dihydroxydinaphthylazo dyes. These dyes are best known under the Geigy trade names Eriochrome Black T and A and Eriochrome Blue Black R and B. Of these dyes, Eriochrome Black T (Erio T) was selected for use as a metal indicator on the basis of the high stability of its magnesium complex. It is one of the first and perhaps most widely used of the metallochromic indicators. While there are numerous applications of Erio T in EDTA titrations, there are essentially no applications for solutions more acidic than pH 6.5. Procedures for the analysis of ores, alloys, and concentrates using Erio T as an indicator have been described by T. Kinnunen, and EDTA titrations with Erio T in pharmaceutical analysis have been developed by R. Pribil. Other applications of Erio T include its use as a chromogenic agent in spectrophotometric determinations, use in fluorometric determinations, and as an indicator in titrations of magnesium with other chelons. The sensitivity of the reaction of metal ions with Eriochrome Black T is amazingly high but unfortunately, Erio T is unstable in solution. This led Harvey Diehl and F. Lindstrom in 1960 to develop calmagite, 1-(1-hydroxy-4-methyl-2-phenylazo)-2-naphthol-4-sulfonic acid, as a replacement indicator which is

stable in aqueous solution; it has a sharper color
change and can be substituted for Erio T without requiring changes in procedure.

Eriochrome Blue Black R and B have also been
employed as metal indicators in chelometric titrations,
and these dyes are somewhat similar to Eriochrome Black
T. An important application of Eriochrome Blue Black R
(Calcon) developed by Hildebrand and Reilley is in the
titration of calcium. The color and fluorescent reactions of both dyes have been utilized in spectrophotometric and fluorometric determination of several metals.
Other o,o'-dihydroxyazo dyes have been used as metallochromic indicators in the direct EDTA titration of metal
ions--e.g., Eriochrome Blue SE, Eriochrome Red B, the
Acid Chrome Blue dyes, and the dye of Patton and Reeder.
These dyes are similar to Eriochrome Black T but appear
to have superior characteristics in specific applications. Thorin (Thoron or APANS) and PAN are two o,o'-
disubstituted azo dyes that have been utilized as indicators for EDTA titration in acidic solutions. Thorin
has an arsono group, $ASO(OH)_3$, and a hydroxyl group as
ortho substituents. This azo dye has been used as an
indicator in the direct EDTA titration of bismuth in
nitric acid (pH 1-3), and it can be used as a chromogenic agent in the spectrophotometric determinations.
PAN, 1-(2-pyridylazo)-2-naphthol, was introduced in
1955 by K. L. Cheng and R. H. Bray as an indicator for
the direct EDTA titration of copper, zinc, and cadmium.
The determination of ultra-micro amounts of copper and
other metals was developed by Hermenegild A. Flaschka,
who is now at the Georgia Institute of Technology.

By introducing iminodiacetic acid groups into acid-
base indicators, Schwarzenbach, Flaschka, and co-workers
were able to develop the metallochromic indicators
Metalphthalein, Calcein, and xylenol orange. An improved synthesis for phthalein-type indicators which
yields the desired product in a pure form, was developed by R. Pribil. Harvey Diehl and J. L. Ellingboe
used Calcein in the direct EDTA titration of calcium
in the presence of magnesium. The calcium derivative
of Calcein is brown and fluorescent, while the indicator
alone is green and non-fluorescent. Although the color
change can be used to detect the endpoint in this titration, as was done by Diehl and Ellingboe in the original
application, the disappearance of the fluorescence is
better and the titration is best carried out in the
dark under ultraviolet light. Morin (2',3,4',5,7-penta-
hydroxyflavone), a reagent used to detect and to determine many metals, has also been used for this purpose.

During the late 1940s and early 1950s a number of
other aminopolycarboxylic acids were also under

investigation, primarily by Schwarzenbach and his co-workers, for use in complexometric titrations. Historically, nitrilotriacetic acid (NTA) is next in importance to EDTA, and it has been widely used in complexometric titrations. The main type of reaction for which NTA is more convenient than EDTA is where its dialkali metal salt is used, followed by a back titration to determine the concentration of hydrogen ion that has been liberated by metal complex formation. Uramildiacetic acid, a similar chelating ligand investigated by Schwarzenbach, forms exceptionally stable complexes with Li^+ and Na^+. A study in the early 1960s by Irving and da Silva of the effect of methyl substitution in uramildiacetic acid on the stability constants for alkali metal complexes led to the suggestion that the ligand forms a sterically favored conformation with a cagelike structure to accommodate small ions which favor a tetrahedral environment.

Bis(aminoethyl)glycol ether N,N,N',N'-tetraacetic acid (EGTA), another structurally related aminopolycarboxylic acid, was developed in the late 1950s by Schmid and Reilley as a selective titrant for calcium in the presence of magnesium. They used a mercury indicator electrode as no good visual endpoint method is available for this titration.

Polydentate amines received attention during the 1950s as potential chelometric reagents. Relative values for the stability constants of metal ions with polydentate amines show a much wider variation than with ligands of the EDTA type. These stability constants were measured primarily in the research groups of G. Schwarzenbach, C. N. Reilley and R. W. Schmid, J. Bjerrum, and H. B. Jonassen. Because of the difficulty of obtaining pure polyamines, few titrations using them as reagents have been described. Nevertheless, methods using polyamines as titrants were reported in the late 1950s by Flaschka and by Reilley and co-workers at the University of North Carolina.

Potentiometric, photometric, conductometric, high frequency, thermometric, amperometric, and chronopotentiometric methods have been developed to detect the endpoint of chelometric titrations. Of these, two types of electrodes are of importance: mercury-mercury(II) EDTA, described by Reilley and Schmid in 1958, and the silver indicating electrode of T. S. Fritz and B. B. Garralda (1964). Various instrumental methods for endpoint detection in chelometric titrations were described by numerous workers: Reilley and Porterfield in 1956 (potentiometric), Reilley and Scribner in 1958 (chronopotentiometric), Pribil in 1951 (amperometric), and Hara and West in 1954 (conductometric). Applications

HOBART HURD WILLARD, 1881-1974

   After obtaining BS and MA degrees at Michigan, Willard went
to Harvard University where he studied under T. W. Richards, earn-
ing his doctorate in 1909.   He then joined the staff at the University of Michigan where he remained until his retirement in 1951.
Willard received many awards in recognition of his excellence as a
teacher and analytical chemist.   He and his students were active
in organizing an annual informal conference known as MUAC (Midwest
University Analytical Chemists).   His scientific accomplishments
include work in homogeneous precipitation, bimetallic electrode
pairs, the chemistries of perchloric and periodic acids and cerate
oxidimetry.   He was coauthor of many popular textbooks.

of instrumental methods for the EDTA titrations were
extended by Kolthoff, Ringbom, Pribil, Laitinen, and
their co-workers.

Of the various instrumental techniques used for
endpoint detection in chelometric titrations, the spectrophotometric method is next in importance to potentiometry. A large variety of photometric titrations have
been reported which utilize complex-formation reactions,
but the titration of various metals with EDTA is one of
the most fruitful applications of photometric titrimetry. The principles of the photometric EDTA titration
were studied in the early 1950s by A. L. Underwood,
H. V. Malmstadt, A. Ringbom, and D. N. Hume. The first
photometric EDTA titration was conducted by Biedermann
and Schwarzenbach to identify the endpoints in the
visual EDTA titrations of zinc and magnesium with Eriochrome Black T.

Photometric and colorimetric methods of analysis
represent another major analytical application of complexation reactions. M. G. Mellon, professor of chemistry at Purdue University and the foremost American
worker in colorimetry and spectrophotometry, was responsible for the development of many new spectrophotometric
reagents and methods. The use of complexing agents in
quantitative photometric analysis is well illustrated
by the applications of 1,10-phenanthroline, α,α'-dipyr-
idyl, and α,α',α''-tripyridyl. These ligands which contain the ferroin group are widely used as spectrophotometric reagents for iron and copper. An early application of 1,10-phenanthroline to the colorimetric determination of iron was reported by Hobart H. Willard, professor of chemistry at the University of Michigan.
Willard and his students were involved in the development of new spectrophotometric reagents and methods for
the determination of metals related to ferrous metallurgy. Many modified 1,10-phenanthroline derivatives
were investigated in the 1940s and 1950s by G. Frederick
Smith and his students at the University of Illinois.
Studies of the stability and analytical properties of
metal complexes of substituted, 1,10-phenanthrolines
were being conducted simultaneously in England by H.
Irving. The research efforts of these groups led to the
development of bathophenanthroline and bathocuproine as
selective spectrophotometric reagents. More recently,
Blair and Diehl at Iowa State University have introduced
the use of disulfonic acid derivatives to overcome the
poor water solubility of bathocuproine and bathophenanthroline.

8-Hydroxyquinoline (oxine) may be used for the
colorimetric determination of many metal ions. Alten,
Weiland, and Loofman, for example, reported in 1933 a

colorimetric determination of aluminum in which they
coupled the hydroxyquinolate of aluminum, in the precipitate, with a diazo compound to obtain a strongly
colored dye, which was then compared with a standard.
Lynne L. Merritt, Jr. and his students at Indiana University during the 1940s investigated the use of selected
steric factors in 8-hydroxyquinoline to obtain selective
or specific analytical reagents. Irving and his co-
workers in England about this same time were also involved in designing selective chelating agents based on
stereochemical differences in substituted 8-hydroxy-
quinolines.

Fluorometric methods of analysis based on complexation reactions have been developed, and these are often
more sensitive than the usual colorimetric ones. As
early as 1867 the intense green fluorescence produced
by adding morin (3,5,7,2',4'-pentahydroxyflavone) to
solutions of aluminum salts was reported by Friedrich
Goppelsröder. In 1943 this reaction was used by White
and Neustadt for the fluorometric determination of small
quantities of aluminum. Other common fluorometric reagents used by White and co-workers include benzoin,
Pontachrome Blue Black R, and 1-amino-4-hydroxyanthro-
quinone. Diehl and co-workers reported a direct determination of magnesium in the presence of calcium without prior separation, employing o,o'-dihydroxyazobenzene
as the fluorometric reagent.

Another early application of chelating agents began
with Lev A. Tschugaeff's 1905 discovery that dimethylglyoxime reacts with nickel ion to give an insoluble
red compound. This reaction was studied extensively by
Tschugaeff and later by Fritz Feigl at the Technical
University of Vienna. These investigations revealed
that only the antiisomers of symmetrical dioximes form
the characteristic precipitate with nickel(II). The
demonstration in 1924 by Brady and Mehta of the existence of two tautomeric forms of the oxime groups led
Pfeiffer to propose that the nickel ion is bonded to the
nitrogen atoms of the dioxime group rather than to the
oxygen atoms. In 1930 Brady and Meurs correctly postulated the existence of internal hydrogen bonding in
these complexes to explain the lack of reactivity of the
hydroxyl group. This theory was verified in the early
1950s by the crystallographic work conducted at Iowa
State University by R. E. Rundle and co-workers. X-ray
analysis showed that the nickel-dimethylglyoxime complex
has a planar configuration in which the $-OH^-$ and $-O^-$ are
strongly internally hydrogen bonded. Surprisingly, it
also revealed the existence of metal-metal bonding in
this complex. The planar structure and the tendency of
nickel to form weak metal-to-metal bonds in the solid

MELVIN GUY MELLON, 1893–

Following his graduate education at the Ohio State University, Mellon joined the faculty at Purdue University (in 1919), where he spent his entire career, now holding the title of Emeritus Professor. He has always been fascinated by color and its significance in chemical analysis, and has contributed heavily to our understanding of its origin and utility. Mellon also made himself an expert in the functional design of academic chemistry buildings.

state has been used to explain the increased insolubility of nickel-dioxime complexes compared with the corresponding copper(II) complexes where such bonding does not occur. Palladium(II)-dioxime complexes are similar to the nickel complexes both in structure and in insolubility.

Other 1,2-dioximes which are more water soluble than dimethylglyoxime and give more favorable conversion factors have been investigated. α-Furildioxime was one of the twelve 1,2-dioximes reported by Tschugaeff to form colored complexes with nickel. It was not until 1925, however, that Byron A. Soule, working under the direction of Professor E. D. Campbell at the University of Michigan, described it as a water-soluble compound, suitable for analytical work and recommended it as a specific reagent for nickel. A satisfactory method for preparing α-furildioxime from furfural was described by Reed, Banks, and Diehl in 1947. The late Charles V. Banks and co-workers at Iowa State University and Ames Institute for Atomic Research showed that although α-furildioxime is a satisfactory reagent for separating and determining palladium, it leaves much to be desired as to solubility in water and as an analytical reagent for nickel.

In 1924 Wallach reported that 1,2-cyclohexanedionedioxime (nioxime) yields a scarlet precipitate with nickel and is a very sensitive qualitative test for nickel. Seven years later Feigl pointed out that in view of its water solubility this compound should be an ideal reagent for nickel. It was not until 1945, however, that Rauh, Smith, Banks, and Diehl succeeded in obtaining a sufficient quantity of nioxime to study its uses as an analytical reagent. In 1946 Voter, Banks, and Diehl reported that nioxime could be used satisfactorily for the gravimetric determination of nickel in the presence of many of the common anions and cations. Although nioxime offers several advantages over dimethylglyoxime as a reagent for nickel, its utility is nevertheless limited. The advantages exhibited by nioxime led Voter and Banks to investigate the properties of some of the higher homologs of 1,2-cyclohexanedionedioxime. In this regard, they developed a method of preparing 1,2-cycloheptanedionedioxime (heptoxime) from cycloheptanone. Their results reported in 1949 showed that heptoxime possesses almost all the good characteristics of both dimethylglyoxime and nioxime without their disadvantages.

THERMOMETRIC TITRATIONS AND ENTHALPIMETRIC ANALYSIS

This area provides an interesting "case history" of a development where automatic instrumentation proved to be not merely a convenience, but an essential prerequisite. The basic idea is as "old as the hills"; it involves the obvious experimental approach: perform a conventional titration in an adiabatic cell and determine the endpoint by monitoring the concomitant change in temperature. Indeed, the first report of such an "enthalpy titration" published more than half a century ago (1913), was intended as a procedure for the preparation of a solution of ammonium citrate. The idea caught on in Europe, especially in France and Switzerland, yielding several series of publications. However through the twenties and thirties thermochemical titrations remained a sort of oddity ("an art"). This situation continued as long as manual burets and mercury thermometers were used. Two important instrumental breakthroughs in the fifties have converted thermometric titrations into a rigorous science and into a promising method of modern instrumental analysis.

 I.   Thermistors were introduced as temperature sensors of high sensitivity and instantaneous response, in lieu of the sluggish Beckman thermometers of yesteryear. This crucial advance was pioneered by L. B. Rogers and D. N. Hume at MIT.

 II. "Personal variables"--which have haunted earlier work--were effectively eliminated, by combining the Rogers-Hume thermistor circuitry with automated constant-flow titrant delivery systems. This development emanated from J. Jordan and his students at Penn State. The "coming of age" of thermochemical titrimetry was brought to the attention of the scientific community by Jordan's "Frontiers of Chemistry" lecture at Wayne State University in 1958.

Since the sixties, R. M. Izatt and J. J. Christensen at Brigham Young University have initiated a vigorous program of titration calorimetry which has produced a wealth of thermodynamic data and information on biochemical thermodynamics. Second generation methods of enthalpimetric analysis have proliferated, including direct injection enthalpimetry (Jordan et al., Penn State, 1964), gas enthalpimetry (Hume and Duffield, MIT, 1964), kinetic titrimetry (Carr and Jordan, Penn State, 1973) and enzymatic enthalpimetry (McGlothlin and Jordan, Penn State, 1975). Advances pioneered in England have included continuous flow (P. T. Priestley et al., 1965) and catalytic indicator methods

(G. A. Vaughan, 1966). Three authoritative monographs on thermometric and enthalpimetric titrations have appeared in print since 1968. Their perusal reveals that the field of enthalpimetric analysis has indeed blossomed during the last decade, encompassing a bibliography of some five hundred entries. Significant applications have transpired in inorganic, organic, physical, biological and clinical chemistry, including aqueous and non-aqueous solvents, as well as fused salts at elevated temperatures. Research groups in the field of enthalpimetric analysis are currently active in Canada, Great Britain, Germany, Hungary, Japan and Sweden. In the United States, centers of relevant research and development include American Instrument Company, Silver Spring, Maryland (C. D. Miller, H. Cullis); Brigham Young University (J. J. Christensen, R. M. Izatt, L. D. Hansen, D. J. Eatough); University of Georgia (P. W. Carr); Penn State (J. Jordan), University of Texas at Austin (N. D. Jespersen); Tronac, Inc., Provo, Utah. Commercial instruments for thermochemical titrations and enthalpimetric analysis are currently manufactured in Canada, Hungary, Japan and the United States.

From a general historical viewpoint, modern analytical chemistry was dominated by reliance on "matter-energy interactions" on which all of the so-called instrumental methods of analysis are based. In this context, it is paradoxical that the most universal energy parameter of chemical processes, the heat of reaction, had not been extensively made use of earlier. During the last decade, enthalpimetric analysis has filled this gap.

FUNCTIONAL GROUP ANALYSIS

Functional group analysis as well as nonaqueous titrations played an important role in the analysis of organic compounds before the development of gas chromatography and mass spectroscopy. Functional group analysis was not discovered cataclysmically; rather it evolved slowly. Organic materials were first measured by determination of elements which they contained. Since many organic compounds contain the same elements, this approach is not sufficient, though quantitative organic elemental analysis is very useful in identifying pure organic compounds.

The first inklings of functional group analytical methods began to appear as qualitative chemical tests for the several groups. Mulliken in 1904 came out with the first compendium of such tests, followed by Shriner

and Fuson. As stated, these tests were geared toward
qualitative identification. Though they did contain
some quantitative methods such as saponification and
neutralization methods for esters, acids, and bases,
their end purposes were identification.

Niederl and Niederl in 1938 published a text consisting mainly of elemental methods but which described
some functional group methods. Other methods were
scattered through the literature--for example, the
determination of carbonyl groups by reaction with hydroxylamine which can be traced to 1909. An excellent
method for the measurement of alkoxyl groups was originated by Zeisel in 1885.

The term functional group analysis was first used
by S. Siggia in 1947. He had written a book which he
entitled, "Quantitative Organic Analysis via Functional
Groups" to be published by John Wiley. The editor
assigned to the book wanted to shorten the title to
"Quantitative Organic Analysis," but Siggia insisted
that the modifying phrase ". . . via Functional Groups"
be kept since it differentiated this type of analysis
from quantitative organic analysis via the elements.
Siggia won the issue, and the book appeared in January
1949 with the full title, and the designation has stuck.

Many functional groups can be measured directly by
instrumental methods such as infrared absorption,
nuclear magnetic resonance, and electrochemical methods
as well as by other titrimetric and gravimetric methods.
Functional group analysis goes further. If compound A
cannot be measured directly by any of our available
measurement methods, then A can be allowed to react
with B to permit the indirect measurement of A.

Functional group analysis began to develop in the
1930s with increased industrial efforts in the direction
of organic compounds. It is not surprising then that
functional group analysis grew up in the industrial
laboratories with the academic sector beginning to make
major contributions in the early 1950s.

One of the first laboratories to work in this area
was the DuPont research laboratory in Wilmington, Del.
There W. M. D. Bryant and D. M. Smith, in 1935, concluded that quantitative analyses for oxygen-containing
functional groups in organic compounds were inadequate.
They made important contributions to acidimetric methods
for measuring aldehydes and ketones by oximation in the
presence of pyridine, hydroxyl groups by acetylation
with acetyl chloride in pyridine, and saponification of
esters and anhydrides of carboxylic acids.

John Mitchell, Jr., entered the DuPont scene in
1935. His initial assignment was in the research division of the Ammonia Department. Mitchell's principal

contributions to functional group analyses were based
on both acidimetric and non-acidimetric procedures. A
new concept in organic analysis was devised, employing
the Karl Fischer reagent to measure water used or produced in organic functional group reactions, as in the
determination of alcoholic hydroxyl and organic acids.
This method was followed in later years by publications
on analyses for acid anhydrides, carbonyl compounds,
amino alcohols, primary plus secondary amines, primary
amines, and nitriles. Major contributions to acidimetric procedures include semi-microsaponification of
esters, carbonyl compounds in the presence of organic
acids, aldehydes in the presence of ketones, small concentrations of carbonyl compounds by a differential pH
method, and hydroperoxide groups by selective reaction
with sulfur dioxide followed by infrared analysis.

While the DuPont laboratory was developing, another
functional group effort was growing at General Aniline
and Film's research laboratory in Easton, Pa. This
effort was led by S. Siggia. Siggia was inspired by
and trained by A. A. Benedetti-Pichler at Queens College.
Siggia also had acquired strong organic chemical training
under Albert H. Blatt at Queens and with Herman Mark at
the Polytechnic Institute of Brooklyn.

It was in 1949 that Siggia compiled the above mentioned text in which he described the most general
methods for determining the various functional groups
which had been studied to that date. Recognition of
industrial analytical problems resulted in the establishment of courses in organic analysis at a number of
universities. Michigan State University was an early
entrant in this field through the efforts of Frederick
R. Duke from 1945 to 1948 and Kenneth G. Stone from 1947
until his untimely death in 1965. Both men had worked
in the organic chemical industry for a year following
their doctorates, Duke's from Illinois and Stone's from
Princeton.

During the late 1940s a functional group laboratory
was established at the Union Carbide Corp. in South
Charleston, West Virginia, initially under the direction
of W. W. Sutherland, just prior to World War II. He was
joined in 1941 by J. B. Johnson who had received a B. S.
degree from Ohio University in 1940. After interruption
due to the war, Johnson and Sutherland returned to the
functional group activity in 1947 and subsequently
established the science of functional group analysis at
Union Carbide. Sutherland was called into the Korean
War and was killed there.

F. W. Critchfield joined the group at Union Carbide
in 1953 after receiving a Ph.D. in physical-analytical
chemistry from West Virginia University. Working with

Johnson, he developed methods for α,β- unsaturated compounds, amines, and carbonyl compounds. In 1963 Critchfield published the book, "Organic Functional Group
Analysis," which described the methods in use at Union
Carbide at that time. Some of these, developed from
1947 to 1953, had not been published previously.

Stemming from the influence of the microelemental
methods of analysis prevalent in the 1920s and 1930s,
functional group determinations on a microscale were
among the first to be devised. The classical micromethods for determining functional groups were explored
and further advanced by T. S. Ma. His work began during
the 1930s as part of his Ph.D. thesis work at the University of Chicago. He began with the Pregl micromethods for the elements and immediately recognized the
need for functional group methods. After World War II,
and with the assistance of graduate students at New York
University and Brooklyn College, he proceeded to test
experimental procedures and published the textbook,
"Organic Functional Group Analysis by Micro and Semi-
micro Methods." At this writing, Ma is professor of
chemistry at Brooklyn College.

R. Belcher also entered functional group analysis
via his early interest in microelemental organic anal-
ysis which he studied at the Pregl Institute in Graz,
Austria, while on leave from the University of Sheffield.
Belcher returned to Sheffield, and after two years at
Aberdeen went to his present location at Birmingham.
He and his associates modified the existing method for
alkoxyl groups among other contributions to the field.

Further advances of functional group analysis rest
upon instrumental methods such as absorption spectroscopy and fluorometry, as presented by J. G. Hanna and
D. M. W. Anderson. Dr. Anderson is professor of analytical chemistry at the University of Edinburgh.

A great deal of work on colorimetric and fluorometric methods has been done on pharmaceuticals by M.
Pesez and J. Bartos of the Roussel-UCLAF Co. in France.
Pesez, who is now director of the analytical division
at Roussel-UCLAF, has published steadily since 1935.
Bartos, who is head of analytical research, joined Pesez
in 1947 and has also published prolifically.

Much research appeared in 1959 and the early 1960s
on acylation and acetylation methods for alcohols; the
acid-catalyzed acetylation methods of Fritz and Schenk
inspired a number of base-catalyzed acylation methods
which have been summarized in a history of functional
group analysis written by G. H. Schenk (1968).

The biggest surge in functional group determinations occurred in the 1950s when the chemical industry
made huge advances in the production of organic

compounds. Acid-base, oxidation-reduction, and gasometric methods were the most prevalent analytical
approaches.

Other instrumental methods, such as gas chromatographic, nuclear magnetic resonance, spectroscopic,
radiochemical, and electrometric measurements greatly
expanded analytical capabilities. Also within the past
25 years kinetic methods for the analysis of functional
groups were developed by Siggia and Hanna. This permitted the analysis of mixtures of alcohols and carbonyl
compounds. Their success with the kinetic approach
stimulated many others to investigate kinetic methods
for inorganic systems as well.

KINETIC METHODS OF ANALYSIS

Analytical applications of chemical kinetics can
be traced back at least as far as the mid-to-late 1800s.
Early examples involved analyses performed on or with
the aid of enzyme preparations and included the detection of hydrogen peroxide with peroxidase and the determination of carbohydrates in foods. Other types of
analyses which began to appear as early as the late
1920s exploited catalytic reactions for trace analyses
and kinetic differences among similar reactions, for
simultaneous two-component analyses. In a 1929 paper
H. Baines described a "stop-watch method" for copper in
silver nitrate and proceeded to describe a method for
small quantities of iodine in mixtures of halides, based
upon the catalytic effect of iodine on the oxidation of
thiosulfate by nitrous acid. In an admirable show of
candor, Baines stated that "This method (for iodine),
however, appears to be of little practical importance
. . . but is probably worth placing on record . . .
since some modification may enhance its practical
value." This statement was prophetic because it was
just four years later (1934) that E. B. Sandell and
I. M. Kolthoff published their classic paper describing
the exploitation of the catalytic effect of the iodine
catalysis of the Ce(IV)-As(III) reaction for the quantitative determination of trace levels of iodine or
iodide. Modifications of this method have been used
extensively throughout the last three decades for the
determination of iodine in a wide range of sample types
including body fluids and tissues, foods, and natural
waters. Numerous other analytical methods based upon
the concepts described by Baines have been summarized
in a 1966 monograph by K. B. Yatsimirskii, who has been
one of the most prolific authors in this particular
area. The unique feature of most of these methods is

that they exploit the catalytic behavior of the analyte
to provide chemical amplification so that extremely
small concentrations can be determined with conventional
detection systems.

Within a year of the report by Sandell and Kolthoff,
H. B. Hass and P. Weber described an alternative
approach which used differences in the rates of reaction
of some monochloroalkanes with potassium iodide for
selective determinations of monochlorides in two-component mixtures. Their method for the simultaneous determination of 1-chloro-2-methylbutane and 1-chloro-3-meth-
ylbutane was one of the earliest so-called differential
kinetic analysis methods. This procedure, like many
others to be developed later, was devised so that difficult separation steps could be avoided. In the four
decades since this early report, hundreds of published
papers have described simultaneous kinetic methods for
a wide variety of organic and inorganic species as well
as mathematical procedures for processing the kinetic
data. While it is not possible to acknowledge all contributions in this area, it appears appropriate to mention the work of S. Siggia and L. Fowler in 1955 and
1961 and their co-workers, whose pioneering efforts were
focused on practical applications of the kinetic concept
to real industrial situations.

The other major areas which became important during
this period involved enzymes, from the point of view of
determining enzyme activity in enzyme preparations or
in body fluids (B. Hess, 1963) and of using enzymes as
selective reagents for substrates (H. U. Bergmeyer,
1963). Applications of enzymes have represented extensive uses of kinetic methods in the past and probably
will continue to do so in the future.

By about 1960 most of the basic chemical approaches
to kinetic analyses had been developed, hundreds of
reaction systems had been evaluated, and the common
kinetic expressions had been subjected to numerous
mathematical manipulations designed to present kinetic
data in numerical or graphical formats that would facilitate interpretation. However, despite these early
developments, except for the biochemical area where
kinetic measurements were essential for enzyme activity
determinations, and a few specialized examples such as
the catalytic determination of iodine, the enzymatic
determination of glucose and scattered applications to
organics such as alcohols, aldehydes, and ketones,
kinetic methods were not used extensively for routine
analyses in this country. In fact, those who were pro-
moting the kinetic concept at that time were frequently
asked why an analyst would ever choose a kinetic method
if any other viable choice were available. To some

enthusiasts, the answers to this question lay in potential advantages of the kinetic methods which had been illustrated by the early workers in the field. These advantages included short analysis times, ultra-high sensitivities based upon catalytic reactions, the ability of the approach to differentiate among similar species according to differences in kinetic behavior, and the remarkable selectivity exhibited by some enzymes for selected substrates. Furthermore, some workers in the field felt that the unsavory reputation of kinetic methods resulted more from the unsatisfactory experimental procedures and instrumentation which were in common use than from any inherent limitations in the kinetic concept.

Prior to about 1960 most kinetic analyses were done with instrumentation which had been designed for equilibrium methods. Kinetic procedures usually called for a limited number (often as few as two) of discrete observations to be made manually during the reaction. Experimental conditions were usually adjusted to require several minutes for each analysis, and the procedures required almost constant attention from the analyst, especially when more than one sample was being run. Unfortunately, important variables such as reaction temperature were not always controlled rigorously. Also, the buildup of high concentrations of reaction products could often lead to interfering side reactions, and kinetic parameters were not well understood. Hence it was not uncommon for long and laborious procedures to yield questionable results. Some research workers felt that if these experimental difficulties could be overcome, kinetic methods would make real contributions toward the solution of many practical problems. This is the primary reason why several workers devoted much of their research effort during the 1960s to the development of instrumentation for kinetic analyses.

While many have contributed to this area, those who began their efforts early and continued throughout the 1960s include Walter Blaedel and Philip Hicks at Wisconsin, Howard Malmstadt at Illinois, Harry Pardue at Purdue, and Stanley Crouch at Michigan State University. All of these workers emphasized procedures based upon continuous monitoring of kinetic reactions early in the reaction before reactant or product concentrations had changed significantly. Their efforts focused on improved detectors capable of determining small concentration changes with high reliability and upon on-line computing systems which would convert reaction-rate data into concentrations automatically. While carefully designed potentiometric and amperometric detectors were used throughout this period, photometric detection has proved most useful. Several relatively simple photometer designs which have been developed as a result of this effort offer noise and drift characteristics which are orders of magnitude better than most of the photometers used through the mid-1960s. Also, temperature control capabilities and rapid mixing mechanisms were included as integral parts of the photometer systems requiring little special attention from the analyst. The net result was that by the mid- to late-1960s, instrument systems which could measure reaction rates with precision and accuracy comparable with equilibrium systems were available in several research laboratories.

The earliest computing systems were special purpose analog computers which sampled some variable and converted it into an electrical signal which was proportional to the concentration of the analyte. In the past 10 years several distinctly different measurement approaches which have evolved from these studies, as well as their relative merits, have been discussed in original papers and reviews by H. A. Laitinen and W. E. Harris and by H. L. Pardue, H. V. Malmstadt, and co-workers. These partially automated systems eliminated much of the tedium formerly associated with kinetic methods. Thus, the concerted, parallel efforts aimed both at improved detectors and automatic computing systems removed two of the major drawbacks of kinetic methods. Subsequent incorporation of these and other concepts into commercial instrument systems designed specifically for kinetic analyses removed one of the last barriers so that by the late 1960s, routine applications of kinetic methods were beginning to multiply rapidly, and that growth has continued to the present time.

The analog computational methods mentioned earlier persisted until the late 1960s when digital components and digital computers became readily available. Dale Margerum, Harry Pardue, and their associates at Purdue have described on-line regression methods which are applicable with high reliability to two- and three-component mixtures of species which undergo similar reactions but with different rate constants. The approach has been applied to both slow and fast reactions using stopped-flow spectrophotometry.

In most of the instrumental developments discussed to this point, primary emphasis has been on the detection and computation steps. Several workers have emphasized reagent and sample handling systems. One representative system is that developed by N. G. Anderson, C. D. Scott, and their co-workers at the Oak Ridge National Laboratories in 1973. In this system (known

by the acronym GeMSAEC as its development was sponsored
by the Institute of General Medical Sciences and the
U. S. Atomic Energy Commission) several samples and
reagents are loaded into compartments in a centrifuge
rotor system. When the rotor is spun at high speed,
centrifugal force brings reagents and samples together
and mixes them in a fraction of a second. After mixing,
each sample is rotated past a photometric detector several times every second so that a record of absorbance
vs. time is obtained, from which the concentration of
analyte can be computed. This system, as well as
numerous other more conventional sample and reagent
handling systems, have been developed commercially by
several companies so that a variety of instruments
designed specifically for kinetic analyses is now
available.

These instrumental developments which have evolved
during the last decade have had a dramatic impact in at
least one area of vital importance to our society,
namely clinical chemistry. In the 1950s and early 1960s,
enzyme assays were based upon the crude manual methods
described earlier, and these analyses represented a
fraction of the work load in clinical laboratories.
Currently, the clinical chemist has a choice of numerous
semi-automatic and automatic systems for enzyme assays,
and the number of enzyme activity measurements has grown
very rapidly. For example, data presented by A. N.
Bowers in 1971 indicated that in one hospital laboratory, the number of enzyme tests performed annually rose
from about 6,000 in 1955 to about 91,000 in 1970, and
the percentage of the total work load increased from
about 9% to about 21% in that same period. While enzyme
assays represent the most dramatic change, there have
been significant increases in routine applications of
kinetic methods for other species such as glucose, urea,
uric acid, cholesterol, and creatinine, and others will
surely follow.

In this writer's viewpoint, the most significant
chemical aspects of kinetic methods of analyses were
developed between 1930 and 1950 and the most significant
instrumental developments occurred from 1960 to 1970.
This is not to say there were no important chemical
developments during the latter period; there were many.
For example, Margerum and co-workers at Purdue developed
unique approaches for trace metals and organic ligands
based upon ligand exchange reactions; Guilbault at
Louisiana State has developed a series of fluorometric
indicator reagents for enzyme reactions; Hicks, Guilbault, Rechnitz, and others have adapted the technology
of immobolized enzymes for a variety of analytical
applications; Mottola at Oklahoma State has reported a

series of new catalytic titrations; Pardue and co-
workers have used catalytic reactions for simultaneous
multicomponent determinations; Hercules at Georgia has
adapted chemiluminescent reactions for trace determinations of some metal ions; and Winefordner and co-
workers at Florida have taken advantage of phosphorescent decay rates for one- and two-component determinations of drugs and other organics. Some of the characteristics of kinetic measurements have triggered other
types of studies as well. For example, Crouch and
Pardue have reevaluated photometric errors as they apply
to kinetic analyses; Kuwana at Ohio State and Pardue
have devised mechanical and electronic (vidicon)
approaches to rapid scanning spectroscopy and have
applied the instruments to fundamental kinetic studies
of reaction mechanisms as well as multicomponent analyses; and several authors have described routine applications of stopped-flow spectrophotometry.

Pardue fully expects the latter chemical and instrumental concepts to play more dominant roles in
kinetic analyses in the future. Indeed, because of the
many developments alluded to in this brief historical
account which have improved the operational characteristics and reliability of kinetic methods, it is expected that kinetic methods will soon be viewed as a
viable complement to the more common equilibrium
methods, and that kinetic methods will play a more
dominant role in the total discipline of analytical
chemistry. As indicated above, clinical chemists have
already adapted these methods extensively, and other
groups are expected to follow suit in the near future.

CHAPTER III

ANALYTICAL SPECTROSCOPY

Man has been interested in the area we now call
spectroscopy ever since he was pleased by the colors of
nature and became curious as to the cause. Aristotle,
in the 4th century B.C., recognized that light was
necessary for color to exist. He used the term "contamination" to explain his idea that colored substances
impart different kinds of blackness to the incident
white light. If this famous Greek philosopher had
coined the word "absorption," his interpretation of the
phenomena would be remarkably close to that now used to
explain the origin of absorption spectra as due to
selective absorption of different wavelengths of the
incident radiation.

In its modern sense, spectroscopy traces its beginnings to Sir Isaac Newton's observations of the prism
spectrum of the sun, published in 1672. (Similar
though less detailed experiments had been reported 20
years earlier by Marcus Marci, but this work was without
lasting influence.) Newton allowed rays from the sun
to pass through a small opening into a darkened room
and, after passage through a prism, to fall on a screen.
He distinguished the colors red, orange, yellow, green,
indigo, blue, and violet. In further experiments he
established that the colors were a property of the
original light, not of the prism, by using prisms of
different materials and by combining the dispersed
beams into the original white light with a second prism.
He pointed out that increased spectral purity, at the
cost of intensity, could be obtained by using a very
narrow rectangular opening, a crude forerunner of present-day slits.

Thomas Melville, a 26-year old Glasgow scientist,
reported in 1752 his observations on spectra of mixtures

of spirits (alcohol) with sea salt and other substances.
His spectroscope had no slit, but he did note an abrupt
transition from the bright yellow light to the fainter
color adjoining it when the flame contained salt. If a
slit had been used, and if Melville had not died the
following year, spectrochemical analysis might have
gotten a much earlier start.

Infrared radiation was discovered in 1800 when the
astronomer F. W. Herschel noted differing sensations of
heat while viewing the sun through combinations of colored glasses. He then placed a thermometer with a
blackened bulb in various parts of the sun's spectrum.
The temperature rise was twice as great in the red as
in the green, and there was a still greater increase
well beyond the red, where no light could be observed.
Of parallel significance was J. W. Ritter's work a year
later which laid the foundation for photography of the
spectrum and revealed the presence of the ultraviolet
region. Ritter's first announcement, as translated by
Twyman, reads:

> On February 22nd I discovered solar rays
> at the violet end of the color spectrum, be-
> yond the same, finding them by means of silver
> chloride. They reduce more strongly than the
> violet light itself, and their extent is very
> great.

The wave nature of light was demonstrated by Thomas
Young in 1802. He used a glass micrometer scale with
500 lines per inch as a rather crude transmission
grating and was able to calculate the wavelengths of
the spectral colors of the sun observed by Newton. His
results, in nanometers, were:

Red	650	Blue	498
Orange	609	Indigo	470
Yellow	576	Violet	442
Green	536		

Spectral features, beyond the simple observation
of color, were apparently first described by W. H.
Wollaston in 1802. He used a very narrow opening for
the sunlight, as had Newton, and observed it through a
prism from a rather large distance (10-12 ft). He was
able to observe the now well-known dark lines. He also
observed discontinuities in the light from a candle
flame but apparently did not attach much significance
to them. He wrote: "It is, however, needless to
describe minutely appearances which vary according to
the brilliancy of the light, and which I cannot undertake to explain."

It remained for Josef Fraunhofer, starting in 1817,
to map the details of the dark lines, which bear his
name, in the solar spectrum. Initially he was interested

only in the precise measurement of refractive indices
and dispersion of various glasses. He was a practical
glassworker whose immediate goal was to make achromatic
lenses. By mounting a theodolite, to measure angles,
and a prism together, and illuminating the prism through
a slit, he constructed the first spectroscope. His
first work was with artificial light. In search of
greater precision, however, and to see if sunlight and
artificial light gave similar refractive indices, he
placed his theodolite in a darkened room 24 ft from a
narrow opening. He saw many (several hundred) dark
lines of varying intensity and designated the prominent
ones with letters, starting with "A" at the red end of
the sun's spectrum. No such dark lines were seen in
light from a lamp, but bright lines, now known to be
due to sodium emission, were observed in precisely the
position of the "D" lines in the sun's spectrum. The
sodium "D" lines are frequently mentioned today, using
Fraunhofer's original designation.

Being a glassworker, Fraunhofer paid special attention to the required properties of the prism, pointing
out that the surfaces must be very flat and the glass
free of imperfections. He commented too that English
flint glass was inferior, being satisfactory for
observing only the stronger lines. In writing of this
work, F. Twyman, possibly motivated by national pride,
added the following footnote:

> Over forty years' experience in testing
> French, German, and English optical glass,
> including very recent and careful comparisons,
> enables me to say that modern English optical
> glass is in no way inferior to the best of
> the others.

Fraunhofer continued his work to include observations of light from Venus, which showed a spectrum like
the sun's, and to the bright star Sirius, which showed
a very different spectrum. He also made diffraction
gratings superior to those used by Young and observed
spectra from flames and electric sparks through them.
He attempted no explanation for the bright and dark
lines, but he did show how to measure their positions
with precision as high as 5 parts in 10^5.

Some historians credit the Scottish worker W. H.
Fox Talbot with the discovery of spectrochemical analysis because of a series of experiments which he began,
reported in 1826. He observed flames colored by many
different salts using a crude but effective spectroscope. He stated:

> . . . whenever the prism shows a *homogeneous*
> ray of any color to exist in a flame, this
> ray indicates the formation or the presence

of a definite chemical compound. . . . a
glance at the prismatic spectrum of a flame
may show substances which it would otherwise
necessitate a laborious chemical analysis to
detect.

In an 1834 paper he continues:

The strontia flame exhibits a great number
of red rays well separated from each other by
dark intervals. . . . The lithia exhibits one
single red ray. Hence, I hesitate not to say
that optical analysis can distinguish the
minutest portions of these two substances from
each other with as much certainty, if not more,
than any other known method.

There is little doubt that spectral analysis could
have grown from extension of Talbot's work, but it was
to find little use for several decades.

In the years which followed, drawings of the spark
spectra of several metals were made by Charles Wheat-
stone, the solar spectrum was photographed by E. Becquerel and by J. W. Draper independently, G. G. Stokes
(1852) used fluorescence produced in quinine sulfate to
observe Fraunhofer lines in the ultraviolet, and H.
Helmholtz made solar observations with a quartz prism
spectroscope. Little was added to what Talbot had said
regarding the analytical use of spectra until Kirchhoff
and Bunsen published their work. In the opinion of
most, their work marks the true beginning of analytical
spectroscopy and is important enough to deserve a special section here.

Kirchhoff, Bunsen, and Work Based Directly on
Their Contributions. The spectral observations of Gustav Kirchhoff and Robert Wilhelm Bunsen in 1859 and
1860 provide one of the earliest examples of spectroscopic discoveries which depended on work in a completely
different area. Bunsen had invented his well-known
burner just a few years earlier, and for the first time
it was possible to make spectral observations on a
nearly transparent non-luminescent flame. Both emission
and absorption effects were much easier to observe than
with previous flames. It is interesting to note that
the general laws of emission and absorption of light,
the explanation of the origin of the Fraunhofer lines,
and the establishment of spectrochemical analysis all
depended on the lowly burner which has been used by
every chemist since Bunsen's time.

In 1859 Kirchhoff published the first paper of his
classic series. It dealt with general laws of emission
and absorption of light and with the Fraunhofer lines.
He observed that bright lines could be seen in the flame

ROBERT WILHELM BUNSEN, 1811-1899

After winning his doctorate at Göttingen at the age of 19, Bunsen became associated briefly with several German universities, finally settled at the University of Heidelberg. His interests and abilities were unusually varied, as he did pioneering work in organic arsenicals, electric batteries, photochemistry, and calorimetry. In analytical chemistry he is best known for his contributions in spectroscopy.

spectrum when metal salts were introduced, but that if
a light of sufficient intensity was placed behind the
flame, dark lines appeared in the spectrum at precisely
the same location. He stated:

> I conclude from these observations that a
> colored flame in whose spectrum bright sharp
> lines occur, so weakens rays of the color of
> these lines, if they pass through it, that
> dark lines appear in the place of the bright
> ones, whenever a source of light of sufficient
> intensity, in whose spectrum those lines are
> otherwise absent, is brought behind the flame.
> I conclude further that the dark lines of the
> solar spectrum . . . occur because of the pres-
> ence of those elements in the glowing atmos-
> phere of the sun which would produce in the
> spectrum of a flame bright lines in the same
> position.

He concludes that the Fraunhofer "D" lines are due to
sodium in the sun's atmosphere, that the "A" and "B"
lines are due to potassium, and that the absence of a
Fraunhofer line corresponding to lithium emission in
the flame means that there is no, or at least not much,
lithium in the sun.

In a later publication, Kirchhoff states his law
of emission and absorption: "For rays of the same wavelength at the same temperature, the ratio of the emission power to the absorptive power is the same for all
bodies." This deceptively simple law was to form the
basis for later theoretical developments by Planck on
the quantum theory of radiation and in turn for Bohr's
explanation of the origin of atomic spectra. The full
significance of this law to the analyst was, however,
to remain unappreciated for nearly a century.

When Kirchhoff drew his conclusions regarding the
composition of the sun's atmosphere, he knew of observations published a year later with Bunsen. The first
paper dealing specifically with spectrochemical analysis
begins:

> It is well known that certain substances
> possess the property of imparting definite
> colors to flames in which they are heated.
> When the colored light thus produced is ana-
> lyzed by a prism, spectra exhibiting differ-
> ently colored bands or lines of light are
> seen. Upon the appearance of these lines of
> light an entirely new method of chemical
> analysis can be based.

Their light source consisted of a Bunsen burner
flame into which salts could be introduced on a platinum
wire. Two telescopes were used, one for illuminating

and one for observing the dispersed light from a carbon disulfide-filled prism. The prism could be rotated to bring the desired portion of the spectrum into view. Later versions of the spectroscope included a scale which allowed settings to be reproduced and included provision for illuminating the entrance slit from two sources for comparison. Their instrument contained all of the essential features of a modern spectroscope.

They experimented with flames of different temperature and with various salts of the known alkali and alkaline earth elements. They state:

> Among the great number of the salts we have examined which are suitable for spectrum analysis in the flame, we have not met a single one which, in spite of the great variety of the elements combined with the metals, has not exhibited the lines of the metals. One can therefore assume that in all cases the lines of the spectrum of a substance are entirely independent of the elements with which they are associated.

This statement clearly established the agent responsible for the observed spectra and justified the popular opinion that Kirchhoff and Bunsen should be credited with the discovery of spectrochemical analysis.

The method was soon put to practical application. It led to the discovery of new elements at the rate of one per year for the first four years of its existence [Cs, Rb (1860), Tl (1861), In (1864)].

Soon thereafter, A. J. Ångström used improved diffraction gratings to measure wavelengths and to compare flame spectra with that of the sun. Observations using electrical spark discharges became more common, and the groundwork for quantitative analysis was laid by J. N. Lockyer and W. C. Roberts through observations of line lengths.

Despite the power of this new tool in the hands of the chemist, it found restricted use. Spectrochemical analysis became a customary operation in Bunsen's laboratory, but the use of a spectroscope for practical qualitative analysis seems to have been neglected after his time. M. Slavin writes of his own experience:

> I remember during my course in sophomore physics in the early 1920's our professor's carefully removing a brass Bunsen spectroscope and speculum-ruled grating from the instrument cabinet and exhibiting them to the class. Such things were for display, not for use. In the class in qualitative analysis our only contact with spectroscopy was the flame tests for sodium, lithium, and potassium done by the

platinum wire, Bunsen burner and cobalt glass technique.

The library copy of Slavin's book we used in preparing this history has the comment "Still in 1971" scribed by an unknown reader in the margin beside this passage.

Some reasons for the early neglect of the method are discussed by Twyman:

    1. In certain cases the extreme sensitivity was an inconvenience. The yellow lines of sodium always appeared whether or not the element was intentionally added.

    2. Flame sources showed good sensitivity for only a very few elements. The alkali metals gave strong spectra, the alkaline earths, indium, and thallium showed feebly and other metals weren't seen.

    3. Electrical discharges were well known to reveal the spectra of nearly all metals, but full use was not made of this fact until later because:

        a. Convenient means of providing electrical current were not available until many years after 1861.

        b. Spark and arc spectra are often quite complex and, to the uninitiated, unraveling such a maze of lines must have seemed much more difficult than doing a conventional analysis. One must consider also that there were no wavelength tables to assist in spectral interpretation until thirty years later, and that photographic recording, which became so valuable in later years, was not in common use.

We agree with these reasons and, judging from reactions of modern scientists, would like to add another. Spectral analysis was a drastic departure from the accepted and conventional way of doing things. It could not quickly overcome the inertia of the scientific community, and only years later when its great power had been overwhelmingly proved did practicing analysts flock to the techniques.

In 1910 H. Kayser stated, "There is little prospect that in the future qualitative analysis will apply spectroscopic methods to a large extent . . . I have come to the conclusion that quantitative spectroscopic analysis has shown itself to be impractical." The few who did continue the development of the method were lone spirits. In 1922 A. de Gramont wrote, "French chemists have an indolent dread of spectral analysis . . . M——— has declared publicly that ever since Bunsen and Kirchhoff, spectral analysis has been a deception and has made no progress from a practical point of view." Walsh, undoubtedly thinking of the difficulty in the late 1950s to gain acceptance of atomic absorption, states, "Then as now, the art of spectrochemical analysis obviously had to do battle against the doubts, cynicism and indolence of reactionaries."

Thus the method that would eventually revolutionize metals analysis was, until the 1930s, largely abandoned by chemists and left for astronomers, physicists, and others to develop. Slavin states,

> Thus by 1920 all the conditions needed for a system of chemical analysis by spectroscopy existed. We had excellent instruments, good photographic emulsions, a power distribution network, and basic theory. However, chemists were very slow to take advantage of this powerful tool, even for simple qualitative identifications. They still relied on the classical instruments, the test tube, the blowpipe, the eye, and the nose.

At this point it is helpful to divide the field into several areas and to follow the development of each to modern times rather than to follow all developments chronologically.

ATOMIC SPECTROSCOPY

Theory. It would be easy to exaggerate the influence of the development of atomic spectral theory upon the development of analytical atomic spectroscopy. There is no obvious point at which theoretical developments were felt immediately in the history of applications. After discussing theoretical developments, W. F. Meggers states:

> Parallel with the quantum theoretical interpretation of atomic spectra there occurred a rebirth and phenomenal development of spectroscopy applied to chemical analysis. It is strange but undeniable that these two events have little in common except coincidence in time.

Practical analysts did undoubtedly take comfort in theoretical explanations because it made their work more intellectually satisfying--less like black magic. A more tangible benefit was the ability to recognize lines arising from similar atomic transitions which could, therefore, be expected to behave similarly.

In the early days there was no theory of atomic spectra worth mentioning aside from empirical observation of certain regularities in spectra. This remained the case until 1913 when Niels Bohr proposed stationary electronic states within the atom and discrete energy differences between them to account for the discrete wavelengths of spectral lines. The early 1920s saw direct evidence of spatial quantization of atoms, the interpretation of complex multiplets, and the development of the vector model of the atom. The banner year was 1925; Russell and Saunders showed how complex spectra resulted from addition of orbital momenta of two electrons, Pauli developed his rule for equivalent electrons and his exclusion principle, F. Hund correlated spectral terms with electron configurations, and Uhlenbeck and Goudsmit explained the contribution of electron spin to spectra. That same year matrix mechanics and wave mechanics were introduced. Theoretical interpretations continued into the subsequent decades but mostly on spectra from highly ionized atoms and on extremely complex spectra, neither of which were of much interest to the chemist. Thus in a bit over a decade, the spectrochemist went from having no theory to having more than his work required and more than he really wanted to be bothered with.

Instrumentation. Both prisms and gratings were used in early instruments, but prisms predominated in early analytical applications. In the early 1900s, high quality photographic emulsions which were convenient to use had become available, and Twyman designed the fixed adjustment medium quartz spectrograph. This instrument used a prism made in two pieces--one of right-hand and one of left-hand quartz--to cancel effects due to optical activity. The entire spectrum was in focus on a single flat plate. Other important features of this new instrument included a high quality, adjustable slit, and a rather efficient optical system. In 1912 the large quartz spectrograph, also designed by Twyman, was introduced to deal with complex steel spectra. Instruments based on these designs were soon available commercially from several manufacturers, initially Adam Hilger Ltd., and became the standard units upon which most of the early developmental work was done. Aside from using high quality fused quartz optics, one would be hard pressed to suggest improvements in Twyman's designs today. Spectra from these instruments tend to be crowded at long wavelengths, but in the ultraviolet, where so many sensitive metal lines are located, the dispersion and resolution are quite good.

As recently as 1941, some workers regarded prisms as so superior for analytical work, they confidently predicted that gratings were, "not likely to come into wide use for analysis in industrial laboratories . . ."

Grating spectra had advantages which were more obvious to early physicists than to chemists, and it was to meet their needs, as well as those of astronomers, that gratings were improved. This situation is largely true today if economic factors are set aside.

The successful ruling of large concave reflection gratings by H. A. Rowland, starting in 1882, marks an important point in spectroscopic history. He showed that rulings on a concave mirror surface could be used as both the dispersing and the focusing element of a spectrograph. Rowland's work is the first important contribution to spectroscopy from America. The work on improving the art of grating production was continued at Johns Hopkins University by R. W. Wood and later at MIT by G. R. Harrison.

The history of grating production is in itself a fascinating topic which must be greatly abbreviated here. The mechanical precision required is almost beyond comprehension by most grating users. Not only must all grooves be uniform, parallel, and evenly spaced, but the last groove of a large grating must be spaced the proper distance from the first one to within a few millionths of an inch. Two quotations from relatively modern work illustrate this point. Harrison states:

> The success of a ruling engine depends on how compensation has been made for the inevitable changes in shape and size that result from variation in friction, temperature, elasticity, and internal strain. The designer may well imagine his engine as constructed of rubber, thus visualizing the stresses that must be controlled when strains of the order of a micro-inch become of great importance.

Somewhat later, R. F. Jarrell emphasized the operator's role:

> . . . it should be emphasized that the output of a successful ruling engine will depend fully as much on the skill of the operator in diagnosing and correcting its continual minor, and occasional major, maladies, as on the original soundness of design and care in construction. Grating ruling is still very much an art.

In spite of the precision required, a number of successful engines were constructed. Each installation had its own set of special problems, as indicated for one commercial enterprise in a personal letter to the authors from James L. Jones of Applied Research Laboratories:

> At sometime during the late forties, Dr. Hasler decided that the time might come when Pearson would be too old to continue production.

Consequently, he dug a laboratory into a hillside
at his home in Glendale and, with Pearson's help,
installed a couple of ruling engines. Sometime
during the fifties, Pearson did indeed give up,
and subsequently, all ARL gratings were produced
on Hasler's engines until we switched over entirely to B&L replicas. For a number of years
all gratings were originals, ruled on speculum
metal, which was alloyed and cast with a small
portable facility behind the Engineering building.
The main difficulty in those days was that the
proper shape of the ruling diamond was obtained
by starting with a chip and ruling with it until
it wore in enough to give the desired characteristics. Then they would produce gratings like
mad until the diamond wore out. This was such an
uncertain process that they would sometimes go
for weeks without producing a good grating, with
obvious disadvantages to the production schedule.
One of the primary criticisms of early gratings
was that they wasted light in unwanted orders. Astronomers, who were using most of the gratings at that time,
could not afford the light loss. Work was started by
R. W. Wood as early as 1910 on the control of groove
form to concentrate the light in one area of the spectrum. H. D. Babcock, in 1944, gave a quantitative
assessment of the effect of groove shape from which our
modern blazed gratings are derived. An equally important advance in grating production--indeed one which
necessarily preceded application of Babcock's calcula-
tions--was the production of gratings ruled on aluminum.
In the mid-1930s J. Strong, using the recently developed
high vacuum techniques, was successful in evaporating
highly reflecting aluminum coatings onto glass surfaces.
Almost immediately R. W. Wood recognized the advantages
of the softer, more reflective surface and had actually
ruled the first grating on aluminum in 1935 prior to
publication of Strong's work. The aluminum surface
greatly reduced wear on the ruling diamond, made control
of groove shape practical, and increased ultraviolet
reflectivity by nearly an order of magnitude.
Until after World War II, grating production was a
primary limiting factor in their use. Replication of
gratings had been attempted, but most instruments used
original rulings. Evaporation of aluminum was soon to
be used in a new way. During the late 1940s W. Fraser
and J. White perfected a technique by which aluminum
was evaporated onto a master grating, separated from it
only by a thin "parting layer" of an organic substance
to assist later in pulling the replica from the master.
The replica was mounted on an appropriate support before

separation from the master. This technique produced
replicas fully as good as the master at about one-tenth
the cost. Production rate was also eliminated as a
controlling factor in grating use.

At about the same time, improved control to remove
errors which had always plagued grating manufacturers
appeared. In 1950 Harrison wrote:

> In setting up the Michelson ruling engine,
> I was determined not to spend the remainder of
> my life bumping against the same difficulties
> that had defeated other workers. . . . Our prob-
> lems, while as great, could at least be new ones.
> Accordingly it was decided to attempt the appli-
> cation of interferometric control to the ruling
> engine.

The attempt was successful, and since then replicas of
master gratings ruled on interferometrically controlled
engines have become the basis of an explosive increase
in the number of spectroscopic instruments, but in 1950,
were chemists demanding more or better gratings?
Hardly! Harrison's goal was to produce echelles, rather
coarse gratings of high resolution. His reason was to
study Zeeman patterns for classification of lines to
meet the needs of physicists. Echelles were also used
by astronomers because they produced compact, high resolution spectra when used with a low resolution dispersing element as an "order sorter." Only recently,
and, to the authors' knowledge, through only one manufacturer, has the high resolution of the echelle become
available to the analytical chemist. There is presently
little indication that echelle spectrometers will soon
be popular.

In recent years chemists have certainly taken
advantage of quality gratings in increasing number.
Commercial grating spectrographs became available in
about 1935, and until the early 1950s nearly all used
concave gratings. Then W. G. Fastie rediscovered the
optical arrangement based on a plane grating which H.
Ebert had described in 1889. This mount gave stigmatic
spectra--that is spectra in which the lines were in
both vertical and horizontal focus simultaneously--which
most concave grating mounts did not. The mount required
two reflections from a mirror, for collimation and
focusing, in addition to reflection from the grating.
Introduction of added optical components, which had
previously had a disastrous effect on intensity, could
now be readily tolerated because mirrors and gratings
with greatly improved reflectivity were readily available. The Ebert mount and the similar one described by
M. Czerny and A. F. Turner are used in many commercial
units today.

Most spectroscopic instruments now use gratings. They may be designed for photographic recording of large spectral regions or for isolating one or several specific wavelengths. In most cases, the available resolution and spectral purity are entirely adequate to meet the current needs of analytical atomic spectroscopy. Indeed, the problem to the user is now more often in selecting the best instrument for his needs from the dozen or so which may be available, each claimed to be superior to all others by its manufacturer. It can be as hard as selecting a new automobile. Only those on severely restricted budgets need to be instrument-limited. At long last, however, pressure for fundamental instrument improvements may now be coming from chemists. Some users of the inductively coupled plasma are now encountering ghosts and stray light due to grating imperfections which may be limiting the analytical utility of that source. Gratings produced by holographic methods may be required to meet that need.

The development of certain pieces of auxiliary equipment was nearly as important as improved spectrometers to the early user of analytical atomic spectroscopy. Photography and photographic photometry probably never were limiting factors because they were needed by physicists and astronomers before chemists became interested in quantitative spectral analysis. Microphotometers were known before 1900, and an improved version specifically for spectral work was described by W. F. Meggers and P. D. Foote in 1920. The first application of microphotometry for quantitative analysis was probably by Lundegårdh in about 1929. His work, which we will encounter in other contexts, provides another example of important developments contributed by non-chemists. Lundegårdh was a Swedish agronomist whose primary interest was plant composition and soil-plant relationships. No chemist of his day can be credited with equal contribution toward the advancement of the analytical utility of atomic spectroscopy.

As quantitative spectral analysis became popular during the late 1930s and 1940s, commercial microphotometers were marketed by several manufacturers. In about 1940 combination comparator-microphotometers were introduced which made line identification much easier, especially for inexperienced workers. By about 1950, instruments with variable-speed plate drive and strip-chart recorder read out were commercially available, and, with the possible exception of automation, little change has been seen since. It appears that there was no significant delay in the development of the field from this source.

Electrical discharges of various types have been

used for spectral excitation since Talbot's time. W. N. Hartley, in 1882, used a spark condensed by a Leyden jar to excite spectra from solutions, and Jackson excited powders contained in an electrode cavity using an arc prior to 1900. Arc power supplies presented few problems once electrical current became readily available. Interrupted arcs to improve stability were developed by W. Gerlach and by K. Pfeilsticker in the mid 1930s, and the high voltage ac arc was introduced in 1938. In 1955 Bardocz described an electronically controlled arc power supply. More recently, optical feedback has been used to control the arc electronically.

Spark power supplies based on a high voltage transformer, with a capacitor for storing the charge, were in use before 1920. However, the discharge through the analytical gap was uncontrolled. The Feussner spark, described in 1932, included a rotating interrupter gap in series with the analytical gap. The discharge was forced to take place at both gaps simultaneously with the interrupter providing the desired operator control. In 1949 R. A. Wolfe and J. H. Enns introduced a stationary gap in series with the analytical discharge and quenched this auxiliary gap with a blast of air. This simpler system gave even better control. Power supplies based on the air gap design and minor variations of it became the standard units in the field and were produced by several manufacturers starting in the 1950s. More elaborate electronic controls are only now starting to replace air gap units in commercial instrumentation.

Until the late 1940s the photographic emulsion served as the detector for virtually all spectroscopic work except for some flame work done in Europe. After the war, photomultiplier tubes and the electronic circuitry needed with them became available, and the age of the "direct reader" was born. Instruments in which from one to a dozen exit slits were placed on the focal surface to pass specific lines, with the light being detected by photomultipliers, were described by G. A. Nahstol and F. R. Bryan in 1945, by M. F. Hasler and co-workers in numerous papers between 1944 and 1948, and by J. B. Saunderson, V. J. Caldecourt, and E. W. Peterson in 1945. When compared with photographic instruments, these units lacked versatility, required a more carefully controlled environment, and were complex and expensive. However, they excelled in photometric accuracy and especially the speed with which analysis could be carried out. Hasler and co-workers at Applied Research Laboratories promoted their instruments quite vigorously, and these soon became the primary analytical tools of the metals industries. The high initial cost was justified because a batch of steel could be analyzed

for all important metallic components to an accuracy of
1-2% in a matter of minutes. The results were available
quickly enough to be used to control the process. A
few years later carbon, sulfur, and phosphorus were
added to the list of elements that could be determined
when evacuable instruments were introduced.

The design of multi-channel instruments is little
different in principle today from that of these early
units. The electronic circuitry is now considerably
more sophisticated, a computer may assist in the control
of the instrument as well as in data processing, the
units are more compact and versatile, and design improvements have reduced the need for environmental control.

With the direct reader came a dramatic increase in
the amount and complexity of electronic circuitry to
the spectroscopic laboratory. This change was not made
without some problems. Meggers, in a 1954 review
article, wrote, "A new approach to direct reading spectrochemical analysis has been described, but it is so
elaborated with electronics that it is incomprehensible
to an old fashioned spectroscopist." Dependence on
electronics has continued to increase. If all transistors and integrated circuits were removed from our
laboratory today, operations would be limited to qualitative analysis (photographically) and coffee breaks.

Improvements in electronics of course were not made
primarily to meet the needs of chemists. The great commercial success of radio and television was a much
greater source of incentive. Recent developments from
space exploration, to production of improved computers,
to the commercial success of hand calculators have all
produced better electronics which are being used in
chemical instrumentation.

Techniques. Since very early in the history of the
technique, qualitative spectral analysis has been relatively simple, assuming the availability of appropriate
equipment and an operator with some experience. Quantitation became accepted considerably later and yet
today often presents a significant challenge to even an
experienced analyst.

The first work on quantitative analysis was done,
typically it seems, by an astronomer, not by a chemist.
In 1873 and 1874 J. N. Lockyer published several papers
in which he described "long" and "short" lines. He
formed an image of a spark on the spectroscope slit,
thereby causing each segment along the length of the
spectral lines to arise from radiation at different
points between the electrodes. Some of the lines which
he observed originated only near the electrodes while
others extended throughout the spark gap. He called

these "short" and "long" lines respectively. If a flame was substituted for the spark, only the long lines appeared, and if the atmospheric pressure was reduced in the spark, the long lines remained visible to lower pressures. Lockyer states:

> While the qualitative spectrum analysis depends upon the position of the lines, the quantitative analysis depends not upon their position, but upon their length, brightness, thickness, and number as compared with the number visible in the spectrum of a pure vapor.

And later,

> Since beginning with an alloy giving only the longest lines in the spectrum, by increasing the constituents other lines can be produced in the order of their length, the measurement of their length might give a measure of the quantity present.

Lockyer and Roberts attempted quantitative analysis based on changes in line length for a single constituent, changes in the position of equal brightness for lines from different metals in the alloy, and changes in the relative lengths of lines from alloying elements. The last approach is quite similar to the internal standard method which was not to be described further for another half century. Five alloys of cadmium and zinc were prepared, differing by 1% and ranging from 50-54% cadmium. Lockyer and Roberts wrote, "observations by means of the spectroscope at once enabled us to arrange these alloys in correct order." Their results are quite surprising considering the small differences in composition.

The next steps toward quantitative analysis were initiated by Hartley at the University of Dublin and were continued there by J. H. Pollok and A. G. G. Leonard. Hartley's work started about 1884, and it was for this group that Twyman designed the first medium quartz spectrograph in about 1909. The group worked with solutions of the metals which were caused to wet first a graphite and later a gold electrode. Excitation was with a condensed spark. The electrode arrangement used is shown in Figure 1. Pollok published line designations based on their appearance when photographed with the medium quartz spectrograph as shown in Table II.

This is obviously the forerunner of what would be called semi-quantitative or rough quantitative analysis today. One of their procedures is given below.

Analysis of Minerals

> To prepare minerals for spectrographic analysis they should be decomposed in the ordinary way--the solution separated into the

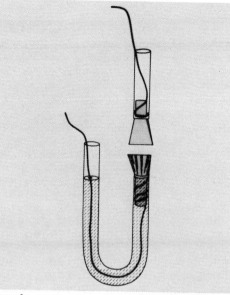

Figure 1.   Electrode arrangement used by Hartley, Pollok and Leonard.

various analytical groups, and these groups then dissolved in hydrochloric acid, or, if necessary, nitric acid, ammonia or caustic soda and made up to a fixed volume, such as 20, cc. each for every two grams of sample taken, and these solutions then sparked. If only a small quantity of an element is present, much more of the original material must be taken, and the solution made of such a strength as to contain not less than 1 per cent of the element sought for. Iron should be separated from the ammonia precipitate by tartaric acid and sulphide of ammonia, as there

Table II. Line Designations by Pollok

Line Designation	Seen With	Not Seen With
τ	Metal	Strong solutions
σ	Strong solutions	1% solutions
φ	1% solutions	0.1% solutions
χ	0.1% solutions	0.01% solutions
ψ	0.01% solutions	0.001% solutions
ω	0.001% solutions	

are so many iron lines that it is difficult to
detect other elements when it is present. A
somewhat similar difficulty occurs with cerium,
but cerium can be completely removed by caustic
soda and chlorine.

Silica gives no lines in an acid solution,
but very characteristic lines when dissolved in
caustic soda or with soluble silicates. Tungsten gives its lines when dissolved in ammonia;
the other metals may be sparked in acid solution. The non-metallic elements present do not
give spectra when treated in this way; they
must be sparked in the gaseous condition; at
reduced pressure, in Geissler tubes.

Here we see not only an early practical procedure
for the analysis of metals but also an appreciation for
the limitations of the method and a way to enhance its
utility through chemical separations. Another contribution from this group was the preparation of an index
of the principal lines of the spark spectra of the
elements.

A. de Gramont worked at the Sorbonne in Paris on
the quantitative analysis of minerals, in the early 1900s.
His excitation method was also the condensed spark, but
he worked mostly with solids. He became interested in
lines which remained observable as the amount of the
element present was gradually reduced. Those lines
which remained observable to very low concentrations
were named *raies sensibles* by him in 1907, and the line
which was the last to disappear when the quantity was
reduced was called the *raie ultime*. The *raies ultimes*
were noted to be of great sensitivity and to be the
same line whether the excitation was with spark, arc,
or a hot flame. It was noted that they were not necessarily the strongest lines in the spark spectrum of the
metal, that the same line was found to be most persistent whether the sample was an alloy, a mineral, or a
fused salt, and that they were in general agreement with
the results obtained by Pollok and Leonard for solutions. Some of de Gramont's conclusions have required
modification, but the importance of his contribution is
well summarized by Twyman:

. . . the work of de Gramont, like that of
Hartley, Pollok, and Leonard, has been of in-
estimable assistance to all subsequent workers
in guiding them to where in the spectrum to
look for the lines likely to be present when
only very small quantities of a metal are contained in a substance.

Lewis, starting in about 1916, developed a pellet
method for quantitative analysis. The steps in his

method were:
1. The sample was converted to a sulfate or a
   sulfated ash.
2. The ash was finely ground and mixed with an
   equal weight of pure aluminum sulfate, and the
   mixture was pressed into a pellet.
3. The pellet was placed on the lower electrode
   of a copper or silver arc and arced for two
   minutes.
4. The resulting photograph was analyzed qualitatively.
5. Synthetic pellets were synthesized until the
   spectrum of the unknown was matched.

An important advance in quantitative spectral analysis took place in 1925 when W. Gerlach and E. Schweitzer
introduced the concept of internal standardization with
selected pairs of lines. The value of using ratios of
line intensities to correct for source instability was
recognized almost immediately. The following is an
account given by Twyman and credited to D. M. Smith.

The intensities of the impurity lines are
compared with those of neighboring lines due to
the predominant metal in the alloy. This obvi-
ates any difficulties arising from small variations in the intensity of the spectrum as a
whole (and hence the intensities of the impurity
lines) which may arise from fluctuations in the
light source, development of the plate, etc.

Care should be exercised in the choice of
lines as intensity standards. For example, the
copper "spark" lines appearing in the arc spectra of copper samples are quite unsuitable if
one is working with a spherical condensing lens,
and unsatisfactory even when a spherocylindrical
condenser is used, on account of the unavoidable
wandering of the arc discharge around the poles
of the electrodes. Moreover, it is difficult
to compare sharp and diffuse lines with exacti-
tude and results obtained in such a case may
not be comparable unless exactly the same slit
width is used for all analyses . . .

The internal standard method is now almost universally used in quantitative analysis with arcs and
sparks. Its value has probably been enhanced rather
than diminished by other advances in the field. Refine-
ments in measuring line intensities have removed many
of the restrictions on line selection, and minor variations in source conditions assume greater significance
because of the demands for greater precision and accuracy placed on the method by modern users.
Even with internal standardization, quantitative

analysis was severely limited by the need for visual interpretation of the photographic plate. The logarithmic sector was introduced by G. Scheibe and A. Neuhausser in 1928. In this method, an opaque, rapidly rotating disc with the periphery cut to a logarithmic curve was placed in front of the slit of a stigmatic spectrograph. The fraction of the time that the slit received light from the source then varied logarithmically along its length. The resulting lines varied in apparent intensity (or actual photographic exposure level) from one end to the other. The lengths of these "carrot-shaped" lines were then used for calibration purposes.

However, the endpoint of such a line was difficult to define. A refinement to reduce this problem was introduced in 1937 by J. S. Foster and H. Horton. A special optical comparator was used to position two lines until they were adjacent and to move them until they tapered off together. The method was soon outdated by the microphotometer.

As mentioned earlier, Lundegårdh was the first to use microphotometry for quantitative spectral analysis, starting in about 1929. During the 1930s and early 1940s, the requirements for accurate spectral line intensity measurements were worked out by Twyman, Webb, Seidel, Harrison, Scribner, and others. Methods for emulsion calibration by known variations in light intensity and changes in the calibration caused by wavelength, emulsion storage, plate-to-plate variations, instrument conditions, and many other factors had to be established before photographic recording could be used for quantitative analysis. Early workers had to change their source intensity by known amounts in order to calibrate because exposure times were well known to affect emulsion response to a given amount of light energy. Calibration was greatly simplified in 1933 when J. H. Webb showed the conditions under which emulsions responded accurately to the integral of intensity and time. The so-called "reciprocity failure" was overcome by using very short exposures such as those produced by a rapidly rotating stepped sector at the spectrograph slit. A known step ratio could then be used to vary exposure levels along the length of a line for calibration. The more difficult job of producing known variations of intensity with constant exposure time was avoided. In favorable cases, accuracies of about 2% could be achieved photographically by carefully controlling all conditions.

By today's standards, emulsion calibration seems very laborious. To appreciate the advance that quantitative atomic spectroscopy represented, one needs to compare it with alternative wet chemical methods used during the 1930s. They too were very lengthy. Calibrations with the spectrograph, once carefully done, could be applied to many samples, whereas the lengthy chemical procedures had to be repeated with each sample.

The period from about 1930 until the mid 1950s might be regarded as the golden years for arc-spark atomic spectroscopy. In discussing the early part of the period, Slavin has written:

> This decade of the 1930's saw the beginning of the industry producing the large grating spectrographs of today, together with densitometers and specialized power supplies. One of the few beneficial results of the great economic depression were the M.I.T. Wavelength Tables. Serious studies of the photographic process were instituted to learn how it could be used as a photometric tool. Studies of light sources, the arc and the spark, were started in an endeavor to make them more reproducible. It is no exaggeration to say that now, 30 years and hundreds of publications later, little has been added that was not started then. This decade of the 1930's changed analytical chemistry from wet to dry, from the era of litmus paper and burettes to the era of optics, electronics, and computers.

There was a very rapid proliferation of methods, of variations of methods, and of applications. In 1946 Meggers commented on the situation.

> Twenty-four years ago only three methods of making quantitative spectrochemical analyses were in use; they were known as the length-of-line method (Lockyer), the residual spectrum method (Hartley), and the intensity-comparison-with-standards method (de Gramont). In the next ten years at least a dozen new methods were proposed. These were called the cathode-layer method, the electrolytic concentration method, the exploded-wire method, the globule method, the high frequency spark method, the homologous-pairs method, the internal-standard method, the logarithmic-sector method, the spark-in-flame method, the twin-spark method, the star-trail method, and the wedge method. More than two dozen new methods were invented during the next decade; the dilution method, the direct photoelectric method, the external-standard method, the filter method, the half-cylinder-sector method, the hollow-cathode method, the interrupter-arc method, the kinematic method, the microscopic method, the

multiple-film method, the photon-counter
method, the pyroelectric-concentration method,
the ratio-quantitative method, the relative-
line-width method, the solution-spray-in-spark
method, the spark-vapor-cloud-spread method, the
step-diaphragm method, the step-sector method,
the step-wedge method, the synthetic spectrum
method, the variable-inductance method, the
variable-exposure method, the total energy
method, etc.

Fortunately, this confusion of so-called
methods is not as bad as it sounds because some
are only modifications of others, and many have
so little practical value that they have been
used only by their inventors.

The reason so many methods were developed was that
each worker was attempting to deal with some small part
of the problems inherent in quantitative spectral analysis. The method is quite indirect, and line intensities were known to reflect concentrations accurately
only under rigidly controlled excitation and exposure
conditions for samples and standards. Much effort went
into the study of "extraneous element effects" and ways
to control them. Samples were often diluted with "spectroscopic buffers" to reduce matrix variations, usually
at great cost in sensitivity. The many variables which
could not be controlled between laboratories forced each
worker to seek optimum conditions within the limits of
his equipment, habits, and prejudices. Each time a
variation which led to improved results in a given
laboratory was discovered, a new method or variation of
an existing method usually was published.

The main stream of atomic spectroscopy was associated with the metals industry and the analysis of various alloys. Here the speed of the analyses and the
ability to analyze numerous components simultaneously
more than compensated for the high initial cost (to a
laboratory director accustomed to buying burets, beakers,
and an occasional platinum crucible, a spectrograph
must have seemed horrendously expensive). The condensed
spark using the sample as one or both electrodes was
particularly convenient and rapid for conducting alloys.

In the United States the National Bureau of Standards (NBS) prepared alloys of known composition for use
as standards. Analytical procedures in the metals industries were improved, and most inter-laboratory variables were defined through the work of The American
Society for Testing and Materials.

If metals analysis was the main stream, then trace
analysis soon became a major tributary in spectrographic
work. The increased need for measurements at the part-

per-million level brought about by nuclear technology
and advances in the biological sciences were two primary forces in this direction. The work on biological
materials by R. L. Mitchell and co-workers at the
Macaulay Institute deserves special mention. That group
took advantage of both the sensitivity and the specificity of spectrographic methods. Some trace metals
were measured directly on the ash of plant or animal
tissues. For elements for which even the spectrograph
lacked sufficient sensitivity, a chemical enrichment
was used. This technique was not chemical separation
of the usual type. The goal was to separate as many
important trace metals as possible, in a single group,
from the major constituents of biological samples
(alkali metals, alkaline earths, and phosphorus). Advantage was taken of the specificity of the spectrograph
to measure the individual trace components simultaneously in the separated mixture. A co-precipitation
method was developed which recovered about 15 elements
at 10-100 fold increase in concentration compared with
the original sample ash. An added benefit from the
separation was better control of the matrix in the
separated fraction. The errors due to matrix or extraneous element effects were greatly reduced.

The period of extremely rapid expansion for arc-
spark spectroscopy closed in the mid 1950s. However, it
would be incorrect to leave the impression that nothing
of significance has been added in the past 20 years.
The range of applications has been extended to include
nearly every type of sample one could think of, including lunar rocks, and the manufacturers now produce
instruments which are pleasant, easy, and safe to use
with the bonus of improved capabilities.

Fundamental studies of sampling and excitation
mechanisms have been made possible by controlled sparks
and nanosecond time resolution of events taking place
within the spark. Studies of this type have been done
by Bardocz, H. Kaiser, and others. J. P. Walters at
the University of Wisconsin is currently active in this
area. The fundamental understanding that these types
of studies produce helps to ensure improved methods in
the future.

The use of high resolution echelle spectrometers
in conjunction with vidicon detectors under computer
control holds promise of still more versatile instruments with improved performance.

During the period of expansion in spectroscopic
methods sketched above, relatively few people were concerned with the flame as an excitation source. The
range of elements to which available flame methods could
be applied was too restricted for most workers. In

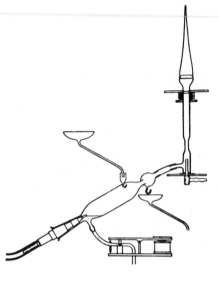

Figure 2. Spray chamber and nebulizer-burner of the type used by Lundegårdh.

fact, to a surprising degree, flame and arc-spark spectroscopy have separate histories as we have noted. Early attempts at flame quantitative analysis were limited by sample introduction methods. The pneumatic nebulizer was used for that purpose by L. G. Gouy as early as 1879, but he was investigating emission processes not quantitative analysis.

The modern era of flame photometry begins with the familiar name Lundegårdh. He used a premixed air-acetylene flame, pneumatic nebulizer sample introduction, and photographic detection. Figure 2 shows the burner which he used. His initial work was on a medium quartz spectrograph of Twyman's design, but he eventually developed a completely automated system that changed samples, controlled the exposure, developed the exposed film, and recorded a microphotometer tracing of the spectral lines. He also developed the spark-in-flame method in which a condensed spark discharge was passed through the flame to enhance excitation of some elements---All from a man whose primary interest was plant physiology!

Lundegårdh's methods were adopted and improved by several groups, most notably by R. L. Mitchell in England. Lundegårdh tried direct photometry of the flame spectrum but did most of his work photographically. W. H. Jansen, J. Heyes, and C. Richter improved on direct photometry, while Schuhknecht isolated sodium

and potassium lines from the flame with filters, starting
in 1937. The filter photometers used selenium barrier-
layer photocells with galvanometers and led to the first
commercial flame instruments.

Advancements were undoubtedly slowed by World War
II, but filter photometers had become sufficiently popular in Europe that Meggers in a 1949 review wrote,
"The flame photometer appears suddenly to have come into
vogue for the quantitative determination of sodium,
potassium, and calcium in almost anything."

In 1949, largely through the work of P. T. Gilbert,
convenient flame attachments became available for existing spectrophotometers. These instruments advanced
the art because the photomultiplier detection system
increased sensitivity and because good wavelength resolution was available without the inconvenience of using
photographic detection. Gilbert also introduced a combination nebulizer-burner which is still widely used.
The flame gases were mixed only in the combustion zone,
and the use of fuels yielding hotter flames, oxygen-
hydrogen, and oxygen-acetylene was thereby made practical. Also, this technique was claimed to be safer to
use with combustible solvents such as gasoline. The
nebulized solution was injected directly into the base
of the flame, and the term "total consumption burner"
was applied to them because there was no spray chamber
in which the larger droplets could settle. The high
temperature flames provided increased emission from
elements familiar to the flame spectroscopist and also
gave useable emission from additional ones.

Flame spectrophotometers of this type quickly dominated the field, especially in the United States. The
units were relatively inexpensive, readily available
from commercial sources, and were easy and convenient
to operate. Even as more advanced instruments with
grating monochromators (or polychromators) and red-
sensitive photomultipliers were developed, the total
consumption burners manufactured by Beckman Instruments
in the United States and Zeiss in Germany were retained.
We emphasize this point because today most flame work
is done on burners that are indistinguishable in principle from the ones used by Lundegårdh. The direct injection of solvent droplets into the flame was slowly
revealed to be the source of numerous interferences due
to incomplete solvent and analyte vaporization.

The 1950s saw rapid expansion of the application
of flame methods. The advantages of using volatile
organic solvents, rather than water, and of extracting
chelates of the elements of interest was developed by
J. A. Dean, internal standardization in filter instruments was used by R. Herrmann in Germany, a multi-

channel flame instrument for the simultaneous determination of alkali and alkaline earth elements in the biological materials was described by M. Margoshes and B. L. Vallee, the fuel-rich flame which aided in the atomization of oxide-forming elements was developed by V. A. Fassel, and the use of a high-temperature flame burning cyanogen and oxygen was described by Vallee and A. F. Bartholomay.

The cyanogen-oxygen flame never really got started on the road to popularity, in spite of its high temperature which would have been very advantageous for emission work. There are several reasons for this. Cyanogen's toxicity was discouraging, there were no commercial sources for the gas, and the temperature of the flame was severely quenched with the usual sample flow rates in a total consumption burner. What is probably the most important reason for the flame's demise is the topic of the next section.

The year 1955 saw the independent publication of papers by C. T. J. Alkemade and J. M. W. Milatz and by A. Walsh describing the advantages of observing absorption rather than emission in flames. This fundamental change again was suggested not by chemists but by physicists. The requirements for observing absorption in flames were described by Kirchhoff and Bunsen, the phenomenon of resonance absorption was well known, and astronomers had used absorption spectra all along. The hollow cathode lamp was described by F. Paschen in 1923 and was well known as a source of very narrow spectral lines of precisely the type needed for absorption.

It might seem that atomic absorption (AA) came on the scene years, even decades, after its time. A careful look at developments in other areas shows, however, that this is not altogether true. The early flame work of Lundegårdh and the development of arc-spark spectroscopy during the 1930s and early 1940s were based on photographic detection. Atomic absorption can be done photographically, but it is much less convenient than recording emission. The practical development of atomic absorption as an analytical method could hardly have preceded the introduction of electrical detection systems. Since hollow cathode lamps are very feeble sources and since flame emission was sometimes troublesome, the use of photomultiplier detection and ac amplification was more or less essential. The photomultiplier did not come into common use until the mid 1940s. Thus Walsh's first application for a patent on atomic absorption in 1953 followed without great delay the time when the needed technology was readily available.

However when atomic absorption, the method which would eventually thrust its way into analytical chemistry

with explosive force, was demonstrated so successfully
in 1955, it caused little if any excitement in the spectroscopic community. Development of the method was left
to a handful of Australian and New Zealand workers.
Walsh traveled extensively, delivering lectures and
attempting to promote interest in the method. At one
point, he described the United States as an underdevel-
oped country as far as atomic absorption was concerned.
His American friends have not let him forget that remark.

Slowly, first in South Africa, then in England, and
finally in the United States, the method began to receive
attention. Its advantages were rather obvious, though
often exaggerated in its early development. It extended
the range of flame methods to elements which had their
best lines in the deep ultraviolet region, it greatly
enhanced the power of detection for numerous additional
elements, it was much less susceptible to certain types
of interferences than emission methods, it gave precision equal to the best flame emission methods (1-2%),
and the instrumentation was simple and inexpensive. The
method itself was quite simple. Light from a line
source, usually a hollow cathode lamp, containing the
element of interest, passed through a flame into which
the sample was aspirated. The light then passed through
a monochromator to isolate the line of interest from
extraneous source radiation and was measured by a photomultiplier. The attenuation of the beam by sample atoms
in the flame was measured and compared with a standard
curve of absorbance vs. concentration. Using the premixed air-acetylene flame similar to Lundegårdh's, the
method was applicable to about 30 elements.

Atomic absorption was extended to the more refractory elements when Amos and Willis introduced the
nitrous oxide-acetylene flame. This flame showed the
advantages of high temperature and strong reducing power
but still had a sufficiently low burning velocity to be
used in burners of the Lundegårdh type which had become
standard for atomic absorption by then. Elements which
formed stable oxides--aluminum and rare earths for ex-
ample--were now readily measured by atomic absorption.
Over 60 elements could be measured by the technique.
Also certain types of interferences which had been troublesome either disappeared or were greatly reduced in
the hotter flame.

The arguments which had raged between the proponents
of emission vs. absorption flame methods in the early
1960s had died away by 1966. The proponents of atomic
absorption had won because of vigorous promotion by
instrument manufacturers as well as inherent advantages
of the method. However, the nitrous oxide-acetylene
flame is also a powerful emission source, as was first

suggested by M. D. Amos.   In his recent history, Walsh says,

> The introduction of the nitrous oxide-acetylene
> flame was not only a milestone in the develop-
> ment of atomic absorption; in my opinion it
> also represents the greatest single advance in
> emission flame spectroscopy since Lundegårdh's
> original work.

If Dr. Walsh was thinking of improvements in the flame itself and not in associated apparatus, we can agree. Atomic absorption and flame emission are now regarded in many laboratories as complementary techniques, and all major manufacturers build instruments which have both emission and absorption capabilities.

The rate of growth of atomic absorption is shown by the instrument sales in Figure 3.   The graph illustrates the success of the method better than words.   In about 1966 J. B. Willis estimated that if the increasing growth rate continued for 20 years, the entire land area of the earth would be covered with AA units.   The flame remains the most popular source of atoms in spite of many well-known disadvantages.   For certain applications, however, its position is being challenged by newer developments.

In 1961 B. V. L'vov described an electrically heated carbon tube furnace as an atomizer for atomic absorption.   The primary light beam passed through the

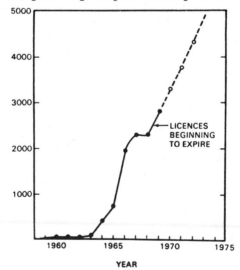

Figure 3.   World sales of atomic absorption spectrophotometers. (*Analytical Chemistry*, 1974)

tube where atomization took place. Though the original
publication clearly showed high sensitivity for the
method, the design was complex, and most people were too
busy exploiting the new-found capabilities of flame
atomic absorption to give L'vov's work the attention it
deserved. A much simpler furnace was described by H.
Massman in 1968, and beginning in 1969, several modifications of his design were introduced commercially.
Furnace atomizers avoid the dilution of the sample with
flame gases and therefore are capable of detecting much
smaller amounts of many elements. It is too early to
judge the full implication of carbon furnace atomizers
on atomic absorption. At this time it appears that
flames are in no danger of being displaced, that the
range of atomic absorption has been extended to somewhat
lower concentrations and to much smaller samples, and
that interference problems are greater than with flames.

Other atomizers such as arcs, glow discharges, and
hollow cathode sources have been used for atomic absorption but have not yet had significant impact on the
method.

The possibility of using atomic fluorescence--i.e.
radiation which is re-emitted by sample atoms after they
have been excited by absorption--for analytical purposes,
was first suggested by Alkemade in 1962 and was first
applied analytically by J. D. Winefordner in the United
States and later by T. S. West in England. The method
has not become popular despite significant advantages
over atomic absorption in some applications. The reasons are not very clear. Lack of commercial instrumentation may be part of the explanation, but more
likely it is the overwhelming popularity of atomic absorption methods. Atomic fluorescence hasn't yet made
it into the club.

Important Publications, Meetings, and Organizations. Certain publications have been so important in
the development of the field that they deserve specific
mention.

Reading tables of wavelengths of spectral lines is
about as interesting as watching paint dry, yet spectral
analysis of unfamiliar material by even an experienced
analyst would be a hazardous undertaking without such
tables. H. A. Rowland published the first, entitled
"New Tables of Standard Wavelengths," in 1893.

In 1907 J. H. Pollok published the "Index of the
Principal Lines of the Spark Spectra of the Elements,"
and de Gramont listed *raies sensibles* and *raies ultimes*
for many elements. The M.I.T. wavelength tables were
published in 1939 under the auspices of the Works Progress Administration and have been called "one of the

few beneficial results of the great economic depression..." A. Gatterer and J. Junkes published a three-volume set entitled "Atlas der Restlinien," the first in 1937 and the last in 1949. Since then many other tables have been published.

The first journal paper to appear in the United States on spectrochemical analysis was published in the *National Bureau of Standards Scientific Papers* by W. F. Meggers, C. C. Kiess, and F. S. Stimson in 1922. Their paper was titled "Practical Spectrographic Analysis," perhaps to avoid scaring away the chemist whom they wanted to reach. During the 1930s, 1940s, and early 1950s, the *Journal of the Optical Society of America* was the principal outlet in the United States for analytical atomic spectroscopy. The first journal devoted specifically to spectroscopy was *Spectrochimica Acta* which started publication in 1939. Since then a number of other specialized journals have appeared.

Dozens of books on various aspects of atomic spectroscopy have been published. "Chemical Spectroscopy" by W. R. Brode, with editions in 1939 and 1943, was one of the earliest which could be used as a text. Twyman's book, "The Spectrochemical Analysis of Metals and Alloys," was particularly valuable for this work because of its excellent section on history. Lundegårdh published a book on leaf analysis in 1945, and a translation by R. L. Mitchell appeared in 1951. Mitchell's own contribution, "The Spectrographic Analysis of Soils, Plants and Related Materials," appeared in 1948 and remains a classic work in the areas covered.

The first meetings devoted to analytical atomic spectroscopy that we know of were held at MIT during the 1930s. Slavin has described them better than we could hope to:

> Impetus for growth of the field, at least in this country, was given by the series of summer conferences organized by G. R. Harrison at the Massachusetts Institute of Technology (M.I.T.). Beginning in 1933 and continuing to 1940, when the conferences had to be terminated because of the approaching war and the involvement of M.I.T. in classified work, the meetings were increasingly well attended. These meetings were held for five days in the month of June, in a small lecture hall seating about 80 persons. Only toward the end of the period were there enough participants to fill the room, and more than half of them were organic chemists working with the spectrophotometer, not emission workers. The emission subjects discussed ranged from sample preparation to

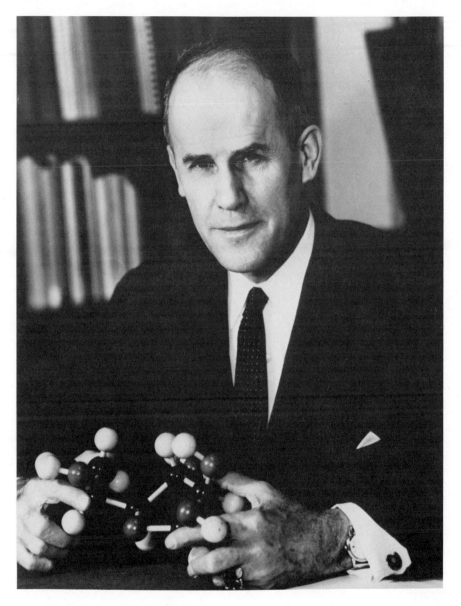

WALLACE REED BRODE, 1900-1974

After completing graduate studies at the University of Illinois, Brode spent a few years on the staff there, then worked at the National Bureau of Standards for two years. He then joined the Ohio State University faculty, where he remained from 1928 to 1947. In that year he returned to the NBS as Associate Director. In 1958 he became Science Advisor to the Secretary of State. He was President of the ACS in 1969.

specific procedures, instrumentation, optical problems, photographic problems, and even literature sources, for the journals covering spectroscopy were unfamiliar to most of the people in attendance. It was a truly egalitarian group; everyone was equal in his ignorance.

The MIT meetings were not resumed after the war, but many others were started. Analytical spectroscopists seem to have developed an insatiable appetite to sponsor and to attend scientific meetings, which continues unabated today. In Europe, the Colloquim Spectroscopicum Internationale was organized, while in the United States, meetings of the Optical Society soon had competition from the Pittsburgh Conference, the Eastern Analytical Symposium, the Mid-America Spectroscopy Symposium, and others as forums for exchange of information and ideas on analytical applications of spectroscopy. Meetings for the same purpose were organized in Canada and somewhat later in Australia. In 1967 an International Conference on Atomic Absorption was started in Prague, and meetings have been held every two years since in various parts of the world.

In the United States dissatisfaction with this proliferation of meetings led to the formation of the Federation of Analytical Chemistry and Spectroscopy Societies. This was an effort to consolidate numerous small meetings into one larger one. The first FACSS meeting was held in 1974.

Just after World War II, local groups in many major U. S. cities sprang up because of a common interest in spectroscopy among the members. Meggers, in his 1949 *Analytical Chemistry* review, mentions a "half dozen or more" societies for applied spectroscopy. Some of the meetings discussed above were sponsored by these groups and were initially quite local. Most of these same groups exist today as local sections of the Society for Applied Spectroscopy.

Important Current Developments. The history of atomic spectroscopy is characterized by many long lags between the time a technique was first described and the time its full potential was realized. The same is surely true today, and it seems worthwhile to mention a few things that may be of increasing importance in the future, things which may cause future historians to wonder how spectroscopists in the mid-1970s could have been so blind as to ignore them.

Atomic fluorescence methods have never enjoyed much popularity. However, the simple instruments based on resonance detectors (no monochromators) which are being developed by Walsh's group at CSIRO may change this. The glow discharge first described by W. Grimm also appears to have more analytical potential as an emission source than has yet been realized.

Plasma emission sources of several types have been investigated vigorously for the past several years. The inductively coupled argon plasma, described by S. Greenfield in 1964 and elaborated by Fassel's group in the United States and by P. W. J. M. Boumans and co-workers in the Netherlands, appears to hold the greatest promise. Its primary attractions are multi-element capability and freedom from interferences. The primary limitation is likely to be the high cost of radio frequency power supplies and multi-channel spectrometers. Overall, the future for this excitation source is extremely promising.

Finally it is interesting to speculate on the analytical utility of lasers. They have been used as a sampling device in the laser microprobe and as a light source for atomic fluorescence, but neither application has become very popular. Given the established utility of lasers in other fields, it seems reasonable to predict eventual application to analytical problems. Perhaps inter-cavity quenching of laser radiation which has been described recently will prove very useful. More likely, however, it will take a new idea, one which will make many of us wonder why we didn't think of it, to exploit the potential of lasers for analytical purposes.

MOLECULAR SPECTROSCOPY

The absorption of visible light as an analytical tool was utilized to some extent long before the true nature of the phenomenon was understood. This general approach has traditionally been known as "colorimetry," a term used by physicists in a different sense. In its analytical context, the word refers to the selective attenuation of certain colors of light caused by the presence of corresponding species (usually ionic or molecular) in a solution. Thus color is a unique property of specific chemical systems and can be used to estimate concentration.

It has been reported that Pliny (A.D. 60) used an extract of gallnuts to test for the presence of iron in vinegar. One of the first documented colorimetric methods was that of Wilhelm August Lampadius (1838) who estimated the amount of iron or nickel in a cobalt ore by comparing the colors of a sample solution with those of standard reference solutions in glass cylinders. Augustin Jacquelain, in 1846, devised a method to estimate copper based on the color of the copper-ammonia complexes.

In the following decades progress was slow in the development of colorimetric methodology. T. J. Hera-path's thiocyanate method for iron (1852), Nessler's method for ammonia (1856), the phenoldisulfonic acid test for nitrate (1864), the hydrogen peroxide method for titanium (1870), the methylene blue method for hydrogen sulfide (1883), and the molybdosilicic acid method for silicate (1898) were typical colorimetric methods used in the late 19th century.

Most colorimetric analyses in those years were carried out by the standard series technique, using Nessler tubes. Comparators for matching colors by adjusting the thickness of the solution through which incident light passes were designed by Alexander Müller (1853), by Jules Duboscq (1854), and others. Müller designated his instrument a "Komplementär Kolorimeter" (Figure 4); the solution to be examined was placed in the glass cylinder A, provided with a millimeter scale d. A concentric tube a was capable of vertical motion. The lower ends of both cylinders were closed by plane cover glasses. A glass filter was provided at g, of color complementary to that of the solution. As observed from above against white light reflected by the adjustable mirror, if the inner tube were raised, the color of the solution would predominate, while if it were lowered to virtual contact at b, the color of the

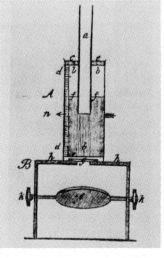

Figure 4. Müller's "Komplemen-tär Kolorimeter."

Figure 5. The original Du-boscq comparator.

filter would be seen. At some intermediate point the
two would balance, and an approximation to white would
be observed, with perhaps 10% uncertainty in scale setting. Müller claimed to be able to determine as little
as 10^{-4} mg of iron by the thiocyanate reaction with this
device.

The obvious deficiency in Müller's colorimeter lay
in the lack of control over the light source. The
Duboscq design (Figure 5) overcame this difficulty by
utilizing two similar sets of cylinders and comparing
the color density of the analyte directly with that of
a standard. The light beams from the two cylinders were
combined by a prism and lens system so that the observer
perceived a split field of view, half corresponding to
the analyte, half to the standard.

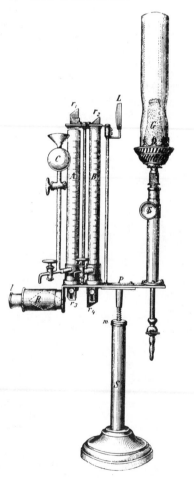

Figure 6. The colorimeter contructed by Krüss.

An interesting colorimeter designed by Gerhard and Hugo Krüss (1895) is shown in Figure 6. The variability associated with daylight as a source is obviated by the use of a gas flame with a Welsbach mantle G as illuminant. Light gathered by the lens L was reflected downward through a pair of sample tubes A and B by the reflecting prisms r_1 and r_2; the two beams were again reflected at the lower end by prisms r_3 and r_4, and combined through the rhomb R to form a divided field in the eyepiece l. The levels of liquids in the two cylinders could be adjusted to give equal intensities in the eyepiece, and the positions of the two menisci were read on the millimeter scales. Gerhard Krüss' book "Kolorimetrie und quantitative Spektralanalyse," published in 1891, was the earliest comprehensive treatment of colorimetry.

Figure 7 depicts a modification of the Duboscq comparator for turbidity measurements. It was designed by Kober about 1917 and was subsequently manufactured by the Klett Manufacturing Co. This instrument is provided with an extended light source, so that the pair of cylindrical cuvets can be illuminated uniformly from the rear. The light scattered by colloidal material in the cuvets is then compared in the split field of the eyepiece.

With these instruments visual colorimetry had reached its peak.

Figure 7. The Duboscq instrument modified for nephelometry.

An early application of qualitative spectrophotometry was the identification of very minute quantities
of vitamin A in certain oils by Woodrow (1928) and by
R. A. Morton and co-workers. A similar observation was
made by Capper (1930), who found that substances extracted from the liver of rats fed on carotene gave absorption bands identical with those of vitamin A.
O. Warburg (1930) established the identity and function
of the "respiratory ferment" by correlating the absorption spectra of the living cells with the variation of
the photochemical effectiveness of the incident light.

Progress in analytical molecular spectroscopy was
relatively slow during the latter part of the 19th and
early part of the 20th century, with very few scientists,
at least by present-day standards, being involved in
fundamental investigations. Practicing analytical chemists did develop colorimetric methods whenever possible
to solve their particular analytical problems, but colorimetry was not especially popular with analysts. It
was necessary to prepare a reference standard colored
solution for each color comparison in order to minimize
errors although some effort was expended to develop permanent color standard solutions and colored glasses as
standards.

Visual Spectrophotometry. Advances were made in
improving visual instruments to facilitate color com-
parisons, primarily with respect to attenuating the
beams of light passing through the reference and sample
solutions and to isolate certain regions of the incident
spectrum. In 1873 Carl Vierordt discussed apparatus for
obtaining absorption spectra and suggested the possibility of quantitative analysis by absorption spectroscopy. He may be considered the founder of present-day
absorption spectrometry.

The slit of Vierordt's apparatus was divided into
two parts, such that the width of the upper and lower
sections could be adjusted separately with micrometer
screws. A glass cell was placed before the slit, partly
filled with the solution to be examined. The light from
the two parts of the slit entered the spectroscope verti-
cally displaced from each other. If the slit widths
were equal, the spectrum formed by the light beam passing
through the solution was always weaker than that passing
over the surface. By narrowing the upper slit, the two
intensities could be made equal. The adjustment screw
on the upper slit had a scale divided into 100 equal
parts, which gave a relative measure of the transmission
of the solution. Using this apparatus, Vierordt determined the spectra of many colored substances, such as
permanganate, chromate, cuprammonium, fuchsine, even

blood stains. He was the first to publish tables of extinction values.

Vierordt's method of intensity control by alteration of the slit width caused changes not only in the intensity but also in the spectral quality of the light, so that the light incident on the two solutions was not quite identical. This defect was overcome (independently) by Paul Glan and Carl Hüfner, who decreased the light intensity by polarizing the light in one path, leaving the slit width unchanged. Intensity ratios were then determined from the angles of rotation of the Nicol prisms.

W. A. Miller, an early investigator of absorption spectra, found no definite relationship between constitution and light absorption, though he wrote in 1864:

> The most interesting fact disclosed by these various experiments is the persistence of either the diactinic or the absorbent property in the compound, whatever be its physical state, a circumstance which proves that the property under examination is intimately connected with the atomic or molecular nature of the body, and not merely with its state of aggregation.

In 1872 Walter N. Hartley came into possession of the instrument that Miller had used, improved it, and continued the investigations. Hartley, and workers following him, developed a photographic method in which the wavelengths at which various thicknesses of a given solution ceased to transmit, were recorded. By progressively diluting the solution, he could follow the absorption to its maximum and plot a curve of equivalent thicknesses of standard solution (or their logarithms) against the observed limiting wavelengths transmitted, thus producing an absorption spectrum.

Another important piece of early work is H. W. Vogel's 1877 determination of carbon monoxide in blood. Branly (1882) described an absorptiometric method for determining hemoglobin. His spectrophotometer was of the polarization type using Nicol prisms, arranged so that the $\tan^2$ law applied. For convenience, in view of the linear relationship between the logarithm of the transmittance and the concentration, as discovered by Beer, the early instruments were calibrated directly in units of extinction.

On the basis of extensive measurements of absorption spectra, Hartley, and later E. C. Baly, established an empirical relationship between the chemical constitution of an organic molecule and its absorption spectrum. They found that similarity in spectra often corresponded to similarity in structure and used this observation to elucidate molecular structure when

recognized chemical methods were inadequate. It was
found that the development of color in a compound could
be attributed to the presence of certain atomic groups
called chromophores that were already known to be present in dyes. Absorption measurements were also found
to be applicable to the study of keto-enol tautomerism.
Hartley must undoubtedly be considered a pioneer in this
branch of spectroscopy.

Around the turn of the century Arthur König and
F. F. Martens developed an excellent visual spectrophotometer. It employed a polarization photometer in which
the light was split into two polarized beams by a Wollaston prism such that the planes of polarization were
respectively parallel and perpendicular to the dividing
line of the split field. The fields were matched by the
rotation of a Nicol prism. Two American firms, the
Bausch and Lomb Optical Co. and the Gaertner Scientific
Co., manufactured visual spectrophotometers based on a
similar principle. However, eye fatigue and difficulty
in obtaining reliable readings below about 430 nm and
above 680 nm made the obtaining of complete absorption
spectra with these instruments a very tedious task.

Several visual filter photometers were developed
and manufactured in this era. The Pulfrich photometer
manufactured by Carl Zeiss used a series of glass filters having different spectral band widths and transmittance levels. Sample and reference beams were atten-
uated by adjustment of diaphragms with readings taken
from micrometer drum heads. Adam Hilger, Ltd., in England, manufactured the Hilger-Nutting photometer utilizing polarization attentuation. The Aminco neutral
wedge photometer of the American Instrument Co. used
a series of filters together with an optical wedge
attenuator in the reference beam. The scale readings
corresponding to wedge positions were convertible to
absorbance values.

The review on instrumentation by Ralph H. Müller in
the *Analytical Edition* of *Industrial and Engineering
Chemistry* (January 1939) summarizes the state of the art
at that time. In his opinion, "For colorimetric chemical analysis, the visual Duboscq colorimeter is still
the most versatile and useful instrument." Further, in
his October 1941 review in the same journal, Müller says,

> The assumption that any photoelectric instru-
> ment must be more accurate and reliable than a
> visual instrument is wholly unwarranted. . . .
> However, the future does seem to lie in the
> direction of the photoelectric types, for there
> is no inherent limit in the attainable sensi-
> tivity and objectivity of the measurement.
> Fatique effects again incline toward the photo-

RALPH HOLCOMBE MÜLLER, 1900–1970

    Müller held degrees from the Universities of Pennsylvania,
Columbia and Göttingen. He was Professor of Chemistry at New
York University from 1923 to 1951. From then until 1962 he was
in charge of special instrumentation problems at Los Alamos Scientific Laboratory. At the time of his death, he was Visiting
Professor at the Louisiana State University. He served 24 years
as a contributing editor of *Analytical Chemistry*.

electric type, although squinting at a micro-
ammeter needle for protracted periods is not a
pleasant pastime.

Photographic Spectrophotometry. About 1910 Adam
Hilger, Ltd., introduced a rotating sector photometer
which, with a suitable source and spectrograph, consti-
tuted a photographic spectrophotometer. The radiant
energy from the source was passed through reference and
sample cells; the two beams were then deviated by wedge
lenses to a biprism at the slit of the spectrograph. A
rotating sector interrupted the two beams so that the
spectra of sample and reference beams were juxtaposed
on the photographic plate. The sector in the sample
beam had a large fixed opening, while that in the reference beam could be changed in angular aperture to correspond to transmittance values between zero and one.
    Later a modified variable-diaphragm photometer
called the Spekker photometer, was introduced by Hilger
which was easier to read and to adjust. Sector photometers were manufactured in the United States by Gaertner, by Bausch and Lomb, and by Applied Research Labora-
tories-Dietert, each designed primarily to be used with
the spectrograph manufactured by the same firm. Numerous devices were developed to reduce the time required
to obtain absorption spectra by photographic means. An
example of this approach is Hilger's echelon cells in
which the thickness of solution was varied stepwise in
logarithmic increments, permitting several stepped spectra to be obtained simultaneously. Despite the considerable time and effort required, the photographic spectrophotometer made it possible to obtain absorption
spectra in both visible and ultraviolet regions, and
many spectra were recorded initially by this method.
    Wallace R. Brode, Professor of Chemistry at The Ohio
State University, was one American chemist who made a
significant contribution using photographic spectrophotometry. As an organic chemist with a great interest
in dyes and organic structures, Brode with his students
reported the absorption spectra of many compounds and
made extensive correlations between spectra and structures. Later, with the publication of his book "Chemical Spectroscopy" (1939 and 1943), he did much to popularize both absorption and emission spectroscopy. It
appears that Professor Brode initially obtained spectrographic apparatus to investigate Raman shifts but found
absorption spectrophotometry more informative and experimentally more tangible than Raman spectroscopy.
    George R. Harrison of MIT and Kasson S. Gibson of
the National Bureau of Standards are two American physicists associated with the advancement of spectrophoto-

metry in the 1920-1940 era. F. Twyman of Adam Hilger,
Ltd., in England also contributed markedly to the progress of the field during this period.

Photoelectric Spectrophotometry. The photoelectric
effect was discovered by Wilhelm Hallwachs in 1888 and
was observed by others with considerable interest in
subsequent years. However, it was not until 1900 that
Philipp Lenard showed that electrons were ejected from
metals when irradiated, and J. Elster and N. Geitel
showed that the rate of emission was proportional to
radiant power. The photovoltaic effect was discovered
by W. Adams and P. Day in 1876, when they observed that
a potential was generated when light irradiated a selen-
ium-platinum junction. Much early work on photoelectric
cells was conducted in the United States by Herbert E.
Ives of the Physical Research Laboratory of the United
Gas Improvement Co. of Philadelphia, especially with
respect to studies on wavelength dependency, linearity,
and composition of photocathode surfaces. It was not
until 1917 that T. W. Case found that fused thallium
sulfide showed a change in resistance upon illumination
and ultimately developed the Thalofide cell containing
thallium, oxygen, and sulfur, as the detector which J.
Kaplan of the Naval Research Laboratory used in near
infrared spectrometry.
The first utilization of photoelectric detectors
for absorption measurements seems to have been made by
Wilhelm Berg, who obtained a German patent in 1911 for
a photoelectric colorimeter. Early similar colorimeters
developed in America used a single photovoltaic cell.
The Sheard-Sanford design was used in an instrument
designated the Photelometer by Central Scientific Co.
The design by Evelyn was used by the Rubicon Co. in the
Evelyn photoelectric colorimeter. Klett Manufacturing
Co. and Fisher Scientific Co. were among the first to
offer photoelectric colorimeters with two balanced photovoltaic cells, permitting automatic correction for line-
voltage fluctuations and convenient blank subtraction.
All of these instruments used glass filters to isolate
regions of the visible spectrum and microammeters for
readout or to indicate a potentiometric balance. Most
of the photocells used in these instruments were photovoltaic (barrier-layer) cells manufactured by Weston
Electrical Instrument Corp. under the name Photronic
cells. The advent of reliable, direct-reading instruments sparked great interest in colorimetric analysis
and in absorption spectrophotometry.
In the early 1940s two photoelectric spectrophotometers equipped with diffraction gratings for dispersion
and single photovoltaic cells for detection became

commercially available. Both used deflection galvanometers for readout. The Cenco-Sheard Spectrophotelometer (Central Scientific Co.) used an Eagle-mounted
concave grating and provided selectable bandwidths from
2.5 to 20 nm. Coleman Electric Co.'s model 14 "Universal" spectrophotometer had a fixed 35-nm band width
and a plane transmission grating. Coleman also marketed
briefly (1940-41) a double-monochromator spectrophotometer with two plane gratings to reduce stray light; an
external galvanometer served as null indicator for a
potentiometric circuit.

The incorporation of gratings in place of prisms
eliminated the necessity of adjusting the slit width
for each wavelength setting because of the near constancy of dispersion throughout the spectrum characteristic of gratings. The main limitation, aside from the
restriction to the visible region, was the time required
to obtain spectra by point-to-point measurements. A
rather wide spectral bandwidth was necessary to obtain
sufficient signal from the detector--a serious factor
if spectra have sharp changes in bandwidth.

The relatively low cost of these rugged instruments
and their ease of operation led to widespread applications of spectrophotometers in clinical, metallurgical,
and agricultural determinations of minor constituents.
About 1938 a double prism monochromator of the van
Cittert type with a unique polarization photometer in
which the vacuum phototube served only as a null point
detector was designed by A. C. Hardy of MIT and soon
became available commercially as the General Electric
Recording Spectrophotometer. With the availability of
adequate photoelectric instruments (by 1946 it was
estimated that there were about 100 of these in use),
there began several decades of exceptional progress in
the development of new and improved analytical methods
and the use of light absorption spectrometry in other
analytical studies and research fields.

Professor Melvin Guy Mellon of Purdue University
obtained the second General Electric spectrophotometer
to be manufactured, a non-recording model which was in-
geniously converted to a recording instrument by Dr.
Swank, then one of Mellon's graduate students, and subsequently a Director of the DuPont Co. For many years,
new colorimetric methods were developed in Mellon's
laboratory, and the effects of solution variables, particularly diverse ions, were studied and delineated.
Color-forming reactions involving heteropoly acids,
metal chelates, and dye formation were investigated. In
1952 Professor Mellon received the Fisher Award in Analytical Chemistry for his contributions in colorimetric
analysis and spectrophotometry. Professor John H. Yoe

of the University of Virginia was another analytical
chemist who with his graduate students developed many
new colorimetric methods using organic reagents. In
1957 the Fisher Award was presented to Professor Yoe.
Other Fisher awardees who made significant contributions
in the chemistry involved in absorptiometry are Professor
G. Frederick Smith, of the University of Illinois for
his development of the ferroin type reagents, and Professors Harvey Diehl and Charles Banks of Iowa State
University for their studies on the dioximes and other
organic reagents. The multi-volume compendium "Colorimetric Methods of Analysis," by Foster Dee and Cornelia
Snell, and E. B. Sandell's "Colorimetric Determination
of Traces of Metals" embody the contributions of many
American analytical chemists. In 1976 light absorption
spectrometry had attained the status of a classical
method of analysis.

Ultraviolet Absorption Spectrometry. The first
systematic investigation of the ultraviolet absorption
spectra of simple organic compounds was done by Victor
Henri (1919) and his pupils. Henri used a quantitative
method that enabled him to plot molar extinction coefficients (absorptivities) against wavelength. The first
result of Henri's investigations was that the spectrum
of a compound is not specifically characteristic of the
whole molecule but only of particular atomic groupings
within it. Henri extended the use of the term chromo-
phore, previously restricted to the particular groups
associated with visible color, to include groups responsible for selective ultraviolet absorption as well.
Although many ultraviolet absorption spectra had
been obtained by photographic means, it was the introduction of the Beckman Model DU Quartz Photoelectric
Spectrophotometer in the early 1940s that catalyzed
interest in such spectra for analytical purposes. For
the first time it was possible to obtain an ultraviolet
absorption spectrum within a reasonable time (even
though point-by-point readings were required) and with
a minimum of experimental difficulties and relatively
inexpensive instrumentation. One analytical application
was the qualitative identification of compounds through
their absorption spectra. Although such identifications
were purely empirical, the correlation of structure with
absorption spectral features was particularly useful in
studying unsaturated organic compounds. The realization
that many inorganic species also exhibit characteristic
absorption in the ultraviolet prompted extensive investigations and development of analogous methods for
inorganic constituents.
The historical impact of the model DU was as

significant in the 1940s as the advent of the Duboscq
colorimeter had been almost 90 years earlier, with respect to the development of commercial chemical instrumentation. The design of the DU was carefully thought
out. A prism monochromator was selected in preference
to a grating to minimize stray light. The instrument
featured variable slits, a hydrogen lamp source for the
ultraviolet, and an incandescent automotive headlight
bulb (operated at reduced voltage for stability) for the
visible region. Two phototubes were employed, one for
the ultraviolet, the other for the visible. A dc amplifier measured the voltage drop across the phototube re-
sistor. The absorbance reading was obtained by null
balancing of the meter, with readout taken from the
calibrated dial of the balancing potentiometer. Although
the monochromator was designed to cover the spectrum
from 200 to 2000 nm, no detector was available for the
regions below about 220 nm or above 1000 nm. The appearance of the DU ensured the demise of absorptiometry by
means of the spectrograph with its dependence on the
inconvenient and imprecise processing and measurement of
photoplates.

During the 1940s, much progress was made in electronics. Reliable photomultiplier tubes were developed,
and the need for electronic stabilization of the light
source was recognized, and means were devised for accom-
plishing it. Concurrently inverse feedback amplifier
circuits of high stability were developed. In clinical
laboratories the demand continued for instruments that
were cheap, convenient, and versatile. This was also
reflected in chemical laboratories by a continuation of
the trend to offer accessories to the basic instruments,
such as flame photometer modules, fluorescence accessories, and reflectance attachments.

The desire for recording instruments increased, not
only at the level of highest quality and flexibility for
research applications but particularly for medium-priced
instruments suitable for routine use. One of the first
recording ultraviolet spectrophotometers on the American
market was the Beckman model R, which consisted of a
standard DU with the addition of a robot mechanism to
turn switches and dials in imitation of a human operator.
Since a single-beam spectrophotometer requires zero adjustment for every increment of wavelength, the resulting
spectrum consisted of a series of plotted points rather
than a continuous line.

A continuously balancing double-beam recording
spectrophotometer soon became available in the first of
the Cary line, announced in 1946. Since then many firms
in the United States and abroad have entered the field,
and many models have been produced, including specialized

spectrophotometers, such as the dual-wavelength instruments; in these two wavelengths are passed through the sample simultaneously to compensate for turbidity of the solution. Stopped-flow spectrophotometers allow scanning of the spectrum in a fraction of a second, with oscilloscope readout, useful in studies of reaction kinetics.

The Absorption Laws. Concurrent with the study of molecular absorption spectroscopy, attempts were made to describe mathematically the phenomena of molecular light absorption. The relation that was eventually deduced is known today as the Beer-Lambert law.

The earliest contribution was that of Pierre Bouguer, Royal Professor of Hydrography at Le Havre, who published in 1729 a work entitled, "Essai Optique sur la Gradation de la Lumière," in which he described the attenuation of light as it passed through successive thicknesses of glass. He concluded that "equal layers [of glass] should absorb, not equal amounts, but rather proportional amounts. That is, if a certain thickness intercepts half the light, the following equal thickness will intercept not the entire second half, but only half of this half, reducing it accordingly to one-quarter of its original brilliance." Johann Lambert, a German physicist and astronomer, familiar with Bouguer's work, and writing in 1760, gave a more exact mathematical formulation to the same or analogous observations.

It was nearly a century later (1852) when August Beer, a mathematics professor at Bonn, entered the picture. He showed that the logarithmic relation of Lambert could be extended to solutions of absorbing substances in nonabsorbing solvents, in which case the concentration is mathematically analogous to the thickness of a pure absorbing material. He, and independently the Frenchman, F. Bernard, in 1853, introduced an absorption coefficient, which was utilized by Bunsen and Roscoe in 1857. This coefficient was defined as the reciprocal of the path length at which the light intensity is reduced to one-tenth of its initial value. Clearly this is not identical with the absorptivity as used today, but the two are directly proportional.

The corresponding extensive property, now known as absorbance, was first called the optical density, or sometimes the extinction. The concept was developed by F. Hürter and V. C. Driffield (1890) as a measure of the deposit of silver in photographic materials; the fraction of incident light transmitted was called the transparency, its reciprocal, the opacity, and the common logarithm of the opacity, the (optical) density. The latter term was adopted by absorption spectroscopists since the logarithmic relation required was identical to that demanded by the Lambert-Beer relation. Hürter and Driffield were only concerned with measurements on white light since silver deposits, at least in the visible region, are not selective in their absorbant powers.

Apparently the first application of absorption spectroscopy in analytical chemistry was in the work of Jons F. Bahr, a Swedish scientist working with Bunsen (1866). Together they made a rough determination of neodymium oxide in gadolinite by comparing the visual absorptions of unknown and standard solutions; the more concentrated solution was diluted until the same band intensities were observed. A simple calculation then gave the desired concentration. It remained for Vierordt to recognize the utility of the absorption coefficient, permitting variation of the intensity of incident light to keep the actual measurements within the linear region of the detector.

The absorption law, then, must be considered the product of a number of scientists, and it is purely arbitrary that it is usually designated as Beer's law. There have been many efforts to improve or to extend the law. One of the significant attempts is the paper of G. Kortüm and M. Seiler in the *Zeitschrift für angewandte Chemie* in 1939, where the authors point out that the invariant quantity is not the absorptivity, ε, but rather $\varepsilon \cdot n/(n^2 + 2)^2$, where n is the refractive index of the solution, itself a function of concentration. This correction is not ordinarily significant in analytical applications, where solutions are almost always very dilute, but it stresses the danger in comparing solutions in differing solvents.

Vibrational Spectroscopy: Infrared. Infrared (IR) and Raman spectroscopy have special significance to analytical chemistry as a whole, not only because of the impact of the techniques themselves (which has been considerable) but also because their development portended a revolution. The revolution, simply stated, was the insertion of powerful physical methods into a discipline that had been primarily pure chemistry.

The genesis of infrared spectrometry was in 1800 with the thermometers of Sir William Herschel. He observed two heat maxima, one in the yellow-green portion of the spectrum and another somewhat beyond the red end of the visible region. He believed that one maximum was due to light and the other to heat energy. However, later his son John Herschel, also A. M. Ampère and M. Melloni (1835), showed that the difference was due only to the degree of refraction. The invention of the bolometer by Langley in 1880 made it possible to utilize diffraction gratings of known geometry for precise wave-length determinations in the infrared.

At the turn of the century, understanding of the absorption phenomena was only rudimentary. Many of the early workers were preoccupied with correlations between the absorption bands and the presence of certain single atoms in the molecule, with molecular weight or size, or with temperature, color, refractive index, dielectric constant, and so forth. Many spent a great deal of time on "harmonic ratios" or regular progressions of absorption bands (water, for example, was found to absorb at 0.77, 1.0, 1.25, 1.50, 1.94, 2.05, 3.06, 4.7, and 6.1 μm), an apparent analogy to the series observed in the atomic spectra of hydrogen. Several investigators noted that selective absorptions seemed to be associated with definite groups of atoms, but the reason for this correlation was unknown. The use of infrared spectroscopy to determine molecular structure was apparently foreseen by W. deW. Abney and R. E. Festing, however, who in 1881 commented as follows:

> In our minds there lingers no doubt as to the easy detection of any radical which we have examined, but it will require more energy and ability than we possess to thoroughly classify the different modifications which may arise. We may say, however, it seems highly probable by this delicate mode of analysis that the hypothetical position of any hydrogen which is replaced may be identified, a point which is of prime importance in organic chemistry.

In 1900 an impecunious graduate student named W. W. Coblentz entered Cornell University to work with Professor Edward L. Nichols in the Department of Physics. His first project, sensitizing photographic plates to record infrared radiation (0.8 to 10 μm) was not successful. He then began to build a Nichols radiometer to study the radiant luminous efficiency of lamps. Before long, however, he was supplied with a small mirror spectrometer with a rock salt prism and succeeded in measuring infrared radiation as far out as 14 μm, to the astonishment and delight of his co-workers. Coblentz received his Ph.D. degree in 1903 but stayed at Cornell for two years as a post-graduate student, and became engrossed in measuring the infrared spectra of many organic materials. For this work he constructed a larger spectrometer (Figure 8), using the same rock salt prism as in the earlier instrument. Instead of pursuing will-of-the-wisp correlations with impure natural substances, however, he simply set about in the best manner of pure research to map the infrared absorptions of a large number of pure substances. As he tells it,

WILLIAM WEBER COBLENTZ, 1873-1962

    Coblentz was educated at Case School of Applied Science and
at Cornell University. Following a few years as research associate with the Carnegie Institution, he joined the National Bureau
of Standards, where he was the chief of the radiometry section for
40 years. Well known for the thoroughness and accuracy of his
work, he set standards for radiometric measurements from the ultraviolet through the infrared spectral regions.

Figure 8. Coblentz's large infrared spectrometer at Cornell
University. The Nernst source is at the right (h), the radiometer detector at the left (r).

When I began infrared work at Cornell the
subject seemed old and worn out, and yet it was
new. It meant compiling new data for which
there was no immediate prospective application.
There was no accurate infrared spectroradiometry.
The few infrared absorption and emission lines
and bands that had been recorded (up to 1900)
were uncertain in wavelength. Beyond 3 microns
in the infrared the wavelengths were entirely
incorrect; the maxima of the absorption bands
recorded at 10 to 12 microns were probably at
5 to 8 microns.
Rubens and Paschen in Germany, and Langley
in Washington were determining the refractive
indices of fluorite and of rock salt in the infrared spectrum. Using these data, which, while
fairly accurate, were undergoing improvement,
I began what was the first really accurate survey

of infrared spectroscopy of various substances.
Perhaps it would be better to say spectroradiometry, for that was the method used.

Coblentz went to some lengths to obtain pure materials, even using $54 from his own meager funds to pur-
chase chemicals from a supply house. The point-by-point
process that Coblentz used to obtain the absorption
pattern has been described by R. Norman Jones:

> Having selected a setting of the spectro-
> meter circle, Coblentz recorded the radiometer
> deflections using the cell-in, cell-out tech-
> nique; the ratio of the deflections gave the
> percentage transmission of the samples. Be-
> tween each measurement the iron shutter was
> lowered and the radiometer zero checked. The
> time required for a single transmission mea-
> surement was 1.5 minutes, and the exploration
> of the complete spectrum took 3.5 to 4 hours.
> The operator sat in an outer room, manipulated
> the shutters and cells by means of the cables
> and plotted the spectrum at the same time.
> There does not appear to have been any provi-
> sion for the remote resetting of the spectro-
> meter circle between readings; this would seem
> to require his entering the inner room before
> each measurement, but apparently this did not
> significantly upset the thermal balance of the
> radiometer.

Using this tedious process, Coblentz obtained the
spectra of over 100 organic solids, liquids, and gases
with sufficient accuracy that his spectra are still very
presentable today (Figure 9). Results of this work were
published in 1905 by the Carnegie Institution of Washington and later (1962) reprinted by the Perkin-Elmer
Corp. and the Coblentz Society.

Coblentz was undoubtedly the first to use infrared
spectrometry as a method for monitoring the progress of
a purification process. He writes,

> My purification of ethane by noting the
> disappearance of the infrared absorption bands
> of the impurities, that I removed by liquefac-
> tion and fractional distillation, was probably
> the first practical application of this method
> of controlling a manufacturing process.

One of the most useful features of infrared spectro-
scopy--the fact that certain chemical groups have associated with them specific absorptions or "group frequencies"--had been noted by Julius and others. Coblentz
extended the list of chemical groups and their associated
absorptions and tabulated the results (Table III). Oddly
enough, he did not note any correlation between the

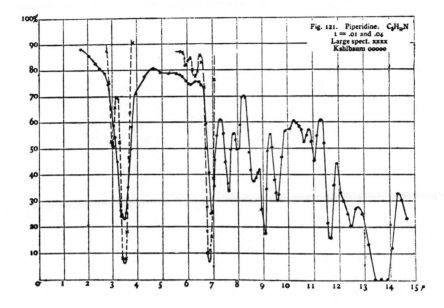

Fig. 121. Piperidine. C₅H₁₁N
t = .01 and .04
Large spect. xxxx
Kahlbaum ooooo

Figure 9. The spectrum of piperidine taken point-by-point on Coblentz's spectrometer.

Table III. Coblentz's Correlations

Group	Characteristic Maxima (μm)
CH_2 or CH_3	3.43, 6.86, 13.6 to 13.8, 14
NH_2	2.96, 6.1 to 6.15
C_6H_6	3.25, 6.75, 8.68, 9.8, 11.8, 12.95
NO_2	2.95
NCS	4.78

presence of a carbonyl group and the intense absorption near 5.9 μm that he observed in many of the compounds he ran.

As an experimental physicist, Coblentz did not fully perceive the implications of his observations to the field of organic structural analysis, nor could he foresee the revolution that would be caused by the application of infrared spectrometry to chemistry.

At about the same time Friedrich Paschen, at the

University of Tübingen, was studying the emission spectra of certain elements, and he is credited with discovery of the Paschen series in the infrared emission spectrum of hydrogen. Professor H. M. Randall of the University of Michigan spent a year (1910-11) working with Paschen on the atomic spectra of cesium and rubidium and thus became acquainted with Paschen's infrared apparatus and ideas. This led him to institute a research program in infrared spectroscopy upon his return to Michigan. By this time Eva von Bahr had shown that there were fine separations in the doublet bands of HCl gas, providing evidence that the rotational energy of the HCl molecule is quantized.

Professor Randall therefore prepared to study band spectra. A high resolution prism-grating spectrometer was constructed and used by Imes and Sleator (1918-19) to study the molecular absorption spectra of the hydrogen halides and of water vapor. An active research group in experimental infrared spectroscopy and instrumentation was developed under Randall's leadership.

Applications of infrared spectrometry to chemical problems began in the 1920s. One of these applications involved the General Motors Corp. (GM) and the University of Michigan in several cooperative projects. The details have been documented by Dr. G. M. Rassweiler, a research physicist and ultimately Technical Director of Basic and Applied Sciences at the General Motors Research Laboratories. In studying the knocking characteristics of hydrocarbons, GM scientists, under the direction of "Boss" Kettering, wished to explore the possibility of identifying pure hydrocarbons and to analyze mixtures of hydrocarbons using infrared spectrometry. With the University of Michigan already actively involved in studying the infrared spectra of hydrocarbons, the contract between the University's physics department and General Motors was a natural one and represents a milestone in the progress of infrared absorption spectrometry. The cooperation, expertise, and dedication of both groups contributed much both to improvements in infrared instrumentation and to analytical methodology. The infrared spectra of 17 pure hydrocarbons were obtained by the laborious point-by-point method. In a 1933 publication of these spectra by Kettering and Slater the following statement appeared: "The spectra shown . . . suggest the possibility of a beginning in qualitative analysis of hydrocarbon mixtures by infrared spectra." In 1931 Randall and Strong described an automatic recording infrared spectrometer using optical amplification. The light beam from a primary galvanometer was allowed to fall on a thermorelay. This thermorelay generated a signal proportional to the deflection

of the galvanometer but with more energy available.
Hence a secondary galvanometer connected to the relay
gave a much amplified deflection which was recorded
directly on photographic paper mounted on a rotating
drum synchronized with the wavelength drive of the
spectrophotometer.

In 1936 another physicist, Dr. R. Bowling Barnes,
then of Princeton University, published an article in
the *Review of Scientific Instruments* entitled "Infrared
Spectra and Organic Chemistry," in which he summarized
several semi-empirical rules relating to the interpretation of infrared spectra, which had been developed
over the past 50 years. Barnes also listed some applications of infrared spectroscopy to structure determination. Also in 1936, Dudley Williams at the University
of Florida published a paper on applications of infrared
spectroscopy to the rubber industry and showed spectra
of some typical natural and synthetic rubbers.

Interest in infrared spectroscopy was growing among
some of the major chemical manufacturers, who saw the
potential value of the technique in their laboratories
and plants. Breaking into the field, however, was not
a simple task. The first step was to hire a physicist,
preferably someone with some training in the field.
These people were available from only a few schools.
The University of Michigan with H. M. Randall was a
training center for many of the infrared pioneers; other
early infrared work was done at Johns Hopkins under
Pfund, Princeton (Barnes), and Ohio State (H. H. Niel-
sen). The physicist constructed his own infrared spectrometer with a prism made from a single crystal of
natural rock salt and a radiometer or dc thermocouple
detector. After calibrating the spectrometer, he was
ready to start the tedious process of accumulating a
library of spectra and finding where the technique could
be applied to solving his employer's problems.

One such physicist, then a postdoctoral fellow at
the University of Michigan, was Norman Wright. He was
interested in using infrared and Raman spectroscopy to
analyze mixtures of amino acids. He comments:

> For some time during and even before the work
> on biological materials, I had become convinced
> that IR was a most promising method for the
> analysis of chemical mixtures, particularly
> organic compounds, and I began to seek an oppor-
> tunity somewhere to prove this. It chanced in
> 1937 that I met my friend Dr. J. D. Hanawalt,
> then director of the X-ray and Spectroscopy
> Laboratory at the Dow Chemical Company, at a
> Washington, D.C. meeting of the American Physi-
> cal Society. I showed him my IR spectra of

amino acids. He immediately proposed that I
consider coming to Dow to add IR to the spectroscopy of his laboratory, which up to then
included X-rays, ultraviolet and visible, and
my career began there on July 1, 1937.

My first task at the Dow labs was to design
and build an infrared spectrometer. (There was
no instrument commercially available even remotely adequate for the purpose.) The mechanical parts of the spectrometer were built at the
University of Michigan Physics Department by
the same machinists who had built the spectrometers for Randall's famous IR laboratory.

By November of 1937, my first spectrometer
was recording spectra, 2-14 microns (rock salt
prism) of compounds of interest to Dow workers.
By early 1938, the IR method had proven useful
in a large number of compound mixtures submitted
by both researchers and production people repre-
senting many types of chemical operations.
There was soon no longer any doubt of the great
utility of the IR method. After early 1939,
the problem was to find time for anything beyond filling urgent requests for analysis by
IR. My first assistant, Lee Gildart, joined
me in August, 1939.

Later in the year of 1939, I made my first
publication of the industrial analytical use of
IR in a talk before a local sectional ACS
meeting in Lansing, Michigan. The first talk
before a National ACS Meeting followed on
September 12, 1940 in Detroit. Entitled "Applications of IR Spectroscopy to Industrial Research," it was published in January of 1941
in *Industrial & Engineering Chemistry*.

At long last, the physicists were starting to talk
to the chemists. Norman Wright's paper represents a
milestone in the development of analytical infrared
spectroscopy, elaborating as it did on a number of specific applications of real interest to chemists, including identification of unknown organic compounds;
identification of impurities in organic compounds; quantitative analysis of impurities; studies of reaction
mechanisms and kinetics, isomerism, association, and
compound formation; polymerization of plastics; study of
geometrical isomers; calculation of thermodynamic properties; and studies of crystal structure using polarized
radiation. His infrared spectrometer, although single
beam, gave a photographic record (Figure 10) of the
2-14 μm region in 20 minutes. Perhaps the most appealing
feature of the technique (to the chemist) was its ability

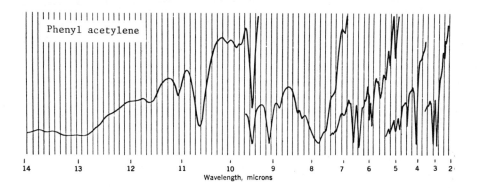

Figure 10. An infrared spectrum recorded photographically by N. Wright.

to do rapid quantitative analysis on complex mixtures of closely related materials.

Two years later, R. Bowling Barnes, U. Liddel, and Van Zandt Williams at American Cyanamid Co. published a paper on the use of infrared spectroscopy for analysis and control of monomers and polymers related to synthetic rubber. Quantitative accuracy of 1% for monomers in mixtures was claimed. Shortly thereafter, the same authors published a paper on industrial applications of infrared containing 363 partial spectra (2000 to 1000 or 800 cm^{-1}) and a small monograph, now a classic, which contained essentially the same material plus a bibliography on infrared (said by the authors to be incomplete) consisting of 2701 references! Other analytical applications by W. H. Avery of Shell Oil, R. R. Brattain of Shell Development, and W. C. Sears of B. F. Goodrich were also published during this same period. The revolution had begun.

Given impetus by wartime needs for synthetic rubber, gasoline analysis, and other industrial requirements, infrared spectroscopy proved equal to the demands placed on it and ensured its value to the chemical industry.

A major chemical research program--to determine the structure of penicillin and if possible synthesize it-- utilized infrared spectroscopy as an integral part of the project. The results of the infrared studies were later published as a monograph, which included a collection of 350 spectra, under the title "Infrared Determination of Chemical Structures" by H. M. Randall,

N. Fuson, R. G. Fowler, and J. R. Dangl. Many obstacles
remained to thwart the widespread adoption of the technique, however. The difficulty of accurately detecting
the small signal and the need for a highly competent
instrumentalist to construct and to operate the spectrometer were two of the most critical problems.

This situation was partially remedied in 1944 when
the Perkin-Elmer Corp. introduced the model 12-A infrared spectrometer. This was a single-beam instrument,
similar to the one built in 1936 at American Cyanamid.
It used a thermocouple detector, whose response was read
with a galvanometer. Shortly thereafter an improved
model 12-B appeared, which used an electronic recorder
to record the spectrum. The signal was subject to drift
from temperature gradients and other outside interferences. If a complete spectrum were desired, point-by-
point calculation and replotting of the data was necessary, but it was a commercial spectrometer on which
spectra could be obtained by relatively unskilled technicians. Other instrumentation had been available previously; both Gaertner and Hilger had built and sold
spectrometers suitable for infrared spectroscopy that
contained mirrors and a rock salt prism but no detector.
National Technical Laboratories, starting in about 1942,
marketed the IR-1 (the first of Beckman Instrument's
line of infrared spectrometers), which was a manual
wavelength setting, manual readout instrument. A significant improvement occurred with the construction of
thermocouple detectors whose response was fast enough to
allow chopping the radiation beam at 13 cps. The Perkin-
Elmer model 12-C had a stable signal and with the addition of a cable-driven variable slit drive to compensate
for the changing emissivity of the source gave a reasonably presentable infrared spectrum.

The principal analytical application of infrared
in the early days was quantitative analysis. To obtain
a qualitative spectrum, one had to calculate and to
replot transmission data; quantitative data at a few
fixed wavelengths could be obtained comparatively easily.
Further, even to this day, quantitative data from a
single-beam spectrometer are more accurate than those
from a double-beam spectrometer.

During the period 1940-46 the Dow group had developed the first double-beam optical null recording spectrometer which presented the spectrum in the format
that is customary today--per cent transmission (ordinate)
against wavelength (abscissa). This instrument was a
prototype of the Baird Associates infrared recording
spectrometer introduced in 1947. At Perkin-Elmer, John
White and Max Liston were developing a double-beam optical null spectrometer, the model 21, which was

commercialized in 1949. National Technical Laboratories used a different system in their IR-3, which was a double beam-in-time spectrometer that used a variable slit, programmed to give constant energy throughout by a magnetic wire memory.

A good summary of the status of infrared instrumentation and techniques in 1948 was written by Van Zandt Williams, then of American Cyanamid, later with Perkin-Elmer.

Having finally discovered the value of infrared, analytical chemists went all out to exploit it. The 1950s were years of ferment, and new developments in techniques, instrumentation, and applications paraded monthly through the journals and scientific meetings. Full-time practitioners became skilled specialists in manipulating samples and interpreting spectra.

In 1957 Perkin-Elmer introduced a low-cost bench top infrared spectrometer, the model 137, which was designed to bring infrared spectroscopy into every chemist's laboratory. This development was not an unmixed blessing; the infrared specialist was relieved of solving some of the obvious or routine problems, but on the other hand, underexperienced and overenthusiastic chemists sometimes misused the technique or misinterpreted their spectra. The result was some disenchantment with infrared and a growing reliance on newer, more glamorous techniques. Thus, the revolution continued with gas chromatography, NMR, mass spectrometry, liquid chromatography and others; each came to the forefront before settling into its proper place in the laboratory operation.

However, the field has continued to advance. Key developments that have made possible the sophisticated instrumentation of the 1960s include the use of gratings blazed to concentrate radiation into one or two orders, along with dielectric wavelength filters for order isolation, and more reliable electronics which utilize solid state devices.

Quantitative infrared spectroscopy also found its place in the industrial plants which manufactured chemicals and petroleum products. As early as 1930 H. Schmick had patented a non-dispersive infrared gas analyzer. Subsequently, improvements were described by A. H. Pfund, K. F. Luft, and others, including N. Wright and L. Herscher in 1946. Other infrared process stream analyzers, both dispersive and non-dispersive, were developed and became commercially available during the 1950s. Most of these, however, were eventually supplemented by less expensive analyzers such as gas chromatographic or other systems. Nevertheless, in some situations, infrared is the only practical on-stream analysis method available.

As libraries of infrared spectra grew to include several thousand spectra, the problem of matching the spectrum of an unknown substance with a spectrum already on file became acute. In the early 1950s, L. E. Kuntzel of Wyandotte Chemicals developed a retrieval system based on the use of precision-punched, machine-sorted cards in which the presence of absorption bands and chemical groups were coded by punched holes. This system was adopted and marketed by the American Society for Testing and Materials, and the data base was later used for computer searches of vast quantities of data. This retrieval system increased the usefulness of infrared as a qualitative tool manyfold, transferring as it did the burden of identification in many cases from the spectroscopist's memory to a routine operation.

The 1950s and 1960s also saw much activity in group frequency correlations--that is, correlating shifts in group frequencies with structural or electronic features of the molecules being studied. Many publications and several monographs resulted from this activity, which now seems to have reached a point of diminishing returns. Most recently (1970s), development of computers as "learning machines" by T. L. Isenhour and others has pointed the way toward virtually automatic interpretation of spectra, although it is unlikely that the spectroscopist will ever be replaced by the computer.

Although the interferometer was invented by A. A. Michelson in 1891 and used by W. Weniger to measure transmissions in the far infrared in 1923, the first person actually to calculate a spectrum from an interferogram, using a numerical Fourier transform, was Peter Fellgett in 1949. Use of the interferometer for measuring infrared spectra was not considered practicable, however; the advantage of higher radiation throughput (and thus shorter measurement time) was more than cancelled by the long computation time (several hours on a large computer). The technique was attractive for studying the low-energy, far-infrared region, however, and some applications in this region developed. In 1966 the Cooley-Tukey fast-Fourier transform algorithm was developed, which allowed calculations of the spectrum from the interferogram in a few minutes. Commercial mid-infrared interferometers were not long in coming; these instruments when integrated with dedicated minicomputers have produced a powerful new kind of infrared spectrometer that is being exploited in situations involving low energy, such as micro samples, rapid-scan techniques for on-the-fly gas-chromatography fraction identification, infrared emission spectrography, and other special applications. More recently, semiconductive laser IR spectrometers and gas (CO_2, CO) laser IR gas-analyzing spectrometers have become available.

Vibrational Spectroscopy: Raman. The scattering of light by various media had long been studied (Rayleigh 1871, Einstein 1910, and others), but no change of wavelength had been observed, with the sole exception of certain types of scattering in the x-ray spectral region (Compton, 1923). That scattering with change of wavelength was theoretically possible had been predicted by A. Smekal in Germany (1923), but it remained for Sir C. V. Raman, of Calcutta University, India, in 1928, to discover this effect. (Raman was apparently unaware of the publication by Smekal.) Professor Raman has recently commented on his discovery [quoted from *The Spex Speaker*, April 1966 (Spex Industries, Inc.)]:

> Looking back over many years of sustained scientific activity, I recall two periods, each of a few months, which stand out vividly in my memory by reason of their having opened new vistas of research which were later followed up. The first period was from September 1921 to February 1922. Experimental studies made during that time established the proposition that the molecular scattering of light in a transparent medium is a universal phenomenon exhibited in various degrees by all such materials, viz., crystalline solids, glasses, liquids, and gases. It was thereby made evident that the study of the scattering of light is a fruitful pathway for the exploration of the structure of matter.

> The second period was from September 1927 to February 1928. It began with my attempts to reconcile the apparent conflict between the ideas of wave-optics and Einstein's idea that light consists of discrete quanta of energy. That a reconciliation was possible between these two concepts of the nature of light was demonstrated by my success in deducing on the basis of the classical wave-principles, the existence, as well as the characters, of the two types of x-ray scattering, respectively with and without a change of frequency. This elucidation of the Compton effect suggested fresh experimental studies on the scattering of light making use of monochromatic radiation. These studies led to the discovery of the type of light-scattering in which a change of frequency manifests itself.

> It may seem surprising but it was neverthe-

less the case that the new phenomenon was, in the first instance, observed visually. This was possible by reason of the availability in the mercury arc lamp of a powerful source of monochromatic light and because also of the extreme sensitivity of the human eye to feeble light under appropriate conditions. The observations which showed the universality of the phenomenon and revealed its origin were all made visually, using a pocket spectroscope of the direct-vision type. They were later confirmed using the photographically recorded spectra.

While infrared spectroscopy was developing rapidly during the 1940s, Raman spectroscopy found only limited analytical applications. The major drawbacks to the technique were the extremely weak signal,[*] which had to be recorded photographically during exposures of several hours and the fact that any fluorescence from trace impurities or from the sample itself often completely overwhelmed the Raman spectrum. Early work was directed toward improving sources, and the mercury arc--filtered to give essentially monochromatic radiation from one of the prominent mercury lines--became the standard source. A fast spectrograph of high aperture and good wavelength discrimination was needed; spectrographs for Raman work were usually constructed by the researcher or adapted from existing commercial monochromators. In the early 1940s, an f/3 Raman instrument using three glass prisms and Schmidt-type camera was introduced by the Lane-Wells Corp. (Pasadena, Calif.). In 1940 R. C. Lord, Jr., and Foil A. Miller at Johns Hopkins University constructed a fast plane grating spectrograph for Raman work. An instrument based on this design was described, in 1945, by R. F. Stamm (American Cyanamid), who also discussed analytical applications of the technique. Under the heading of qualitative analysis, he included: (1) following the progress of distillations and (2) detecting certain chemical groups such as nitriles, conjugated olefins, and aromatics. Quantitative analysis was applied to multicomponent mixtures. Stamm also pointed out some of the pitfalls of Raman spectroscopy. Problems with fluorescence, scarcity of equipment, and the time required for analysis were all major drawbacks that undoubtedly stifled the development of analytical Raman

---

[*]For liquid samples, the total intensity of the molecular scattering is of the order of 10^{-5} of the total intensity, and only 1% of this contributes to the Raman spectrum.

spectroscopy. Its one major advantage over infrared was that water solutions could be easily handled, but in most industrial applications, this feature was not particularly significant. Nevertheless, some petroleum companies found the method valuable for hydrocarbon analysis.

In 1946 the first Raman grating spectrometer with photoelectric detection was described by D. H. Rank and R. V. Wiegand at Penn State, and in 1947 Rank and co-workers published a catalog of Raman spectra for 172 pure hydrocarbons. Photoelectric detection eliminated the necessity of photographing the spectrum and accelerated the data gathering. In 1953 introduction of the highly sophisticated Cary model 81 gave considerable impetus to Raman spectrometry. Invention of the laser was followed shortly by its application as a monochromatic Raman source; in 1962 S. P. S. Porto and D. L. Wood reported use of a pulsed ruby laser for exciting Raman spectra. Commercial instrumentation was introduced shortly thereafter and has proliferated to the point where Raman systems to suit all tastes and budgets are now available. Use of lasers having different exciting wavelengths has to some extent overcome problems of sample fluorescence, and the ability to focus the laser beam to a very small spot has meant that micro-sized samples can be examined with comparative ease.

<u>Rotational Spectroscopy (Far IR and Microwave)</u>. The molecular rotation regions of the spectrum--i.e., the far infrared ($200-10$ cm^{-1}) and microwave regions ($10-0.1$ cm^{-1}) have not found extensive analytical application. The far infrared region is experimentally difficult because of the low energy available and because of background radiation from the spectrometer components. In fact, working in this region is like trying to do visible spectrometry with a white-hot spectrograph! It is therefore interesting that H. M. Randall and F. A. Firestone at the University of Michigan were able to measure the rotational spectrum of NH_3 in 1938 with a high resolution, far infrared spectrometer. Although some group frequency correlation work has been done in the 1950s and 60s by Freeman Bentley and others, this spectral region has not proved as analytically useful as the mid-infrared.

In 1934 C. E. Cleeton and N. H. Williams at the University of Michigan used a magnetron oscillator and echelette grating to study inversion doubling in NH_3 at 0.8 cm^{-1}. Following development of the klystron oscillator and radar technology, a number of laboratories became involved in microwave investigations of gases, principally as a tool for determining molecular structures. Another significant advance occurred in the

1960s with the development of the backwardwave oscillator, which covered a wider frequency range than the klystron tube and gave an almost constant intensity over that range.

Microwave spectroscopy is probably unsurpassed for positive qualitative identification of many molecular species--there is no ambiguity about the identification. On the other hand, some of its limitations are rather severe. The sample must be somewhat volatile, it must have a dipole moment, and sensitivity is best if the molecule is not too complex. Most critical, however, is the problem of adsorption and desorption of water and other materials on the surface of the metal waveguides. This phenomenon severely restricts quantitative analysis because of cross contamination between samples. Other instrumental techniques can be used to obtain the same analytical information, and little analytical microwave spectroscopy is now being done.

Fluorometry and Phosphorimetry. Luminescence is the generic term for those phenomena in which certain molecular or ionic species absorb energy from any of numerous possible sources and subsequently re-emit energy in the form of visible radiation. Fluorescence is that form of luminescence resulting from the absorption of radiant energy, causing electrons to be raised to excited states, after which they fall back to their normal (ground) states with emission of radiation of lower frequency. Phosphorescence is due to similar excitation, followed by intersystem crossing to a metastable excited triplet level, from which the transition to the ground state is less favored, hence delayed. In addition to these, luminescence may be produced by such other processes as chemical activation (chemiluminescence), electrical excitation (electroluminescence), and mechanical agitation (triboluminescence).

An Italian shoemaker and alchemist, Vincenzo Casciarolo, in the early 17th century, became involved with luminescence phenomena when he prepared a new colored material by heating "Bologna stones" (heavy spar, barite), with coal and noticed that at night this material gave off a continuous bluish glow (phosphorescence). This material, called "lapis solaris," created much interest. About the same time it was noted that an aqueous extract obtained from wood, "lignum nephriticum," also produced a unique blue luminescence--the object of much study and speculation. About 1852 G. G. Stokes, using complementary filters, showed that the phenomenon is caused by the absorption of certain wavelengths of sunlight with emission of another wavelength of light. Stokes stated as a general principle that the emitted radiation is always equal to or longer in wavelength than the excitation energy. He is also credited with coining the term "fluorescence." Respecting the accepted name, "dispersive reflexion," he remarks:

> I confess I do not like this term. I am almost inclined to coin a word, and call the appearance 'fluorescence,' from fluor-spar, as the analogous term 'opalescence' is derived from the name of a mineral.

Spectrofluorometry. In 1868 the German chemist Friedrich Goppelsröder used the natural dye morin as a fluorescent reagent for aluminum. Many organic compounds, particularly dyes and plant pigments, exhibit fluorescence, and some of those substances in which the effect is critically dependent on pH have been used as indicators in acid-base titrations. However, most earlier analytical applications of fluorescence were in qualitative identification of substances. F. Feigl used fluorescent effects in many of his spot tests. The first six volumes of the *Analytical Edition of Industrial and Engineering Chemistry* (1929-1934) contain only two papers on fluorescence: A. L. Glantz used the characteristic fluorescent colors of virgin and adulterated olive oil to detect adulteration at the 5% level; and the fluorescent characteristic of rayon was investigated using a special ultraviolet microscope illuminator. In 1935 G. H. Damon suggested the estimation of traces of oxygen based on its effect on the intense green fluorescence of pure acetone vapor. In 1937 there were two papers, one dealing with a new fluorescent test for aluminum by C. E. White and C. S. Lowe, and a visual fluorescence estimation method for riboflavin using standards containing sodium fluorescein. It was the fluorescence of vitamins that did much to accelerate the development of quantitative fluorometric determinations and suitable instrumentation.

Visual comparison of unknown and reference fluorescent standards, analogous to the standard series technique used in colorimetric analysis, was used in early quantitative work. Thus, in 1925 Lutz determined zinc at about 0.2-10 ppm levels with less than 10% error using Nessler tubes. Illumination with ultraviolet radiation was usually from the bottom of the tubes. Visual viewboxes were sometimes used. The Pulfrich photometer, with appropriate filters to remove the ultraviolet before the incident beam reaches the eye, was also used to compare fluorescence intensities. Early reports on the use of photoelectric detectors included those of Matheson and Noyes (1938) for measuring the fluorescence of acetone, Cohen (1935) for lactoflavins,

and Hand (1939) for determining riboflavin in milk.
About this time photoelectric fluorometers appeared on
the market. Instruments soon were available from Photo-
volt Corp., Klett Manufacturing Co., Pfaltz and Bauer,
Coleman Electric Co., Fisher Scientific Co., Central
Scientific Co., and Farrand Instrument Co. The Fisher
and Farrand instruments used photomultiplier tubes. In
addition, fluorescence attachments for several brands
of spectrophotometers became available.

Two commercial spectrofluorometers, the Aminco-Bow-
man (American Instrument Co.) and the Farrand, based on
the work of R. L. Bowman and S. Udenfriend, were first
marketed in 1956-57. These two-monochromator instruments
featured xenon arcs as ultraviolet sources and were designed for use with external recorders. Hence it was
now possible to determine both excitation and emission
fluorescence spectra. The Baird-Atomic Fluorispec, the
Turner model 210 Spectrofluorometer, and the Perkin-Elmer
Spectrophotofluorometer were marketed later. The availability of reliable instrumentation and the improved
sensitivity of fluorometry over spectrophotometry led
to a rapid increase of fluorometric methods, both in
routine analysis and in research.

It is difficult to document the most significant
analytical contributions made in spectrofluorometry, but
several names belong on the record. Professor Charles
E. White of the University of Maryland was a pioneer in
the fluorometric analysis of inorganic substances. His
periodic reviews, dating back to 1939, brought the latest
developments to the attention of analytical chemists.
B. L. van Duuren, S. Udenfriend, G. G. Guilbault, J. D.
Winefordner, D. M. Hercules, and E. Sawicki are among
others who have been closely associated with progress
in this field. Measurements which are capable of detecting and quantifying substances at the 0.1-ppb level
play an important role in assays in agricultural chemistry, biochemistry, clinical pathology, medicine, pharmaceutical analysis, pharmacology, and many research
problems.

Phosphorimetry. The advent of commercial spectrofluorometers ushered in phosphorescence as a potential
analytical technique, inasmuch as many of the same instruments could be adapted to phosphorimeters by the
addition of a relatively simple phosphoroscope and low
temperature sample compartment. It is somewhat of a
paradox that those factors which make phosphorimetry a
more difficult technique than fluorometry are responsible
for the main advantages of the method--namely, sensitivity and selectivity. The enhanced sensitivity is due
to the larger quantum efficiencies that result primarily

from working at 77°K rather than at room temperature. Differences in phosphorescent lifetimes often provide selectivity, if not specificity, in dealing with mixtures of several phosphorescent species. For example, time-resolved phosphorimetry has been used successfully to analyze a ternary mixture of halogenated biphenyls.

Sample preparation consists of dissolving the sample in a rigid transparent glass. A 5:5:2 mixture of diethyl ether, isopentane, and ethanol, designated EPA, introduced by G. N. Lewis and M. Kasha in 1944, is commonly used.

Spectrophosphorimetry as an analytical tool was first brought to the attention of chemists by R. J. Keirs, R. D. Britt, Jr., and W. E. Wentworth, of Florida State University, writing in *Analytical Chemistry* in 1957.

Spectropolarimetry. In 1818 the French physicist J. B. Biot, observed that several naturally occurring organic compounds, such as sugar, tartaric acid, turpentine, and camphor, had the unusual property of rotating the plane of polarized light. However, Berzelius, in 1831, isolated a sample of tartaric acid that was optically inactive, thus posing a dilemma. It was not until 1848 that Louis Pasteur unraveled this puzzle. In studying the crystal structure of sodium ammonium tartrate, an optically inactive salt, Pasteur noted that some of the crystals appeared to be mirror images of others. After painstakingly separating the two kinds of crystals, he prepared two solutions of the same concentration from the two types and measured their optical rotation. The two solutions rotated the plane of polarized light by the same amount but in opposite directions. Hence the mixture of the two forms of an active compound becomes inactive (a racemic mixture), and this was the nature of the tartaric acid sample of Berzelius. The correlation of optical activity with the presence of an asymmetric carbon atom in dissymetric organic compounds was first made by Le Bel and van't Hoff in 1874.

When plane polarized light traverses an optically active medium, the right and left circularly polarized components generally travel at different speeds--a phenomenon known as circular birefringence. Upon emergence from the active medium, the resultant of the two components is plane polarized but with the plane of polarization rotated with respect to the incident beam. The amount of rotation depends on the inequality of n_R and n_L, the refractive indices exhibited by the optically active medium with respect to the two circular components. The optical rotation thus depends on the wavelength of the incident radiation. Optical rotatory dispersion (ORD) is the term used to designate this change in rotation with wavelength. In 1895 A. Cotton discovered that in the region of a spectral absorption band, the refractive indices and the molar absorptivities of the two components of plane polarized radiation vary, hence producing elliptical polarization. The measurement of molecular optical rotation in the vicinity of absorption bands gives very characteristic ORD plots, now commonly called Cotton-effect curves. The measurement of the difference in the molecular absorptivities of the left- and right-hand components of the circularly polarized radiation, the circular dichroism (CD), also gives a characteristic plot when molecular ellipticity is plotted against wavelength.

However, prior to 1955 most polarimetric measurements were made using monochromatic light, either the yellow-green line of a mercury vapor lamp (546 nm) or the yellow sodium line (589 nm). Polarimetric measurements were used to determine the concentration of optically active substances, but precautions were needed because of the variation in specific rotation with concentration. Extensive methodology was developed, particularly for the analysis of sugar products, and has been thoroughly documented by F. J. Bates of the National Bureau of Standards.

The first commercial photoelectric spectropolarimeter, manufactured by O. C. Rudolph in 1953, was used by Professor Carl Djerassi and his students at Wayne State University in ORD studies of steroids. Djerassi demonstrated the correlation of certain features of the ORD curves with structural moieties and thereby showed that spectropolarimetry was of value in structural analysis. Some of the major manufacturers of instruments designed to measure optical rotation at one or a few wavelengths are O. C. Rudolph and Sons, Carl Zeiss, the Perkin-Elmer Corp., Japan Spectroscopic Co. (JASCO), and Bellingham and Stanley. Some of these manufacturers also produced recording ORD instruments designed to cover the ultraviolet and visible regions. Howard Cary and co-workers (in 1964) designed and manufactured a precise recording instrument--the Cary model 60 Spectropolarimeter--which was later modified to do CD as well as ORD. Cary Instrument Co., JASCO, Jouan, and Jobin-Yvon have produced instruments for CD only.

Besides the simple determination of concentrations of optically active substances, polarimetric techniques have been used to study the kinetics and reaction mechanisms of ligand exchange reactions. In 1960 Dwyer and co-workers determined the rate of loss of optical activity, the half-life of optically active ligand exchange, and related phenomena of many metal complexes. C. N.

Reilley and his students (1967) combined optical rotation measurements with NMR to study symmetrical and unsymmetrical ligand exchange.

Kirschner and Bhatnagar, in 1963, used spectropolarimetric titrimetry to study metal ions, strong and weak acids and bases, optically active and inactive ligands, and the number of ligands per metal ion in complexes. In 1970 Pearson and co-workers, utilizing a digital photoelectric spectropolarimeter with flowthrough capabilities, analyzed successfully for many metal ions by means of a stereospecific optically active ligand.

Both ORD and CD have been used extensively in the structural analysis of hormones, proteins, and related polymers. These techniques have also been useful in the structure determinations of many inorganic complexes. Recent advances in instrumentation, including computer interfacing, magnetic techniques (MC, MORD), and differential techniques (DCD, DORD) extend the possible analytical applications of spectroscopy based on optical activity.

X-RAY SPECTROCHEMICAL ANALYSIS

The Early Years. What a fascinating time it was for chemistry and physics in the early 1900s. The university research system was at its peak whereas industrial or government laboratories of stature were almost nonexistent. Personal animosities and national jealousies were strong, based on support of various unproved theories. The competition to "get into print" first was even more fierce than it is today. Thus it was, less than 70 years ago, when x-ray spectroscopy sprang forth suddenly, with many of its principles and capabilities completely obvious in that first historic paper by H. G. J. Moseley in December 1913. In that paper x-ray spectra were shown for Ca, Ti, V, Cr, Mn, Fe, Co, Ni, Cu, and Zn. Each element gave two lines, the $K\alpha$ and $K\beta$ (Figure 11). Moseley stated the simple relationship between frequency, ν, of the $K\alpha$ line and the atomic number, Z (his paper called it N).

$$\nu = (3/4)\nu_0 (Z - \sigma_n)^2$$

These simple, beautiful spectra were photographed with a crystal spectrometer, and the diffraction angle was measured to $\pm 0.1°$. Impurity lines were recognized by their low intensity and the prophetic comment of Moseley:

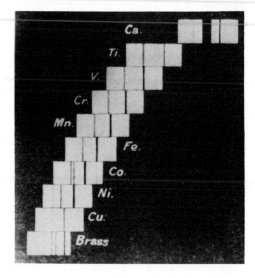

Figure 11. Characteristic x-ray emission spectra according to Moseley. .

The prevalence of lines due to impurities suggests that this may prove a powerful method of chemical analysis. Its advantages over ordinary spectroscopic methods lies in the simplicity of the spectra and the impossibility of one substance masking the radiation from another. It may even lead to the discovery of missing elements, as it will be possible to predict the position of their characteristic lines.

This first paper to show x-ray spectra from a continuous series of elements encompassed nearly all the principles used today in x-ray analysis--the simple relationship between λ and Z, the obvious relationship between intensity and concentration, and the near independence of wavelength on physical state or chemical combination. To appreciate the situation in chemistry and physics at the time of Moseley's work, several factors must be considered.

The Argument of Atomic Weight vs. Atomic Number. Chemists in the early 1900s still held firmly to Mendeleev's principle that the chemical properties of an element depended unambiguously on its atomic weight. However, physicists, under the leadership of Niels Bohr in Copenhagen and Ernest Rutherford in Manchester, were busy exploring the physics of the atom and showing that the charge on the nucleus should be important in determining the properties and reactions of the elements.

In particular, it was known from Rutherford's α scattering experiments that a rather uniform 2:1 relationship existed between atomic weight and nuclear charge. In Amsterdam, van den Broek interpreted this to mean that since the known charge on He was 2, the charge on H must be 1, and that since the atomic weight varied by two units from element to element, the nuclear charge must vary by unity from one element to the next in the periodic table. This charge he called atomic number.

The Early Confused Knowledge of X-Rays. After x-rays were discovered in 1895 by W. C. Röntgen, they were quickly applied in medical radiography, and scientists began to investigate their properties. Before 1910 C. G. Barkla at Liverpool knew that different elements, when excited by primary radiation from an x-ray tube, emitted secondary radiation which had different absorption properties in aluminum foil. He called this secondary radiation "characteristic rays" as contrasted with the "general rays" given off by the x-ray tube. Barkla also knew that some of the characteristic rays from an element were much more penetrating than other rays from the same element. He named the more penetrating rays the K series and the less penetrating rays the L series. (He started in the middle of the alphabet because he presumed that other series would be found later on both sides of the K and L series. He later thought he had observed a J series, and this notion persisted until 1922 when F. K. Richtmyer finally dispelled it.) Barkla and his co-workers A. J. Philpot and C. A. Sadler as well as J. S. Kay and later R. Whiddington all considered these "characteristic rays" to be electromagnetic waves and thought they could *only* be excited by higher energy x-rays. Then in 1912 R. T. Beatty at Cambridge did experiments to prove that "characteristic rays" could be excited directly by electrons as well as by general x-rays. If this seems bizarre when looking back at those early years, remember that the x-ray spectra were not easy to recognize as the rainbow which God made for us.

A big step forward toward the understanding of x-rays came from Munich in April 1912 when W. Friedrich and P. Knipping, under the direction of M. von Laue, published the first x-ray crystal diffraction patterns. They interpreted the patterns as wave interference but thought that the diffracted waves were the "characteristic rays" of Barkla generated within the crystal. The renowned W. H. Bragg at Leeds suspected that the Germans had misinterpreted the diffraction patterns. He contended that x-rays were corpuscular rather than waves because of the way they transferred energy to secondary electrons in a gas. He is reported to have said that if x-rays were waves, their known ability to transfer their entire energy to a secondary electron could no more occur than could a spreading water wave produced by the fall of a rock encounter an identical rock, surrender its entire energy, and project it to the height from which the original fell. Then W. L. Bragg, the son of W. H. Bragg and an undergraduate at Cambridge, observed that the spots on the Laue x-ray patterns seemed related to "avenues" in the crystal lattice and thus were characteristic of the crystal rather than of the x-rays. At first he tried to reconcile the passage of corpuscles through the crystal lattice but soon was forced to conclude that x-rays had to be treated as waves. Shortly thereafter he formulated the simple law which bears his name: $n\lambda = 2d \sin \theta$ where n is the order of diffraction, λ is the wavelength, θ is the angle of incidence between the incident x-rays and planes in the crystal, and d is the spacing between planes. His father, W. H. Bragg, accepted the dual nature of x-rays (particles and waves) and constructed a crystal spectrometer with which the father and son went on to measure x-ray spectra. By November 1912 W. L. Bragg was getting spots by reflection from mica, and he published his results in *Nature* in December.

Enter Moseley. Young Henry Moseley had graduated from Oxford in 1910 and obtained an appointment as demonstrator and lecturer in physics at the laboratory of the already famous Rutherford in Manchester. There he worked on radioactive decay as did all of Rutherford's students. As an aside, it must be said that in today's jargon Moseley was somewhat of an operator; he was personable, capable, accustomed to converting others to his beliefs and to having his own way. Having read the work of Friedrich and Knipping in the spring of 1912, Moseley quickly became interested in x-rays. With the help of mathematician C. G. Darwin, he set out independently of the Braggs to explain the German results which he thought had been improperly explained. Moseley and Darwin arrived at an explanation similar to that of Bragg but found that the Braggs were ahead of them and already well along with the crystal spectrometer and ionization detector. Therefore they adopted the experimental approach of the Braggs and set out to measure the "ionizing properties" of the diffracted x-rays. Here again they were only shortly behind the Braggs, who sent their first results to *Nature* on 7 January 1913; they sent their own results confirming the Braggs on 21 January 1913. By July of 1913 Moseley and Darwin had published a careful study of the diffraction of the continuous and characteristic spectrum from a Pt target x-ray tube. They were explicit in stating that the characteristic

lines were the same as the characteristic rays Barkla
had noted earlier.

In the early summer of 1913 Rutherford had been
visited by Bohr from Copenhagen. Bohr and Moseley discussed atomic theory and x-ray spectra at length (von
Hevesy of later fame in x-ray chemical analysis was also
present at those discussions). By that time the physicists, particularly Bohr, were well on the way to formu-
lating concepts of the atom. Moseley is known to have
suggested that x-rays should help resolve the argument
between atomic weight and atomic number, particularly
for anomalous pairs of elements such as Co and Ni. In
the late summer of 1913 Moseley set up the apparatus for
measuring x-ray lines from a series of elements. He
reverted to a photographic plate to record the lines
because of the difficulties in stabilizing the output of
the pumped x-ray tube and because of the spatial irregu-
larities in the intensity diffracted by the crystal (now
known as the topography of the crystal). By mid-November
he had measured the lines for all elements from Ca to
Zn (except Sc). His historic publication in the December
1913 issue of *Philosophical Magazine* was followed early
in 1914 by further publication of spectra for the additional elements Al, Si, Cl, K, Yt, Zr, Nb, Mo, Ru, Pd,
and Ag. The diagram from his 1914 *Philosophical Magazine* publication left no room for doubt about the simple
relationship between atomic number and x-ray spectra.

At the end of November 1913, Moseley had returned
to Oxford as an independent, self-supporting investigator
in Townsend's laboratory (the paid appointment he had
sought having been given to another applicant). It was
from Oxford that he published the second paper. It was
there also in June 1914 that Moseley was visited by
Georges Urbain from France, who brought samples of rare
earths to be analyzed by the new method. In particular
Urbain wanted confirmation of element 72 which he thought
he had discovered in 1911 and had named Celtium. (Urbain
thought element 72 was a rare earth, and it was not until
atomic physicists showed definitely that 72 should be
homologous to Zr that it was finally found in Norwegian
zircon by D. Coster and G. von Hevesy in 1922 using x-ray
spectra.) However, Moseley's measurements of Urbain's
samples showed no element 72; neither did they show the
then accepted "thulium II" which was expected to be present. They did show mixtures of rare earths, and Moseley
was able to estimate the concentrations of the different
elements.

In the fall of 1914, after a trip to Australia where
he presented a paper on the x-ray method, Moseley en-
listed in the British army and was subsequently killed
in action 10 August 1915 on the Gallipoli peninsula

during the Dardinelles campaign. It is always fruitless
to speculate on what might have been, but there seems no
doubt that had Moseley lived, his clear insight and experimental as well as theoretical capability would have
given him a leadership role in the chemistry and physics
of his time.

    The Years From 1914 to 1932. Even before Moseley's
first publication of spectral series in December 1913,
M. de Broglie in Paris had used a rotating crystal to
overcome the irregular diffraction intensity noted by
the Braggs and Moseley with their stationary crystals.
By the summer of 1914 de Broglie had also gone to fluorescent excitation by placing the sample close outside
the x-ray tube where it could be excited by primary
radiation passing through a thin window. This fluorescent excitation allowed the measurement of volatile or
low-melting elements and was a most important advance.
Unfortunately, the technique was overlooked and not
adopted again until 1948 when H. Friedman and L. S.
Birks at the Naval Research Laboratory in Washington
employed it in what was to become the renaissance of
x-ray spectrochemical analysis. (D. Coster and Y.
Nishina in 1925 and R. Glocker and H. Schreiber in 1928
used secondary fluorescence inside an x-ray tube but
seemed unaware of de Broglie's earlier work. More about
this later.)
    The measurement of x-ray spectra spread quickly to
universities throughout Europe and elsewhere after 1914,
but it was not until 1920, after the war ended, that the
number of papers mushroomed to tremendous proportions.
M. Siegbahn lists over 1500 x-ray papers in the years
from 1920 through 1930, but they were primarily measurements of spectral lines and interpretations of atomic
physics. Many were concerned with valence effects on
emission lines and absorption edges, but, disappoint-
ingly, less than 30 were specifically concerned with
chemical analysis.
    In 1922 A. Hadding at Lund in Sweden published the
first x-ray paper with the words "quantitative analysis"
in the title. His conclusions were, however, that quantitative analysis was not promising because it was too
difficult to relate intensity to photographic blackening
on the film. He proposed to continue working on the
problem, but nothing was heard from him thereafter.
Also in 1922 A. Dauvillier in Paris published x-ray confirmation of Urbain's rare earth celtium (72), but his
work was soon to be discredited. In 1923 Coster and
von Hevesy, who expected element 72 to be a metal,
searched for and found lines definitely ascribed to the
element in Norwegian zircon. They named it hafnium

after the Latin name for Copenhagen just as Urbain had
named it celtium after the Latin name for Paris. Coster,
writing in *Philosophical Magazine* in 1923, went on to
explain Dauvillier's lines as K or L lines from impurities in the rare earths he was examining. In 1925
Walter Noddack and Ida Tacke (Miss Tacke later became
Mrs. Noddack) of the Physico-Technical Office in Berlin,
and Otto Berg of the Siemens and Halske Co. observed
x-ray lines from element 75 which they named rhenium
after the Rhine river.

It is interesting that much of the early x-ray work
was concerned with minerals. Partly this stemmed from
the difficulty of their analysis by other chemical methods, but partly it stemmed from their refractive nature
and ability to withstand electron bombardment and heating
when rubbed into the metal target of the x-ray tube.
von Hevesy recognized the general difficulties with
volatilization and chemical change caused by direct excitation and suggested the fluorescent concept described
by Coster and Nishina in 1925 and independently by
Glocker and Schreiber in 1928 (de Broglie's early work
seemed to have been forgotten). Figure 12 shows the
arrangement schematically. Since the specimen was at
the cathode potential, it was not subjected to electron
bombardment and therefore was not heated to volatilization. In addition, the high background intensity of the
continuum was eliminated (except for scattering). The
intensities were very low compared with direct excitation
however, and fluorescent excitation was not adopted
generally for x-ray analysis.

Before going on, we must return to the problem of
accurate x-ray intensity measurements. The Braggs had
used ionization chambers for which it was originally

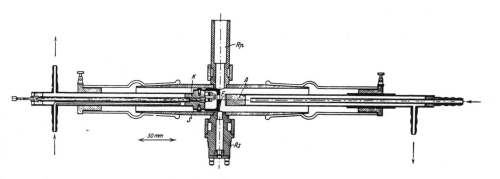

Figure 12. Coster's x-ray tube.

assumed that the amount of ionization was an accurate
measurement of x-ray photon energy and therefore could
be converted to intensity if one knew the energy (wavelength). Arthur H. Compton in 1916 had refined the
Braggs' approach by using the current from the ionization
chamber to deflect a galvanometer; a beam of light reflected from the galvanometer mirror recorded the spectrum on a roll of bromide paper. However, L. Krieges-
mann at Bonn and others had shown later that the ionization was wavelength dependent; L. Grebe explained this
on the basis of Compton effect. Likewise the difficulties with photographic film had long been recognized.
So now we turn to the work of Hans Geiger in 1913 who
experimented with discharges in gases and used the avalanche principle discovered by Townsend (it was Townsend's laboratory at Oxford where Moseley went in 1913).
It was E. Jönsson at Upsala in 1927 who first used the
idea of photon counting in the Geiger counter to measure
accurate intensities of x-ray series lines. Incidentally
he also made use of full-wave rectified, constant potential x-ray tube operation which did not become popular
again until the 1950s. Again we may ask as we did of
de Broglie's early fluorescent excitation, why was Jönsson's work with Geiger counters not recognized as important and utilized for chemical analysis?

We go forward now to the work of C. E. Eddy and
T. H. Laby in Melbourne, Australia, in 1929 and 1930.
They are often credited with the first quantitative
chemical analysis using x-rays, and perhaps rightly so.
Strangely enough, however, they knew of Gunther and
Stranski's work on the effect of an interfering element
on the intensity of the element being measured but disagreed with the conclusions and chose to ignore it.
They also mention the Geiger counter as a detector but
chose photographic film. Their results on alloys were
spectacular; they could measure down to 3 ppm of Fe in
Zn and also measured Pb and other elements at low concentrations. Their average of several measurements
agreed with wet chemical analysis to within 0.1%. Eddy
and Laby made two interesting comments: they concluded
that x-ray analysis was much more important for alloys
than it was for minerals where most of the previous work
had been concentrated. They also concluded that the
only reason x-ray analysis was not being more widely
used, in spite of its advantages, was that x-ray equipment was more expensive than that for other techniques.
(The expense argument is still heard today in spite of
the proved overall lower cost per element for x-ray
analysis.)

Where were the Americans in all this early x-ray
work? W. D. Coolidge at General Electric (GE) had

developed the hot-cathode tube in 1913 which went on to become the standard tube for medical radiography and eventually for diffraction and spectroscopy tubes. W. Duane and F. L. Hunt had shown the important relationship between electron energy and the minimum wavelength of the continuum. Compton had found the inelastic scattering of x-rays in 1923, for which he received the Nobel prize in 1927. However, the first paper on chemical analysis did not come from America until 1931 when G. R. Fonda and G. B. Collins at GE reported the quantitative analysis of Cu-Ni and Fe-Ni alloys and showed the non-linear matrix absorption effects with composition which we recognize so well today.

1932 is an important milestone in x-ray spectrochemical analysis because it marked its apparent demise (fortunately only temporarily). How, one can ask, could this be possible? Moseley had originally prophesied that x-ray spectra should obviously be useful for chemical analysis. de Broglie had shown that any kind of sample could be excited by secondary fluorescence outside the x-ray tube. Jönsson had shown that accurate intensities could be measured with a Geiger counter. Glocker and Schreiber had discussed absorption effects of matrix elements. von Hevesy, in his book in 1932, lays out the whole picture of most effective wavelength for exciting the characteristic lines, the effects of interfering elements with absorption edges or emission lines between lines of the elements being measured, and the use of internal or comparison standards. Nevertheless, from 1932 until 1948, a period of over 15 years, *Chemical Abstracts* shows but a single publication on the subject; von Hamos in Stockholm used a clever curved-crystal arrangement to image the variation in composition of a sample in terms of an individual element (the first micro-analyzer). The papers listed as x-ray analysis during those years are all on powder diffraction to identify different compounds. There are some contradictory bits of evidence to the preceding statements; Losev's review in *Industrial Laboratory* in 1968 states that x-ray analysis was used routinely in Russia in the 1930s for qualitative and semi-quantitative analysis. A listing for a 1939 monograph on "X-ray Spectral Analysis" by Borovskii and Blokhin is known as is the fact that Borovskii began teaching x-ray spectral analysis at Moscow University at about that time. However, in the rest of the world, whatever the cause--worldwide depression in the industrial laboratories, the onrush of World War II--x-ray spectrochemical analysis was not to reappear until 1948.

Renaissance. What led to the rebirth of x-ray

spectroscopy for chemical analysis in the late 1940s? Actually it was not deliberate but rather the result of a chance observation of strong background interference in x-ray powder diffraction patterns of Fe compounds when using a Cu target x-ray tube. We must go back and examine the events which set the stage for this observation.

X-ray powder diffraction--i.e., the diffraction from crystalline powder rather than from a single crystal--was first described by P. Scherrer at Göttingen in 1918. The phenomenon had become popular in industry during the 1930s as a means of identifying different compounds. J. D. Hanawalt at Dow Chemical Co. tabulated the diffraction lines from hundreds of compounds so that an analyst had merely to match his observed lines with those in the Hanawalt table to identify his sample. Mixtures of two or more compounds gave separate lines for each compound, and thus the components could be recognized. Originally, photographic film was used to record the diffraction patterns, but quantitative measurement of line intensities was difficult as always. Near the end of World War II Friedman at the Naval Research Laboratory (NRL) in Washington replaced the photographic film with a Geiger counter which could be moved around an arc to measure the diffracted lines one at a time. The Geiger counter gave more accurate line-intensity measurements and was considerably faster than photographic recording. (This innovation was the direct conversion of equipment assembled by Friedman during World War II for rapid alignment of quartz crystals to be cut into oscillators for radio circuits.) There was immediate interest in the Geiger counter diffractometer by x-ray equipment manufacturers who, by that time, had developed stable, sealed x-ray diffraction tubes and power supplies. Soon Geiger-counter diffractometers had replaced film cameras for power diffraction in many industrial laboratories in the United States. Motor drives were substituted for manual scanning, and improvements were made in the electronics for amplifying and counting the pulses from the Geiger counter. Figure 13 shows an early sample.

Then in the summer of 1947, at Friedman's direction, Birks at NRL was surveying powder diffraction patterns from many different compounds such as ores, alloys, ceramics, and organics. Generally this was done with a Cu target-diffraction tube because it gave high intensity and convenient diffraction angles. However, Fe compounds or alloys gave extremely high and variable background interference which was puzzling at first but then was recognized by Friedman as the fluorescence of Fe in the sample by the Cu radiation from the tube. Changing

LAVERNE STANFIELD BIRKS, 1919-

A physicist by training, Birks has been associated since 1942 with x-ray work at the U. S. Naval Research Laboratories, where he became Head of the Optical Physics Division in 1958. He helped develop instrumental techniques for x-ray fluorescence analysis and electron probe microanalysis. When the Electron Probe Analysis Society of America was organized in 1968, Birks was its first president. He has been active in committee work with IUPAC and ASTM, and has authored many papers and two books.

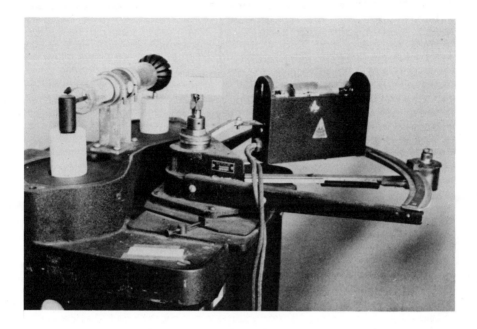

Figure 13. An early Geiger tube goniometer.

to an Fe-target tube eliminated the background difficulties, but Friedman recognized the potential of using
the fluorescent excitation as a means of elemental analysis. The diffractometer was quickly converted to a
spectrometer by placing a rock salt-crystal analyzer
between the specimen and the Geiger counter. As the
crystal rotated through angle θ and the Geiger counter
through 2θ, each wavelength from the sample was diffracted in turn, and its intensity was measured. The
work was reported in *Review of Scientific Instruments*
in 1948, and again the x-ray equipment manufacturers
were quick to produce commercial models of the instrument because the applications to chemical analysis were
obvious.
     Simultaneously with the work at NRL a paper was
given at the Instruments and Measurements Conference in
Stockholm by A. Kochanovska of the Skoda Works of Prague.
He used fluorescent excitation with a focusing crystal
and photographic film to measure elements in alloys and
solutions. He was able to detect 2 ppm of Fe in water
and a few hundred ppm of metals in alloys. The literature

shows no further pursuit of this technique.

The electron microprobe concept was developed at almost the same time as x-ray fluorescence but took much longer to reach fruition. In 1947 Hillier at RCA patented an idea for focusing an electron beam onto a sample and measuring the characteristic x-rays emitted from it, but he did nothing further about applying the concept. Then, independently, A. Guinier and his student R. Castaing in Paris and Borovskii in Moscow developed electron microprobes. Castaing and Guinier reported their conversion of an electron microscope at the Delft Electron Microscope Meeting in 1949, and Castaing went on to discuss instrumentation and data interpretation in his famous doctoral thesis from the University of Paris in 1951. In 1953 Borovskii published his work in *Problemi Metallurgii*, a Russian metals journal, where it went unnoticed by most of the western world. We return to electron probes later because their widespread application did not begin until the late 1950s.

At this point an interesting and important difference between x-ray spectroscopy as developed in the 1950s and the earlier work in the 1920s should be noted. In the 1920s the work went forward almost entirely in the universities; in the 1950s the work went forward almost entirely at government or industrial laboratories. This should not be interpreted as a criticism of the universities but rather as an indication of the tremendous support for research in government and industry in those years (looking back at the "golden age" of the 1950s, it is clear that we shall not see such support again soon, if ever).

As we now follow the course of x-ray spectrochemical analysis as it developed into one of the major analytical techniques, we gradually observe that its success depended not on new x-ray principles but almost entirely on various kinds of improvements in electronics. For instance improved amplifiers, stabilizers, and pulse-counting circuitry in the 50s; solid-state components including the lithium-drifted silicon detector and multichannel analyzer of the 60s; greatly increased availability and speed of computers for efficient data interpretation in the late 60s and early 70s. The exception to the electronics area is the deliberate selection and improvement of analyzer crystals to expand the range of wavelengths amenable to measurement; this has advanced us from a practical lower limit at Ti in 1948 to routine detection down to C nowadays (analysis down to Be has been reported but is certainly not routine).

Early Applications. Within a year after the initial paper by Friedman and Birks in 1948, x-ray fluorescence

(XRF) was being used for semiquantitative analysis of major elements in the steel industry by Abbot and by Cordovi. H. F. Beeghley had applied XRF to gaging tin plate on steel (the first nondispersive application because the Sn lines were not excited and the Fe lines were measured without a crystal spectrometer). The "new" technique was mentioned by H. A. Liebhafsky in the 1950 biennial review of x-ray absorption in *Analytical Chemistry*. He said "... x-ray fluorescence promises to become an important method of chemical analysis," and he promised to discuss it more fully in subsequent reviews. Before the end of 1950, L. S. Birks, E. J. Brooks, and H. Friedman had published applications to quantitative analysis of Pb and Br in gasoline (a big problem in the petroleum industry at that time). The possibility of using liquid samples had been forecast by de Broglie in 1914 and by von Hevesy in 1932, but the measurement on aviation gasoline was the first time this technique had ever been accomplished. A second application to liquids followed quickly with the analysis of U in aqueous solution with varying concentrations of Pb as an interfering element (detection limit for U of 50 ppm). Liquids were, in fact, ideal samples because standards were simple to prepare and families of calibration curves allowed easy interpretation. By 1950 North American Philips was marketing a flat-crystal spectrometer similar to the one developed at NRL, and by 1951 GE was marketing a spectrometer which used a curved mica crystal in transmission (the 331 planes). Applications to practical problems were being carried out in laboratories in both the United States and Europe.

In the spring of 1953 XRF had become of such interest that the American Society for Testing Materials (ASTM) held a symposium of six invited papers to review the state of the art. (Papers by Friedman, Birks, and Brooks from NRL; Sherman from Philadelphia Shipyard; Hasler and Kemp from Applied Research Laboratories; Brissey, Liebhafsky, and Pfeiffer of GE; Noakes of Ford Motor Co.; Carl and Campbell of U. S. Bureau of Mines.) The discussions included multiple spectrometers for simultaneous analysis of several elements, properties of Geiger, gas-proportional, and scintillation detectors, kinds of crystals and crystal optics. They also included application to metals and minerals. (As shown later the importance of mathematical correction cannot be stressed enough because it is one of the prime differences between x-ray spectroscopy and other spectroscopic techniques and the basis for the economic advantages which x-ray analysis enjoys.)

By the time of the 1954 Biennial Review in

Analytical Chemistry, the title of the x-ray review had been changed to include x-ray emission and the number of XRF papers cited had jumped to more than 50. The 1954 review states, "At the present time no instrumental method of analysis is growing in popularity so fast as is x-ray emission." The reasons for such popularity were well deserved--samples could be examined as solids, powders, or liquids with minimal sample preparation; analysis took less than five minutes; results for major constituents were quantitative to within a few per cent relative by using simple empirical calibration curves.

A Decade of Rapid Growth. From the middle 1950s to the middle 1960s the growth of x-ray analysis (including electron probe) was phenomenal. The number of papers cited in the Biennial Reviews in *Analytical Chemistry* had jumped from 127 in 1954 to 231 by 1958 and to 436 by 1962. Of course this was the era when XRF was introduced into many new laboratories, and there was much repetition in the literature. Nevertheless the advances in techniques were important.

Detectors. The long dead-time of Geiger counters limited their use to a few thousand counts per second, which made it difficult to measure both major and minor components with the same operating conditions. Gas-proportional and scintillation detectors had far shorter dead times and could count up to 50,000 pulses per second but required more sophisticated electronics which took time to develop. As a result of efforts, primarily by the x-ray equipment manufacturers, the Geiger counter was phased out during the late 50s and early 60s and was replaced by the scintillation counter for $\lambda < 1.2$ Å, by the sealed proportional counter for $1.2 < \lambda < 2.5$ Å, and by the flow proportional counter for $\lambda > 2.5$ Å.

The gas-proportional and scintillation detectors had a second important advantage over the Geiger counter--namely, the amplitude of each pulse is proportional to the energy of the x-ray photon absorbed. This proportionality leads to the energy dispersion mode (which is so commonplace nowadays with solid-state detectors). Even when used with a crystal spectrometer, it eliminates second-order diffraction interference and much of the scattered background interference. To take advantage of the proportional response, it was necessary to introduce an electronic pulse-height discriminator which passed only the desired pulse amplitude; this had to be adjusted automatically to correspond to the wavelength (energy) as the spectrometer was scanned through the diffraction angles. The added expense of the proportional and scintillation detectors plus the added expense of the more sophisticated electronics was compensated by reduced analysis time and better signal-to-noise ratios.

Analyzer Crystals. The rock salt which had been used in the early spectrometers was replaced by LiF which was not hygroscopic. The diffracted intensity from LiF was greatly improved by abrading it to introduce dislocations and make it more mosaic. Other commonly used crystals of the 50s were quartz, pentaerythritol, ammonium dihydrogen phosphate (ADP), and gypsum.

By the early 60s the interest in measuring longer wavelengths from the lower atomic-number elements led to a search for better long-spacing crystals (Bragg's law tells us that the maximum wavelength which can be diffracted is $2d$ where d is the interplanar spacing of the diffracting planes). The most important of the long spacing crystals turned out to be potassium acid phthalate (KAP) with a $2d$ value of about 26 Å. This crystal (and its successors with rubidium or thallium substituted for potassium) rapidly became the workhorse for the important region from F to Si.

Even the KAP could not reach the important elements C or N and was marginal for oxygen. Henke at Pomona College, Baun and Fischer at Wright-Patterson Air Force Labs in Ohio, and others revived interest in multilayer fatty-acid films which had been investigated by Irving Langmuir and Katherine Blodgett in the 1930s. The best of these pseudo-crystals turned out to be lead stearate decanoate (LSD) with a $2d$ spacing of about 100 Å. Of course with the measurement of longer wavelengths it was necessary to use vacuum spectrometers and ultra-thin detector windows such as stretched polypropylene.

Specimen Preparation. As the analysis of minerals and ores developed through the efforts of I. Adler and J. M. Axelrod at U. S. Geological Survey (USGS) in Washington, D. C., D. M. Mortimore and P. A. Romans at USGS in Eugene, Ore., and H. F. Carl and W. J. Campbell at U. S. Bureau of Mines in College Park, Md., it became recognized that quantitative analysis usually required grinding to smaller than 200 mesh size to overcome heterogeneities. However, there were often so many components that calibration standards were difficult to prepare, and internal standards were frequently used for specific elements. A big improvement in sample preparation was introduced by F. Claisse of the Canadian Department of Mines who fused the sample in borax to make a homogeneous specimen. Other techniques introduced were dilution with low Z material such as starch to improve the linearity of intensity vs. composition in strongly absorbing matrices, also the use of thin samples by Salmon of Denver to reduce matrix effects. Generally, however, the analysis of minerals was not as easy or as accurate as that for alloys where the number of component elements was smaller and the sample preparation consisted merely of smoothing the surface to about 30-50 micro-inch finish (with #00 emery paper). Liquid analysis remained simple and straightforward except for the problems of containing volatile components in a cell with a thin window and reducing bubble formation near the window.

Truly heterogeneous samples or limited quantities of material brought about the introduction of x-ray milliprobes, instruments where the x-ray beam was limited to a small area on the specimen surface. Such instruments usually employed focusing curved-crystal optics to regain some of the intensity lost due to the small mass of emitting material. With these milliprobes it was possible to detect quantities as low as 10^{-8} g of an element (compared with 10^{-6} g for flat crystal optics and to 10^{-14} g for the early electron probes).

Development of the Electron Microprobe. As stated earlier, the electron probe had its origins at about the same time (1947) as the renaissance in x-ray fluorescence, but it was much slower in coming into general use. The French company CAMECA had constructed "commercial" instruments in the early 1950s for Castaing at the French Air Force Labs (ONERA) and for Crussard and Philibert at the Metals Research Institute at St. Germain, but it was not until the middle 50s that suddenly there was an upsurge of interest in the United States and Europe. Within about two years P. Duncumb and W. C. Nixon had constructed an instrument in Cosslett's laboratory in Cambridge, as had Haine and Mulvey at Associated Electrical Industries in Aldermaston, Fisher at U. S. Steel, Birks at NRL, Wittry at Cal Tech, and Schwartz and Austin at Battelle. Each of these instruments used focusing curved-crystal optics and had a "claimed" beam size of about 1 μm and detection limit of about 10^{-14} g. (Although the quantity detectable is about 10^{-14} g for electron probe compared with about 10^{-8} g for XRF, the fractional composition detectable is more favorable for XRF being about 1-10 ppm vs. 1000 ppm for electron probe. The reason for poorer fractional detectability with the electron probe is the high background interference from the Bremsstrahlung.)

Castaing laid out an elaborate mathematical approach for matrix correction in his thesis (see the following section on mathematical corrections), but most of the early analysis was done with the aid of calibration standards. For instance, FeS precipitates in $CuFeS_2$ were identified with standards of chalcopyrite, cubanite, valleriite, and pyrite. Other applications to metals

and minerals occurred near the end of the 50s as more
laboratories constructed instruments or purchased the
first commercial models becoming available in Europe,
the United States, and Japan. These early identifications of segregations and phases often disagreed with
accepted compositions deduced from microscopy; this led
to considerable controversy between probe analysts and
metallurgists or mineralogists and may have breached
some long-time friendships.

   The first biological application--the variation of
calcium in newly formed bone--did not come until 1962
with the cooperative work of Brooks, Tousimis, and Birks.
It was followed by a survey of Ca/P ratios in bone by
Mellor, by measurement of Cu in a membrane of the eye
by Tousimis and Adler, and by measurement of Zn in sperm
by Hall. Generally speaking, biological applications
lagged behind those in metallurgy and mineralogy (and
still do).

   The early 1960s brought considerable work on solid-
state diffusion in metals where the electron probe was
the ideal tool for the size scale involved. It was
possible to identify non-equilibrium phases in metals
and to perfect the phase diagrams which have always been
so important in metallurgy. This was also the era of
most rapid advance in identifying phases in minerals,
information which helped geologists understand the processes which occurred in the evolution of the earth.
(As an aside, it has always seemed to this author (LSB)
that the use of the electron probe to study fundamental
reactions in metals and minerals is by far its most important contribution. Unfortunately, this has never
been pursued to the degree which is possible and, in
fact, has declined considerably. Similar possibilities
for studying reactions in biological systems have never
been pursued at all.)

   Mathematical Corrections for Matrix Effects. As
early as 1928 Glocker and Schreiber discussed the equations for exponential absorption of incident primary
radiation and emerging fluorescence. Values for mass
absorption coefficients were known from the early work
of F. K. Richtmyer; fluorescent yields were known from
the work of P. Auger and of S. T. Stephenson. G. von
Hevesy specifically mentions secondary fluorescence
(enhancement) in his book in 1932. L. von Hámos had
developed formulas for intensity as a function of concentration of matrix elements in 1945. E. Gillam and
H. T. Heal gave expressions for enhancement in 1952,
yet none of this earlier work was referenced by either
J. Sherman or G. E. Noakes at that 1953 ASTM symposium
as they set out to establish equations for matrix corrections. (They should not be faulted any more than the

rest of us involved in XRF at that time; none of us had
bothered to read through the publications of the 20s.)
Sherman set up accurate expressions for matrix absorption by relating intensity from the desired element to
the mass absorption coefficients and concentrations of
the other elements in the specimen. His comments on
their evaluation were not very encouraging however:

> The theoretical correlation of the intensity of
> the fluorescent spectra excited by a polychro-
> matic beam, from a multicomponent mixture and
> the concentration of an element in the mixture
> involves integral harmonic means and the use of
> hyperbolic curves in multidimensional spaces.
> The computational labor involved makes the re-
> lations too complicated for general use.

All of us agreed wholeheartedly with his second sentence.
He did go on to say that for limited ranges of composition a usable approximation would suffice, and he gave
the expression for an n-component system which is the
basis for the empirical coefficient method still in
widespread use today (the terminology has been recast
for modern context):

$$C_i/R_i = 1 + \sum_{j \neq i} \alpha_{ij} C_j \tag{1}$$

where R_i is the relative x-ray intensity of element i,
C_i, C_j is the concentration of element i or j, and the
values of α are determined by calculation or measurement
on samples of known composition. Noakes, at that same
ASTM symposium, set up less exact equations for intensity as related to mass absorption coefficients and concentrations of the other elements. He too arrived at
expressions involving empirical coefficients, but they
are not repeated here because in principle they are
equivalent to Sherman's.

Similar equations were published by H. J. Beatty
and R. M. Brissey in 1954 and by several others since
that time. They all suffer from the same shortcoming--
namely, that intensity can be calculated from known concentrations but what is desired is to calculate concentration from measured intensity. Therefore, it is necessary to obtain concentration by iteration; for instance,
the measured intensities are used as the first estimate
of concentrations to calculate the intensities; the differences between measured and calculated intensities
are used to adjust the estimated concentrations for the
second iteration, etc. The first attempt to automate
some of the mathematics was by J. Hower, L. C. Jones,
and H. D. Burnam of Shell Oil; in 1957 they reported on
using IBM equipment (they did not call it a computer)

to evaluate equations similar to those of Sherman.

A different form of empirical-coefficient expression was offered by H. J. Lucas-Tooth and B. J. Price in 1961. It can be written as

$$C_i/R_i = 1 + \sum_{j \neq i} \beta_{ij} R_j \qquad (2)$$

and has the important difference that concentration is expressed directly in terms of intensity rather than vice-versa. However, the form used by Sherman is the only one which can be derived from the basic relationship involving mass absorption coefficients and fluorescent yields; mathematicians would argue the legitimacy of the transformation to the form used by Lucas-Tooth, but technology often takes such liberties with mathematics.

One of the interesting sidelights on the history of x-ray spectrochemical analysis has been the repeated "rediscovery" of Equations 1 or 2 over the years. The list of persons who have offered modified versions is far too long to mention here, but each of their expressions can be recast exactly in one or the other form as was pointed out by S. D. Rasberry and K. F. J. Heinrich in 1974.

Meanwhile, in electron probe analysis it was difficult to prepare calibration standards for many of the systems of interest. In addition, it was difficult to find even reagent-grade chemicals which were homogeneous on the micron scale. (Some workers attempted to alleviate this problem by expanding the beam size to encompass a larger area, but it was pointed out that matrix effects do not average over a range of composition.) Therefore, the need for mathematical corrections was even greater than in XRF. Castaing's equations were efficacious but tedious if many analyses had to be carried out. Nor was it easy to determine values for the empirical coefficients to be used in equations similar to Equation 1 or 2 above. Birks simplified the calculations by approximating the enhancement correction, but accuracy was impaired for some elements and concentrations. Other approaches were offered by Wittry and by Reed, and modifications to the parameters used in Castaing's expressions were eventually put forward by Philibert, Duncumb and Shields, Henrich, Borovskii, and others. We shall have to wait for the final section to discuss the eventual forms used as computers became available.

Valence Effects. During the late 50s and early 60s shifts in wavelengths of characteristic lines for different compounds of the same element were measured by

van Nordstrand of Sinclair, Holliday of U. S. Steel, and
Baun and Fischer of Wright-Patterson. These valence
effects were a nuisance to x-ray analysts but, of course,
had been recognized as early as 1920 when J. Bergengren
measured the valence effects in the absorption spectrum
of S. In fact, whole schools devoted to spectral fine
structure had been built up by Hayasi in Sendai, Japan,
Parratt at Cornell, Bearden and Shaw at Johns Hopkins,
Kai Siegbahn at Uppsala, and others. The information
was also covered in standard x-ray texts such as those
by Compton and Allison, Blokhin, and Glocker, but except for a few isolated applications, such as S in oil
and Cl in a few compounds, there was not any general
analytical use of the valence information (and still has
not been even in the 70s).

Approaching Maturity. By the mid 1960s XRF was
firmly established as an accepted analytical technique
in industry. Several thousand units of commercial equipment were in routine daily use for steel production,
cement plants, ore processing, petroleum industry, etc.
Nevertheless, research continued for better equipment
and methods to improve XRF's efficiency and capability.
Many changes occurred in the late 60s and early 70s as
we bring this story to a close.

Automatic Data Processing. The 1957 work of Hower,
Jones, and Burnam was followed in 1962 by Marti of Sulzer
Bros., Switzerland, who reported using an IBM 1620 computer to solve Sherman's empirical equations but preferred a simple analog processor for three-component
systems. By 1964 J. W. Criss of NRL was using an IBM
1620 computer to solve fundamental parameter equations
and to perform the necessary iterations for determining
concentration. Siemens Corp. offered a dedicated small
computer (PDP-8S) on their x-ray spectrometer in 1966;
it processed equations similar to those of Lucas-Tooth.
Then in the late 1960s computer speed began to increase
by orders of magnitude; now it was possible to consider
processing the elaborate expressions for matrix effects
described by Sherman first in 1953 and in more detail
in 1955 and 1959. In 1963 Shiraiwa and Fujino of Sumi-
tomo Metals in Japan had rewritten the basic expressions
for absorption and enhancement (secondary and tertiary)
in a form convenient for computer evaluation, and Criss
at NRL had done a similar thing. By the late 1960s
these fundamental-parameter expressions were being run
economically on big computers for systems of 15 or more
elements and an unlimited range of concentration.

In 1971 Criss put his computer program on the CDC
time-sharing system, where it is available for anyone
to try by merely supplying a user number. It has also

been translated for IBM batch processing and will be distributed through Argonne Code Center. The cost is less than 30-50 cents per sample (for all elements). One might well ask why such a powerful approach has not replaced all other calculation methods? The answer seems to be that the fundamental parameters themselves-- spectral distribution, mass absorption coefficient, fluorescent yield--are still not known accurately enough to satisfy the requirements for an industry such as steel, where a fractional per cent Cr in a thousand tons of steel is economically more important than efficient x-ray data processing. In addition, many laboratories seem to prefer a small computer which relies on the empirical coefficients even though the range of compo- sition is limited. It is this author's opinion that the trend will be to the fundamental-parameter method as the parameters become more accurate (see a later sub- section for a discussion of the situation with respect to parameters).

Paralleling the data processing effort in XRF is the history of quantitative electron probe analysis. The empirical atomic number-absorption-fluorescence (ZAF) method of Castaing was made tractable by computer pro- cessing in the late 1960s. The MAGIC program of Colby of RCA is readily available, and more elaborate programs allowing for fluorescence by the continuum were prepared by Heinrich and co-workers at the National Bureau of Standards with the cooperation of J. Henoc from the National Center for Studies of Telecommunication, Mou- lineaux, France. In addition to the empirical method, the electron transport program developed by D. B. Brown for his thesis under Ogilvie at MIT corresponds to the fundamental-parameter method in XRF; it is available from Brown (currently at NRL). Even full-blown Monte Carlo calculations have been used for electron probe analysis by Shinoda Murata and Shimizu in Japan and by others.

Here we have to pause for a surprising comment on quantitative analysis for electron probe. During the middle and late 1960s the enthusiasm for quantitative electron probe analysis was very great. However, at about that time the technique of electronic scanning of surface areas was also growing rapidly in popularity. Gradually, the scanning electron microscope (SEM) with its smaller beam size (down to a few hundred Ångströms) replaced most electron probe analysis. Rapid scanning did not lend itself to quantitative analysis, especially for the rough surfaces of particular interest in SEM. Therefore, the trend was toward qualitative, or at most semiquantitative, identification of elements with simple energy dispersion systems using solid-state detectors

(see next section). Truly quantitative electron probe
analysis is still required for investigating reactions
in metals and minerals and hopefully will not be forgotten only to be "discovered" again at some later date.

Energy Dispersion. By the mid-1960s, the Geiger
counter had been replaced by gas-proportional and scintillation detectors on most crystal spectrometers. The
gas-proportional detector had also been employed by C. F.
Hendee, S. Fine, and D. B. Brown as early as 1956 for
non-dispersive analysis. In 1963 Birks and A. P. Batt
used a multi-channel analyzer with a proportional detector to record the energy spectrum from XRF and electron probe samples, but elements had to be separated by
more than two atomic numbers in order for their characteristic lines to be resolved with the gas-proportional
counter. Hence, the energy dispersion mode was of limited usefulness. What was needed was better energy
resolution in the detector itself, and this eventually
came from the solid-state devices, particularly the
lithium-drifted silicon detector which is so popular
today.

For background in this area we have to go to 1947-48
when it was first observed that Type II diamonds would
respond to γ rays if a strong electric field was impressed across the diamond. Other crystals such as CdS
were found to have similar semiconducting properties,
and Ge was used by B. P. McKay for counting α particles
in 1949. The big advances came in the 1960s with the
work of Walter and Dobbs at Oak Ridge and finally in
1966 the use of Si to measure x-rays by H. R. Bowman,
E. K. Hyde, S. G. Thompson, and R. C. Jared at F. S.
Goulding's laboratory at Berkeley. At that time the
energy resolution was 1.1 keV, and the lowest energy
detectable was 4 keV. The potential merit of Si was
recognized in that only 3.6 eV were required to generate
an electron-hole pair (as compared with an effective 30
eV to create an ion pair in an Xe proportional counter).
This meant a larger number of events per x-ray photon
and hence a smaller relative spread in pulse amplitude
for photons of a given energy; ergo, better energy resolution. At first it was thought that energy resolution
would be limited by ordinary statistics for the number
of events, as it seemed to be for gas-proportional
counters, but as this calculated resolution was exceeded
in practice, it became apparent that different statistics
applied.

Goulding, with the help of J. M. Jaklevic, went on
to perfect the Li-drifted Si detectors in which random
carriers are minimized. The present resolution is about
130 eV, limited by about 80-100 eV of random noise even
at the liquid nitrogen temperatures where the detectors

are operated, and by about 30-50 eV of statistical uncertainty. Perfection of the detectors and the related electronic circuitry have also been carried out by R. S. Frankel, R. Woldseth, and Woo at Kevex Corp., by Gedcke at ORTEC Corp., and by others.

No area of x-ray analysis has grown so rapidly as energy dispersion with solid-state detectors. It has the important advantage that spectra from all elements present, expected or unexpected, are collected simultaneously. It can use radioisotope sources, electron probes, or x-ray tubes and can be operated by personnel with a minimum of background or training in x-ray analysis. The energy spectra can be unfolded and processed conveniently on small dedicated computers. Woldseth of Kevex, Russ of EDAX Corp., and others have provided user-oriented programs for data treatment which allow almost instantaneous recognition of elements present in a sample (the flamboyant claims of quantitative analysis should be regarded with some skepticism, however, until tested on one's own applications). The energy dispersion systems are relatively low in cost (compared with multiple spectrometer instruments) although their cost has been increasing rapidly in the past few years. Some of the limitations which are also important are covered in the trace and microanalysis subsection which follows.

Trace and Microanalysis. As every chemist knows, any desired concentration can be measured if one is allowed to extract from a large enough amount of starting material, but what we are interested in here in trace analysis is the concentration which can be measured in situ or by reasonable extraction. The term microanalysis is arbitrarily reserved for those samples which are naturally limited to very small starting quantities. For such samples it is the minimum detectable quantity in grams which is of interest.

In situ, it has been possible since Eddy and Laby's work in 1930 to detect a few ppm of many elements, and this situation has not improved markedly even today. There are, of course, especially favorable systems such as metals in biological tissue where smaller fractions may be detected, but one soon reaches the limit where statistics of the scattered background limit the detection.

In terms of *reasonable* extraction, Kehl and Russell of Gulf Research Laboratories in 1956 were able to measure 0.01 ppm of uranium in water by precipitation with diammonium phosphate. In 1955 W. T. Grubb and P. D. Zemany of GE first used an anion exchange resin to extract fractional ppm of Mn, Fe, and Zn in maple syrup. The most concerted effort with ion exchange resins came from W. J. Campbell and co-workers at the U. S. Bureau

of Mines. Spano, Green, Law, and others used a variety
of general and specific ion exchange resins in the early
60s to measure components of mineral systems. One advantage of the ion exchange method is that filter paper
can be impregnated with the resin and used to extract
the desired elements from solution; then the dried filter
paper is used directly as the specimen in the x-ray
apparatus. There have not been any dramatic changes in
capability in recent years, but the method continues to
be a viable approach for ion concentrations well below
the ppm range.

Microanalysis, unlike trace analysis, has advanced
rapidly just in the 1970s. These advances were primarily brought about by the need to measure large numbers of particulate pollution samples. At the beginning
of the work, pollution samples were generally collected
on glass-fiber filters and then were washed off and analyzed by atomic absorption, which was able to detect
some components at sub-nanogram levels. However, the
expense of sample handling and the limitation for some
elements made a more economical and more encompassing
technique desirable. Both the plasma-torch emission
spectroscopy method developed by V A. Fassel and co-
workers at Iowa State and the XRF method were likely
candidate techniques, and the final chapter cannot be
written yet on their relative merits. It can only be
said that XRF equipment has been installed at the Environmental Protection Agency (EPA) laboratories, and that
is what is described here.

One of the strong advantages of XRF for pollution
analysis is that the substrate on which the sample is
collected can be examined directly in the x-ray apparatus
without specimen preparation. However, the glass-fiber
filters were not suitable because of the high concentration of impurities which completely masked some of the
elements in the samples. Therefore, it was necessary
to resort to filter paper or to Millipore, Nuclepore,
or similar synthetic filters.

All varieties of x-ray spectroscopy were tried--
radioisotope excitation, excitation by protons or α particles, and ordinary XRF with energy dispersion or crystal spectrometers. Generally, the isotope sources are
too weak for reasonable counting times except in a few
isolated instances; they have been disregarded except
by a few experts such as Rhodes at Columbia Scientific
Co. The α and proton advocates were mainly researchers
in the nuclear physics field such as Cahill at the University of California, Walter at Duke, Johansson at the
University of Florida, and others who had access to
cyclotron or van de Graaff machines. It is true that
the ultimate limit of detection for α and proton

excitation (as defined by a signal above background by at least 3 × the background standard deviation) is in the sub-nanogram range but only if the material is collected on thin carbon or plastic membranes ($\sim$ 10 $\mu g/cm^2$ mass). For XRF with x-ray tube excitation and filter paper or Millipore substrates, either energy dispersion or wavelength dispersion has about the same single-element detection limit of $\sim$ 1 ng for favorable elements, $\sim$ 10 ng for most elements, and $\sim$ 100 ng for a few difficult elements such as Cd. This detection is more than adequate for the usual collection times for either ambient air or source samples.

The main controversy in particulate analysis has raged between the energy-dispersion and crystal-spectrometer advocates but (in this author's opinion) resolves itself ultimately into two simple, distinct situations:

(1) For rapid survey where any unknown major element may be of interest, the energy-dispersion method is more rapid and economical. It has difficulty distinguishing minor constituents whose lines are unresolved from neighboring elements of high concentration; the same would be true for bulk samples, where the concentration range is as large as 10,000:1, as it sometimes is in pollution samples.

(2) For situations where the elements of interest can be defined and are fewer than 20-25, the multiple-spectrometer, wavelength-dispersion instrument is more accurate, more rapid, and more economical. The reason is that each spectrometer can be optimized for a particular element, and there is little if any interference from neighboring elements no matter what their concentration.

Thus it seems that both wavelength and energy dispersion will continue to enjoy strong advocacy and hopefully strong competition from other analytical techniques.

Heterogeneous Samples (Particle-Size Effects). As early as 1958, in the Biennial Reviews in *Analytical Chemistry*, Liebhafsky mentioned the uncertainties in intensity introduced by heterogeneities in the sample. At that time little was or could be done about it. Later, in 1967, Berry and co-workers of Texas Nuclear Corp. approximated particle-size effects for idealized heterogeneous specimens (blocks of uniform size but different compositions arrayed in layers). They could calculate absorption effects for specified geometry and could determine the variation in emergent intensity as the block size was varied. The approach was of limited practical value because real samples did not approximate the idealized model. It remained for Criss, reporting at the 15th International Spectroscopy Colloquium in Madrid, in 1969, to set up mathematics and a computer program which allowed for random particle location and different sizes for different particles. Although absorption effects can be expressed quite generally for such a model, enhancement effects are much more complicated and have not been programmed except for a few specific circumstances. Even the absorption effects are sensitive to the nature of the specimen surface--particles encompassed by a medium (such as a slurry) give slightly different effects than particles which comprise the uneven surface of a dry powder or sectioned particles in a polished solid surface. Although Criss' mathematics is far more powerful and useful than that of Berry or other workers, the calculations are used mainly to predict the range of effects which can be expected from precipitation, grinding size, or packing fraction rather than to analyze specimens directly.

The greatest practical application of the particle-size program is in particulate pollution analysis for low Z elements, as discussed by Criss at the 1974 Denver X-Ray Meeting. To a good first approximation the pollution particles are arrayed so they do not "shadow" each other in the incident or fluorescent beam. Thus only the morphology and size need be considered in the equations. For particle shapes other than long rods or thin plates, a single curve of intensity vs. size times linear absorption coefficient predicts the effect within an uncertainty of about 10%. Figure 14 shows the curve; the

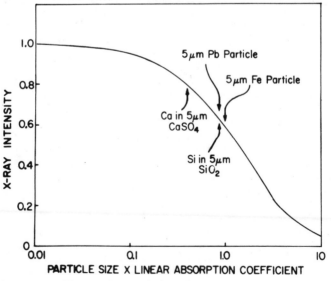

Figure 14. The effect of particle size on x-ray spectra.

intensity is normalized to unity for small particle size
and decreases, for constant total mass, as the particle
size increases. For pollution samples the size can
generally be estimated, but the composition of individual
particles is usually unknown. This introduces an uncertainty in the estimate of mass for each element, but
fortunately it can be held to ± 15% for any system postulated to date. More information on the heterogeneity
problem awaits publication of results by Criss.

    Parameters of X-Ray Spectroscopy. As stated ear-
lier, the thrust of x-ray fluorescence spectroscopy
since 1938 has been toward quantitative analysis. Much
of its success has depended on knowledge of the parameters which describe x-ray generation and interelement
effects in the specimen. No history of the subject
would be complete without some discussion of these parameters and the extensive efforts which have been made to
obtain accurate values for them.

    The first parameter which determines fluorescent
excitation of the specimen is the spectral distribution
of the primary (incident) radiation. The approximate
spectral distribution of radiation generated within
x-ray tube targets was treated by H. Kulenkampff in 1922,
by H. A. Kramers in 1923, and by other early workers,
but those treatments do not give adequate accuracy for
the emerging spectrum, which is what is required for
XRF. Starting in 1962, a program to measure the primary
spectrum was instituted at NRL by Birks and Seal and
pursued by Gilfrich after 1966. It was augmented by
theoretical calculations by D. B. Brown starting in
1968 and completed in 1974. Figure 15 gives results for
rhodium. Note that the comparison in Figure 15 is on an
absolute basis, not on merely relative intensity. The
cost to produce the measured spectrum was approximately
$30,000 and is obviously impractical for the many tar-
gets and operating conditions of interest. Nevertheless,
the work has been proceeding, and the final calculational
technique was perfected and tested only in 1974. It is
expected that tabulations to be prepared shortly will
indeed furnish the kind of spectral distributions required for the fundamental-parameter method of calculation. Attempts by Tertian and others to evoke a single
"effective wavelength" for the primary spectrum have
had limited success in some applications but are not of
general usefulness.

    The second parameter of interest is the absorption
of x-rays by the various elements in the specimen. Mass
absorption coefficients have been measured since the
time of Barkla in the early 1900s and Richtmyer in 1920.
The tables prepared by S. J. M. Allen for the book by
A. H. Compton and S. K. Allison in 1936, and subsequently

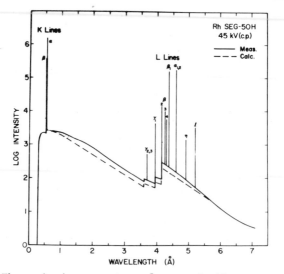

Figure 15. The emission spectrum from a rhodium target, calculated and observed.

used in the "Handbook of Chemistry and Physics," were the accepted values for many years. In 1949 J. A. Victoreen attempted to calculate absorption coefficients, and in 1958 Deslattes repeated measurements on a number of elements. Then in 1967 McMasters and co-workers at Lawrence Radiation Laboratory (now Lawrence Livermore Laboratory) in Livermore, Calif., and Veigele and co-workers at Kaman Nuclear Corp., and others started large-scale computer programs to calculate the scattering terms and to smooth the photoelectric terms for the whole range of elements and energies. This "massaging" of existing data helped to root out some inaccuracies and gave generally better values. The values from the different computer programs were not always in very good agreement, however, as pointed out by Hubbel of NBS in a series of comparison studies. The situation is still not resolved, particularly for the longer wavelengths where absorption fine structure plays an important part. The experimental work of Henke and Elgin at the University of Hawaii has given usable values, however, for much of the long wavelength region, and the work continues. It is the experimental difficulty of accurate measurement of transmission fraction through thin foils, coupled with the effects of impurities, plus the expense of the multitudinous measurements required which has limited the accuracy of the coefficients. Recently, Ebel of Vienna suggested the indirect determination of

absorption coefficients by fluorescent measurements at
a series of take-off angles from solid surfaces. Perhaps this technique will furnish the accurate values so
badly needed. Certainly we have had a surfeit of computer remassaging of old data, and further pursuit in
that direction seems futile. At the moment, the Livermore or Kaman tables appear to be as acceptable as any
values available.

The third parameter is the probability that an atom
will emit a characteristic x-ray after the atom has been
excited (ionized in an inner shell). This probability
is called fluorescence yield. P. Auger in Paris in 1925
was the first to evaluate the probability of characteristic x-ray emission from an ionized atom. The radiation-
less transition which results in emission of a second
electron rather than an x-ray photon (sometimes improperly ascribed to reabsorption of the photon within the
atom) is, by far, the most probable process for low-Z
elements. The best current values for fluorescent yield
were determined by Fink et al. of Georgia Tech in 1966
and revised slightly by the recent *Review of Modern
Physics* publication by Bambynek, Fink, et al. The values
for the K-shell yields are accurate enough for quantitative analysis, but the L-shell yields differ for each
of the three subshells and are of marginal accuracy for
quantitative analysis where L radiation is employed.

In electron probe analysis, there is no primary
x-ray spectrum but rather an incident monoenergetic
electron beam. The parameters which control x-ray generation in the specimen are electron stopping and the
probabilities (cross sections) for producing characteristic lines and Bremsstrahlung. The best values for the
stopping power seem to be those of Berger and Selzer of
NBS. The values of the cross sections have been the
subject of some controversy; the absolute values for
characteristic lines given originally by E. H. S. Burhop
have been criticized by Green, Hink, Brown, and others,
but his relative values seem acceptable and are widely
used. For continuum production, the values of Kirk-
patrick and Wiedmann give the best agreement with measured spectra. Elaborate calculations are underway by
Tseng and Pratt at Pittsburgh and should help to settle
the situation.

Miscellany. Some areas of x-ray analysis have been
neglected because of space limitations and the purpose
of the technique. X-ray diffraction, for instance, is
widely used for compound identification but is not a
technique for elemental analysis. X-ray absorption,
which has contributed so much to our understanding of
atomic structure, can give only the crudest estimates
of composition and is therefore not a viable technique

for chemical analysis. Other areas have been given
scant coverage because of space limitations. For instance, the whole area of radioisotopes has been neglected except for occasional mention. The reason for
this lack of coverage is that whereas the isotope technique seemed to have great promise in the middle 60s,
the availability of low-power x-ray tubes for laboratory
use and the limited application for man-transported,
battery-operated, balanced-filter instruments has resulted in a decline of interest for isotope sources.
In a third category, the ion probe which competes with
the electron probe is not x-ray analysis at all but mass
spectroscopy; it is covered in that chapter.

One particular experiment not discussed heretofore
and certainly of limited application is unique and thus
deserves special mention. Wittry and Arrhenius suggested
in *Geofisica International* (1961) that the sun's x-radi-
ation's striking the moon could be used for an x-ray
fluorescent analysis of the moon from an orbiting satellite. Giaconni, Gursky, and Paolini tried the measurement from an Aerobee rocket in 1962 but could not detect
x-rays from the moon. Adler, Trombka, and Gorenstein
in 1972 succeeded in the experiment during the Apollo 15
mission and were able to measure the variation in Al/Si
ratios across the moon's surface. This specimen probably
will stand as the largest ever analyzed directly. For
the extensive analyses carried out on moon rocks, the
electron probe work of Keil and associates at Albuquerque
and Chodos at Cal Tech and the XRF work by Rose and
associates at the U. S. Geological Survey and the many
other researchers around the world deserves special
mention for the magnitude of the project and the excellent correlation of results achieved.

In an entirely different area, x-ray spectra from
plasmas which are hotter than 10^6 K was mentioned first
in the Biennial Review in *Analytical Chemistry* in 1964.
It was not until about 1972, however, when the big,
pulsed lasers came into vogue, that this application
gained more widespread interest. From 1972 to 1974 the
measurement of x-ray spectra with crystal spectrographs
became a standard diagnostic tool for plasmas up to
10^7 K. In the hot plasmas, all or most of the electrons
are stripped from atoms like Al, and the x-ray spectra
are no longer simple Kα and Kβ lines but whole Rydberg
series of lines from hydrogen-like or helium-like species.
Figure 16 shows the x-ray spectra for Al, Zn, and Gd
from the work of Nagel and associates at NRL. From the
relative intensities of lines for different stages of
ionization, it is possible to estimate plasma temperature
and degree of equilibrium. Here is a completely new
application for x-ray spectroscopy, where the information

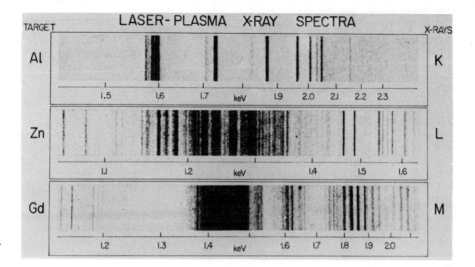

Figure 16.   Spectra of x-rays emitted from a hot plasma.

gained is not primarily the chemical composition but the ionization state of the atoms (of course, the x-ray spectra are also useful for identifying impurity elements in the plasma).

Epilogue. The history of x-ray spectrochemical analysis is important because it explains how the x-ray method has arrived at its present capabilities. What is more important is that it can analyze so many kinds of samples so rapidly, so accurately, and at such low cost. These advantages are the result of the simplicity of the characteristic x-ray spectra and the tractable relationship between concentration of an element and its x-ray intensity. The technical capability of the method depends very strongly on the recent advances in electronics and particularly on the availability of computers for data processing. The economy of the method depends very strongly on the minimal sample preparation required compared with wet chemical analysis or other spectroscopic methods. Although x-ray analysis has matured into a relatively stable situation in terms of bulk elemental analysis, there are already exciting new avenues of interests such as valence effects and plasma diagnostics coming into view. Thus the history is only

partly completed and should be as rich in the future as
it has been in the past.

Finally, it is impossible to recount the contributions of the many hundreds of researchers or analysts
involved in the development of x-ray fluorescence and
electron probe analysis. Some of those names not men-
tioned in the text which should not be forgotten include
Gunn, Yakowitz, Mitchell, Stevenson, Dwiggins, White,
and Rhodin in the United States; J. Brown, Traill,
LaChance, Gillieson, and Leroux in Canada; Hirokawa,
Momoki, Tanemura, Goto, and Ichinokawa in Japan; Narbutt,
Vaĭnshteĭn, and Il'in in Russia; Strasheim, Wybenga, and
Brandt in South Africa; Corona and de Riviera in Mexico;
Lubecki in Poland; Jenkins, Long, and Carr-Brion in
Britain; Harveng, Renaud, Calais, and Remy in France;
de Vries and von Rosenstiehl in the Netherlands; Hans
in Belgium; Pfundt, Weyl, Birchner, Neff, Ottemann,
Bruch, and Niebuhr in Germany; Toussaint, Vos, Ramous,
Gianino, Creton, and Moschin in Italy; Rotter and Klapuch
in Czechoslovakia; Müller in Switzerland, Suominen in
Finland. Let these and the others mentioned by name in
the text stand as surrogates for all those who have
contributed to the field.

X-RAY PHOTOELECTRON SPECTROSCOPY (ESCA)

X-ray photoelectron spectroscopy is the study of
the energy distribution of electrons emitted from x-ray
irradiated compounds. The ultimate parameter measured
by the technique is the electron binding energy. The
principles of x-ray photoelectron spectroscopy have long
been known, and several early attempts were made to
apply the technique in chemistry; however, it remained
for nuclear spectroscopists to provide instrumentation
with sufficient resolving power to enable its successful
chemical application.

Kai Siegbahn and co-workers of the Institute of
Physics at Uppsala University in Sweden first utilized
a double-focusing, iron-free, magnetic spectrometer for
high-resolution energy analysis of photoejected electrons. They discussed the basic theory of the instrument in 1946 and described the double-focusing instrument in 1956. The relevance of x-ray photoelectron
spectroscopy to chemical analysis became evident with
the discovery by the Uppsala group of shifts in core-
electron binding energies of the same element in different compounds. The first chemical shifts were observed for Cu and CuO. The initial studies of the chemical shift for many of the elements led the Uppsala
group to use the acronym ESCA (Electron Spectroscopy for

Chemical Analysis) to describe their technique. With
the publication of the first ESCA monograph by Siegbahn
et al. in 1967, the general utility of the technique to
chemical problems was realized.

The pioneering work of the Uppsala group stirred
the interest of physicists and chemists around the world.
In the United States, D. A. Shirley and J. M. Hollander
of the Lawrence Radiation Laboratory at the University
of California at Berkeley, D. M. Hercules of the Massachusetts Institute of Technology (later at the University
of Georgia and now at Pittsburgh), and R. G. Albridge
of Vanderbilt University began x-ray photoelectron spectroscopic studies with iron-free magnetic spectrometers
similar in design to that described by Siegbahn. Simultaneously, T. A. Carlson and M. Krause at the Oak Ridge
National Laboratory designed an electrostatic spectrometer similar to the prototype first described by Siegbahn in his monograph. The groups employing magnetic
focusing spectrometers were plagued by stray magnetic
fields. Because electron trajectories are influenced
by magnetic fields, it is necessary to have the trajectory determined only by the field of the electron monochromator. Therefore, the earth's magnetic field and
any gradients near a magnetic spectrometer must be reduced to 10^{-4} gauss (G) by a system of Helmholtz coils.
The MIT group found that when using a magnetic spectrometer in an urban area, difficulties with simple Helmholtz systems are encountered, and feedback loops and
additional coils may be necessary. Despite an elaborate
Helmholtz coil system, they observed large fluctuations
in the 2-10 mG range depending upon the time of the day
and the day of the week. The fluctuations correlated
with traffic along city streets as well as a subway
station 600 meters away. Problems such as these slowed
progress using magnetic spectrometers, and thus emphasis
was on electrostatic focusing spectrometers that could
be simply shielded with paramagnetic material.

The lack of commercially available instrumentation
hindered the development of x-ray photoelectron spectroscopy as an analytical tool. Before 1970, to initiate
ESCA studies, one first had to construct the spectro-
meter--obviously, a major project in itself. Then, in
1970, Varian Associates began to market the IEE-15 Photoelectron Spectrometer. This was a spherical electrostatic instrument designed specifically to examine solid
samples with magnesium Kα x-ray excitation. No pro-
visions were available for any in situ treatment of the
sample. Since studies on the solid state are essentially
surface studies (mean electron escape depths up to ca.
10 nm), it is a great advantage to be able to perform
a large amount of sample handling in situ in the

spectrometer. Varian recognized this fact and began to offer a sample treatment chamber in which techniques such as argon ion etching could be used. The initial IEE-15 was installed at the Shell Development Co. in Emeryville, Calif.

Two other American firms, McPherson Instrument Corp. and Hewlett-Packard, Inc., had prototype instruments in operation in 1971. The McPherson instrument used a 36-inch radius hemispherical analyzer without any electron retardation before analysis. Turbo-molecular pumps were used, making the vacuum system compatible with clean surface analysis of solids and with analyses in the gas phase. The system included variable x-ray excitation sources, and ultraviolet and electron gun sources were also under development. Samples could be treated directly in the sample chamber. The Hewlett-Packard instrument was aimed solely at the x-ray market and solid samples. The prototype incorporated both an x-ray momochromator (Al $K\alpha$ excitation) to reduce the x-ray linewidth and a position sensitive detector. The system was compatible with high-vacuum work and contained a sample-handling chamber.

Two English firms, Associated Electronic Industries (AEI) and Vacuum Generators, also began to market instrumentation in 1971. Both systems were composed of hemispherical electrostatic analyzers. The AEI instrument was directed toward the x-ray market and contained a target chamber assembly that could be isolated from the analyzer and was flexible enough to facilitate sample handling in situ. In 1971 the Vacuum Generators instrument was the only one marketed that provided for x-ray, vacuum-ultraviolet, and electron-gun work and was ultra-high vacuum compatible.

In 1973 the Instrument Division of the DuPont Co. began to market a unique electron spectrometer. The DuPont analyzer was non-dispersive and consisted of a series of kinetic energy filters rather than the classic hemispherical design. This instrument was designed for application to the routine analysis of solids.

With time, all of the commercial spectrometers began to add peripheral features more in line with the direction of state-of-the-art research. This meant that features such as ultra-high vacuum compatibility, gas cells, variable temperature probes, variable excitation sources, sample manipulators, ion etching hardware, resolution enhancement accessories, etc. became routinely available on most commercial instruments. In addition, most instruments were either computer controlled or were compatible with such control.

The growth of x-ray photoelectron spectroscopy can also be monitored by considering the conferences and symposia that have been devoted to the technique. The earliest conferences were devoted to both ESCA and ultra-violet photoelectron spectroscopy (UPS). The first conference was sponsored by the Royal Society in London in 1969. The next conference was held at Uppsala, Sweden, in 1970 as a EUCHEM conference. In 1971 an international conference at Asilomar, Calif., was devoted to all aspects of electron spectroscopy (e.g., ESCA, UPS, and Auger). In April 1972 the Chemical Society of London sponsored a summer school in photoelectron spectroscopy at the University College of Swansea, Wales, that was devoted to both ESCA and UPS. In September of that same year, the Faraday Division of the Chemical Society arranged a discussion on the Photoelectron Spectroscopy of Molecules at the University of Sussex, Brighton, England. In April of 1974 J. Verbist and R. Caudano organized an international conference on electron spectroscopy at Namur, Belgium. They felt that the field had expanded to such a point that it was possible to devote the majority of the program to ESCA. In July of 1974 D. M. Hercules organized the first Gordon Research Conference in X-ray Photoelectron Spectroscopy at Wolfeboro, N. H. The number of participants at these last two conferences was greater than 100, indicating that the number of active ESCA investigators had increased very significantly with the ready availability of instrumentation.

In addition to special conferences, most meetings of the American Chemical Society and other similar organizations usually hold symposia devoted to electron spectroscopy. Each year since 1971, for example, the Pittsburgh Conference on Analytical Chemistry and Applied Spectroscopy holds a symposium related to analytical applications of ESCA. Even though fundamental problems may still exist, ESCA has become a standard analytical technique in many laboratories throughout the world.

In the first ESCA monograph the Uppsala group emphasized the use of the chemical shift as a structural probe. Their data suggested that specific functional groups would yield characteristic binding energies. Using the Siegbahn data, Hercules attempted to develop correlation charts relating $S(2p)$ and $N(1s)$ binding energies to functionality. The limited data gave results analogous to those found in the classic Colthup chart routinely used in structural analysis via infrared spectroscopy. However, as more and more data were accumulated, no straightforward single-atom correlations could be established. This situation was exemplified in the study by Jack and Hercules on a series of 60 quaternary nitrogen compounds in which the $N(1s)$ binding energies covered a range of about 5.0 eV. The total

range of N(1s) binding energies was only 10 eV; therefore, unambiguous identification of a species as a quaternary nitrogen based solely on the N(1s) binding energy
appeared impossible. This unfortunate result was attributed to counter ion effects and ring substitution
effects and suggested that a multiple-atom correlation
must be employed.

If proper precautions are taken in interpreting
binding energy data, ESCA can be used for structural
analysis. One of the earliest examples originated in
Uppsala where cystine S-dioxide was determined to exist
as the thiosulfonate structure. At Berkeley, Jolly and
co-workers combined N(1s) binding energies with atomic
charges calculated via extended Hückel techniques to
arrive at a structure for Angeli's salt, $Na_2N_2O_3$. The
Berkeley group was also the first to establish the difference in N(1s) binding energy between linear and bent
nitrosyl ligands in inorganic complexes. This chemical
shift has been used in several subsequent structural
studies on complex molecules. Ginnard and Riggs used
ESCA to determine the structure of fluoropolymers with
considerable success by studying the large chemical
shifts resulting from varying degrees of fluorine substitution along the polymer backbone. Swartz, Ruff, and
Hercules employed P(2p) and N(1s) binding energies to
obtain structural data on the bis(triphenylphosphine)
iminium cation, $\{[(C_6H_5)_3P]_2N\}^+$.

Space limitations dictate that only a few of the
earliest structural studies be mentioned here. The 1974
Analytical Chemistry review by Hercules and Carver gives
a more complete listing. The number of references in
the review clearly indicate that ESCA is now routinely
employed in many laboratories for structural analysis
of inorganic, organic, and biochemical compounds.

The intensity of a photoelectron spectral line is
proportional not only to the photoelectric cross section
of a particular atom but also to the number of atoms of
a particular element present in the sample. Therefore,
ESCA can also be applied to quantitative analysis.
Siegbahn and co-workers first demonstrated the quantitative aspect of ESCA by analyzing some organic compounds for carbon, chlorine, and sulfur and by determining the relative amounts of copper and zinc in brass.
The analyses were accurate to within 5-10%. The ability
of ESCA to analyze quantitatively mixtures of MoO_2 and
MoO_3 has been demonstrated by Swartz and Hercules. Before the advent of ESCA, no instrumental technique
existed that could perform this analysis. By measuring
the intensities of photoelectron lines in spectra obtained from known mixtures of the oxides at binding
energies characteristic of each oxide, a linear

calibration curve was obtained. A least-squares analysis of the data indicated the error to be ± 2% MoO_2. A series of analyses performed on synthetic unknowns yielded results consistent with this accuracy.

In applying ESCA to quantitative analysis, one must have an idea as to the relative sensitivity of detection of the elements. The first sensitivity data were those of C. D. Wagner of the Shell Development Co. The sensitivities of 43 elements were measured relative to the $F(1s)$ or $Na(1s)$ intensities from fluorine and sodium present in the solid compounds. More recently, Berthou and Jørgensen have expanded the listing to 76 elements. In addition, several models have been developed which relate the intensity of photoelectron lines to atomic and instrumental parameters.

Hercules and co-workers have reported a quantitative study elucidating several aspects of ESCA as a quantitative analytical technique. They found that (1) internal standards can be used effectively, (2) the relative standard deviation of calibration curves can be improved by using an inert matrix, and (3) the atomic sensitivity for a given element depends on the compound in which it is contained.

ESCA is primarily a surface technique, the photo-ejected electrons originating within the first ~ 2 nm of the surface. Inasmuch as ESCA has detected fractional monolayers, it has a high intrinsic sensitivity. These data indicate an inherent ability to measure 10^{-8} to 10^{-9} g or less of material. When applied to bulk analysis, ESCA is sensitive to concentrations of only ca. 0.1% even in the most favorable cases. To utilize the inherent sensitivity of ESCA for trace analysis, it is necessary to devise a way for the atoms or molecules of interest to be concentrated on the surface of a substrate. Several techniques have been reported. Hercules and co-workers have used a glass-fiber mat impregnated with a chelating agent such as dithiocarbamate to scavenge metal ions from solution. They reported detection limits of ca 10 ppb for lead, calcium, thallium, and mercury. Brinen and McClure have reported a method by which the trace metals are electrochemically deposited from solution. The electrode surface is then subjected to ESCA analysis. They easily detect 3×10^{-8} g of lead. Czuha and Riggs have reported a method using adsorption of the trace metals from solution by an ion exchange resin. Their data indicate that it is possible to detect 1 ppm of Cu^{2+}, Fe^{2+}, Ba^{2+}, Cd^{2+}, Ca^{2+}, Pb^{2+}, and Hg^{2+} in the resin after minimal exposure of the resin to the solution containing the trace metals. Clearly, ESCA has now developed to the point where it can be used as a very sensitive quantitative analytical probe if a method can

be found to isolate the element of interest on a substrate surface.

As mentioned above, ESCA is a surface technique.
As early as 1967 Siegbahn reported a mean escape depth
of 10 nm for the $I(3d_{5/2})$ photolines from layers of
iodostearic acid. More recent data indicate that escape
depths are closer to 2 nm. The surface sensitivity of
ESCA makes it an ideal technique for studying surface
phenomena such as catalysis and chemisorption. To study
chemisorption, the spectrometer must be compatible with
ultra-high vacuum in order to preserve the integrity of
the surface. The first chemisorption results were reported in 1972 by Brundle and Roberts. They studied the
adsorption of H_2O, CO_2, CO, and Hg on gold. Yates,
Madey, and Erickson at NBS have expanded their surface
science facilities to include ESCA. Winograd and co-
workers at Purdue University have been actively engaged
in studies of oxygen adsorption and oxidation of metal
surfaces. Many other groups throughout the world are
currently involved in ESCA studies of adsorption phenomena; however, it is impossible to mention all of them
here.

The first report to consider the application of ESCA
to catalysis was that of Fadley, Delgass, and Hughes in
1970. Their results unambiguously demonstrated the
value of ESCA as a probe of catalytic surfaces. It is
safe to say that most industrial laboratories with ESCA
capabilities are interested in studying catalysts. This
is evidenced by the early work of Ogilvie and co-workers
at Monsanto and Brinen and co-workers at American Cyanamid. In a report at the Namur conference, Brinen
clearly demonstrated the value of ESCA to studies of
industrial catalysts. Many additional catalytic studies
have been and will continue to be reported, since ESCA
is the only technique capable of elucidating the chemical
structure of a catalytic surface in both a qualitative
and quantitative fashion.

This report has emphasized the development of x-ray
photoelectron spectroscopy as an analytical technique.
Space limitations dictate that many results that have
contributed significantly to this development be omitted.
In addition, the invaluable studies involving analysis
of satellite structure, density of states, theoretical
calculation of binding energies, relaxation phenomena,
angular distributions, and many others have been omitted.
Obviously, all of the people involved in such studies
have played a role in advancing the status of the technique to its present prominent position. X-ray photoelectron spectroscopy is truly Electron Spectroscopy for
Chemical Analysis.

NUCLEAR MAGNETIC RESONANCE

Nuclear magnetic resonance (NMR) has become one of the most commonly utilized methods for obtaining structural as well as analytical and thermodynamic data on chemical systems in the solution phase. The popularity of the technique results from its sensitivity of measurement as well as from the ready availability of user-oriented instrumentation.

That a fundamental interaction is possible between radiant energy and magnetic fields was shown by Faraday in 1845, 20 years before Maxwell's theoretical exposition. Zeeman's 1896 publication describing the splitting of emission lines of atoms by a magnetic field demonstrated that electrons must possess a spin. In a famous atomic beam experiment, reported in 1922, Otto Stern and Walter Gerlach showed that even neutral atoms can possess net magnetic moments.

Magnetic moments ascribable to atomic nuclei were first postulated in 1924 by Pauli; he suggested that the hyperfine structure of some atomic spectral lines is the result of the interaction of the nuclear magnetic moment with the magnetic moments of the electrons in the atom. From today's perspective, a nuclear magnetic moment obviously could arise simply from the spinning of the charged nucleus about an axis. Such a spinning charge would give a magnetic dipole moment parallel to the axis of spin. The idea that nuclei possess spin received considerable support as a result of the discovery of ortho- and para-hydrogen by Dennison in 1927. Nuclear magnetic moments were actually measured in the 1930s by improved versions of the Stern-Gerlach experiment.

If nuclei with magnetic moments are spinning, a static magnetic field should cause a precession of the axis of spin around the lines of magnetic force. This conclusion follows directly from the work of Joseph Larmor, writing in 1900 about electron magnetic moments. If this theory is valid, it should be possible to observe a resonance effect if electromagnetic energy at the Larmor frequency is allowed to interact with the molecules while immersed in the specified magnetic field.

Nuclear magnetic resonance can be detected in one of two ways: (1) the loss of energy from the radiofrequency circuit can be observed as a dip or minimum in voltage as the frequency is swept across resonance, or (2) the energy that is re-emitted from the sample can be picked up by an orthogonal coil, amplified, and recorded. Both methods have been used extensively.

The first NMR spectra were obtained by I. I. Rabi and co-workers in 1939, when they obtained resonance absorption curves for ^{6}Li, ^{7}Li, and ^{19}F in LiCl and NaF molecular beams in high vacuum (see Figure 17). The first direct observations of the expected nuclear magnetic resonance in bulk material (solids and liquids) were reported almost simultaneously in 1945 by Felix Bloch at Stanford University, who worked in the emission mode, and by E. M. Purcell at Harvard, using the absorption method. Their work was so significant that they were jointly awarded the 1952 Nobel Prize in physics. Since these initial discoveries, advances in instrumentation and in chemical applications have been rapid.

Knowledge of atomic structure and information about relative natural abundances of isotopes led to the prediction that a major proportion of the elements could be detected and identified, perhaps even measured, by NMR absorptions. It would be necessary only to establish either the magnetic field strength or the applied frequency and then to scan the other of these quantities over a wide enough region to pick up signals from all these elements in one experiment. This method has not been as practicable as expected and has found relatively little application.

The Chemical Shift. Increased instrumental resolution produced unexpected dividends, however. In 1949 W. D. Knight at the Brookhaven National Laboratory observed different resonant frequencies for ^{63}Cu when he mixed solid copper metal powder and ^{63}CuCl in the same sample tube. Proctor and Yu, at Stanford in early 1950, observed different resonance frequencies for ^{14}N nuclei in solutions of NH_4^+ and NO_3^- ions. Dickinson, at MIT, reported that the ^{19}F nuclei in a series of compounds all had different resonant frequencies. He remarked,

> Most unexpectedly, it has been found that for ^{19}F the value of the applied magnetic field H_0 for nuclear magnetic resonance at a fixed radiofrequency depends on the chemical compound containing the fluorine nucleus. The assumption has generally been made that the time average of all internal magnetic fields is zero. . .

Similar observations were made by H. A. Thomas at the National Bureau of Standards, who detected different resonant field strengths for ^{1}H nuclei in water, H_2, and mineral oil; G. Lindström at the Nobel Institute for Physics, who made similar observations for the protons in water and paraffin wax; and E. L. Hahn at the University of Illinois, who found different resonant fields for the ^{19}F resonances in mixtures of fluorine-containing hydrocarbons.

In 1951 J. T. Arnold and his associates at Stanford obtained the first spectra that showed separate resonances for the hydrogen nuclei in different locations in

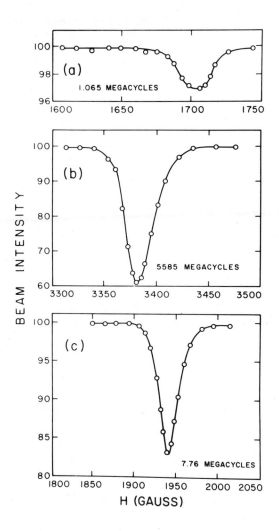

Figure 17. Rabi's magnetic resonance spectra for (a) ^{6}Li, (b) ^{7}Li, and (c) ^{19}F, in molecular beams.

the same molecule. Their spectra of the first five primary aliphatic alcohols demonstrated that it would be
possible to identify the chemically different types of
protons in a molecule from their resonance positions.
Their spectrum for ethyl alcohol (Figure 18) shows peak
separations of 16 ± 3 and 37 ± 5 mG. The ratio of the
areas of the peaks was 1:2.1:3 and immediately led them
to assign the resonances (respectively, left to right)
to the protons of the -OH, -CH$_2$-, and -CH$_3$ groups.
Their success was due to the great care taken to obtain
a stable and homogeneous magnetic field H_0, so that the
entire sample experienced the same instantaneous external field.

These relative changes could be tabulated as "chemical shifts," δ, defined by the relation

$$\delta = \frac{H_R - H_S}{H_R}$$

where H_R is the resonant field for an isotope in some
reference compound, and H_S is that for the same isotope
in the sample. For hydrogen NMR, the protons in water
often served as standards in early work, but now the 12

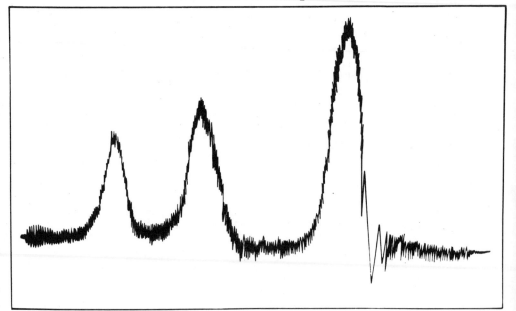

Figure 18. The first published NMR spectrum showing the chemical
shifts in ethanol.

identical protons in tetramethylsilane (TMS), proposed by G. V. D. Tiers in 1958, are almost universally used in this capacity.

The first analytical applications of NMR to be published were described in an article in 1955 by T. M. Shaw and R. H. Elsken on the determination of the total number of hydrogen atoms in organic liquids and in a paper in 1956 by C. F. Callis, J. R. Van Wazer, and J. N. Shoolery on the quantitative determination of various oxyacids of phosphorus in mixtures.

Spin-Spin Coupling. After the discovery of field-dependent chemical shifts, and with a steady improvement in the homogeneity of the external magnetic fields, some compounds were found to exhibit more resonances than expected simply on the basis of the number of different types of nuclei in the sample. For example, the ^{19}F NMR spectrum of PF_3 has two peaks or resonance absorptions, even though there is only one chemically unique type of fluorine present. Furthermore, the separation between these two peaks is field independent, which means that the peaks could not be due to a chemical shift phenomenon. H. S. Gutowsky and co-workers at Illinois (1953) and N. F. Ramsey and E. M. Purcell at Harvard (1952) proposed that this splitting or multiple resonance is due to the interactions between different nuclear spins. In this example, the ^{19}F nucleus can "sense" the spin of a bonding electron. This electron is strongly coupled to other bonding electrons on the phosphorus atom, so that the spin of the ^{31}P nucleus is passed on to the ^{19}F nuclei. The energy of this interaction is given by

$$\Delta E = \hbar \, J_{AB} I_A I_B$$

in which J_{AB} is the "spin-spin coupling constant," $\hbar$ is Planck's constant, and I_A and I_B are the spin quantum numbers of atoms A and B. This theoretical interpretation is that of H. S. Gutowsky and E. L. Hahn and their respective co-workers, both groups reporting in 1951. Figure 19 shows the improvement in resolution obtained during the 1950s.

Progress toward greater resolution and sensitivity has depended on instrumentation. The signal strength varies with the square of the magnetic field, while for a specific resonance, the ratio of the required alternating frequency to the magnetic flux must be constant. Hence to improve the response, the instrument designer must strive toward greater field strength with concurrently higher frequency. For proton resonance, the frequency-to-field ratio (the gyromagnetic ratio) is $4.255 \text{ MHz} \cdot \text{kG}^{-1}$. The state-of-the-art commercial proton

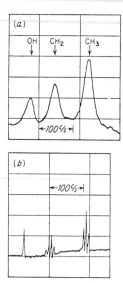

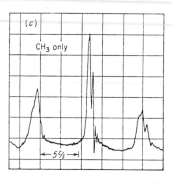

Figure 19. NMR spectra of ethanol at successively greater resolutions, reflecting the improvement in spectrometers during the 1950s.

NMR instruments for a number of years used frequencies and fields as follows:

Year	Frequency, MHz	Field, kG
1953	30	7.04
1955	40	9.38
1958	60	14.09
1962	100	23.50
1966	220	51.70

Since large magnets are expensive, a compromise is often necessary. Most proton NMR instruments in use today operate at 60 MHz, with 100 MHz a strong second. Fields over about 25 kG are produced with superconducting magnets.

The combination of chemical shift data and spin-spin coupling data is immensely useful for determining structural features of a molecule. After the initial discoveries, considerable effort was devoted to tabulating and organizing chemical shift data as well as to correlating spin-spin coupling constants with physical characteristics of molecules. One of the most important and useful correlations has stemmed from the theoretical work of M. Karplus in 1963 on the relationship between the value of spin-spin coupling constants and the dihedral angle between bonds. A plot of Karplus' relation,

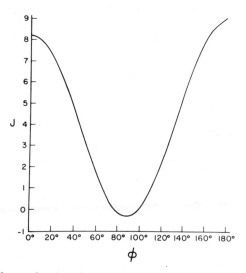

Figure 20. The relation between the spin-spin coupling constant, J, and the bond angle, φ.

utilizing the improved data of A. A. Bothner-By (1965) is presented in Figure 20. The development of this relationship has been the basis for most of the conformational studies done by the NMR technique and also has served as a model for deriving similar relationships for other spin-spin coupled systems.

Double-Resonance Techniques. A further important advance was introduced by V. Royden (1954) and A. L. Bloom and J. N. Shoolery (1955). Their contribution consists in irradiating the sample at the frequency of resonance for a selected NMR-active nucleus, at a power level great enough to cause saturation, while at the same time observing related resonances with the usual low power. This causes the spin coupling of the saturated nucleus to other nuclei to collapse, simplifies spin-spin splittings, and allows the unambiguous identification of the nuclei that are coupled to the other nuclei in the NMR spectrum.

F. A. L. Anet and A. J. R. Bourn, in 1965, brought to the attention of chemists another form of double resonance, known as the nuclear Overhauser effect (NOE). In this technique, saturation of protons at a specific location in an organic molecule produces enhancement of resonances of other protons near the molecule. This result is caused by interference with the normal relaxation mechanism. The effect is useful in assigning spectral peaks to specific protons, and, even more important, in elucidating structure. The latter application was first reported in 1967 by M. C. Woods et al. in connection with studies of a series of 20-carbon multicyclic lactones isolated from the leaves of the ginkgo tree.

Data Processing. Another major concern has been increased sensitivity to allow studies of samples of lower concentration (for example, biological samples), or samples available only in microgram quantities, as well as of nuclei which do not enjoy the sensitivity and natural abundance of ^1H and ^{19}F. One of the first solutions to the problem of weak signals or poor signal-to-noise ratio (S/N) was the introduction of the CAT (Computer of Average Transients) manufactured by Technical Measurements Corp. This device was first reported in connection with NMR by M. P. Klein and G. W. Barton and by L. C. Allen and L. F. Johnson, both in 1963. In the CAT the voltage signal from the spectrometer is converted into digital form, stored and summed in digital counters, while providing for a simultaneous visual display and readout by an oscilloscope, digital counter, or an X-Y recorder. Signal buildup is proportional to the number of sweeps, while the noise accumulates as the square root of the number of sweeps. The result is essentially equivalent to improving the signal by the square root of the number of sweeps while maintaining constant noise level. A serious drawback to the use of the CAT is the fact that even though one can increase the S/N ratio and amplify weak signals, the time required to obtain spectra increases dramatically. For applications to less abundant nuclei such as ^{13}C, the use of the CAT, although it allows one to obtain spectra, requires so much time that its use is impractical.

Probably the most significant recent development in NMR has been the introduction of pulse techniques by E. L. Hahn in 1950 and the use of Fourier transform methods by R. R. Ernst and W. A. Anderson in 1966. In the pulsed NMR experiment, instead of sweeping the frequency range of interest as a function of time, one simultaneously irradiates all the nuclei by applying a pulse of high power radiofrequency energy of the appropriate bandwidth to excite all nuclei at the same time. All of the nuclear frequencies are then recorded together, and by performing an inverse Fourier transform on the observed signal, a conventional NMR spectrum is obtained that contains peaks for all the absorbing nuclei in the sample. The chief advantage of this method is that it is possible to obtain one NMR spectrum in a matter of milliseconds as opposed to a conventional

continuous wave method that requires 200-500 seconds.
By combining the pulse method, the Fourier transform
technique, and signal averaging, the equivalent of thousands of sweeps can be accomplished in the time that it
would have taken to do one sweep by conventional methods.
This improves the S/N ratio by a factor of 50-100. Pulse
and Fourier NMR spectrometers are now the preferred form
for commercial NMR spectrometers, even for nuclei such
as ^1H and ^{19}F where sensitivity is not a problem. (The
large initial cost, of course, rules them out for some
laboratories.) The improvement in sensitivity of these
techniques makes virtually all nuclei with non-zero spins
accessible to NMR measurements.

ELECTRON SPIN RESONANCE

The discovery of the magnetic resonance phenomenon
for unpaired electrons is attributed to a Russian scientist, E. Zavoyskii, who in 1944 observed a resonance
peak due to Cu^{2+} at 47.6 G, using an irradiation frequency of 133 MHz. Cummerow and Halliday in the United
States (1945) followed closely with the detection of
Mn^{2+} in $MnSO_4 \cdot 4H_2O$ excited at 2930 MHz. The next year
Bagguley and Griffiths in England observed resonance
from Cr^{3+} ions in a chrome alum crystal at 9434 MHz.

For the next 10 years paramagnetic resonance research was developed mainly by physicists in the Claren-
don Laboratory in England, at the Kazan State University
in the Soviet Union, and by various workers in America--
e.g., G. E. Pake, W. Gordy, G. Feher, and A. Abragam.
Most if not all of this work was done on solids, usually
as single crystals. During this time physical chemists
were beginning to experiment with paramagnetic resonance
of liquid solutions containing paramagnetic molecules.
Among the early U. S. workers were S. I. Weissman (1952),
G. K. Fraenkel (1953), H. S. Jarrett (1954), and J. E.
Wertz (1955).

Certainly a major advance in the field was the
availability of a commercial electron spin resonance
(ESR) spectrometer in the late 1950s produced by Varian
Associates. Through workshops the Varian staff famil-
iarized interested scientists with ESR theory, the construction and operation of the spectrometer, and the
interpretation of spectra. Soon numerous Varian spectrometers were purchased by schools and industries.
Unfortunately, many of these, particularly in industry,
gathered dust because most of the early attempts to
detect free radicals met with little or no success.
Only very stable or long-lived neutral free radicals
could be kept in solutions at concentrations above the

detection threshold of the spectrometer (10^{-8} M). Ion radicals, however, are more stable, and a surge of ESR investigations of such species occurred during the 10-year period following the availability of the Varian instrument. Early methods of forming radical ions in solution were reduction with alkali metals or other electron donors and oxidation by air or mild oxidizing agents. Analytical chemists in the United States developed electrolytic methods of reducing or oxidizing appropriate compounds to radical ions (Geske, 1960; Adams, 1962), but no quantitative uses of ESR were introduced at this time.

Techniques to detect short-lived, reactive neutral free radicals developed more slowly. Two methods produced many interesting early results. The first was developed in the United States in 1963. It required a unique spectrometer with fast electron irradiation through the pole piece of the magnet, of a non-polar liquid filling the cavity--e.g., propane. This process gave, among other things, the propyl radical. The second method, devised in Europe and England in 1964, involved a rapid flow-mixing system with fast flow of sample through the cavity of the ESR spectrometer. Only recently (1974) have some results using the latter technique been quantitated by Czapski.

Analytical usefulness of the ESR technique has been hindered by the lack of good textbooks or reference books from which to teach and/or to learn. Only Ingram's 1958 monograph or that published by Blois in 1961 were available for the non-theoretical approach to ESR in the early 1960s. Books translated from the Russian, by Buchachenko and by Al'tshuler and Kozyrev, became available by the middle of the decade, and that by Forrester, Hay, and Thomson by 1969. However, none of these were really suitable for teaching a course to introduce the potential applications of ESR to students. Hence many chemists still feel that ESR is a "difficult" area, which must be approached from a theoretical point of view and which has few if any analytical applications. Reference to two review articles by E. G. Janzen in *Analytical Chemistry* (1972 and 1974) shows that this impression is slowly changing. The analytical methods listed are directed on the one hand toward complex ions of those transition metals with unpaired electrons, and on the other, toward drugs and other organic compounds that can exist as, or be converted to, comparatively stable radical ions.

NUCLEAR QUADRUPOLE RESONANCE

Nuclear quadrupole resonance spectroscopy (NQR) is that branch of magnetic resonance spectroscopy concerned with the absorption of energy from radiofrequency radiation by matter in zero external magnetic field. The only requirement is that the sample contain nuclides with quadrupole moments. Even though about 70 of the known elements have such moments, and therefore are available for examination by NQR, only the ^{35}Cl and ^{14}N isotopes have seen extensive investigation and use in analytical work.

In sharp contrast to NMR, the frequencies of NQR depend solely on the nature of the molecule of which the quadrupolar nucleus is a part, and can range in practice from a few hundred kilohertz to over one gigahertz for some of the heavier nuclei.

The first zero-field quadrupole resonance to be observed was by W. Nierenberg, N. F. Ramsey, and S. B. Brody in 1946, using a molecular beam technique. The first successful NQR experiment in solids was reported by H. G. Dehmelt and H. Krüger in *Naturwissenschaften* in 1950. Their instrument used a super-regenerative electronic oscillator--a device that was improved and used extensively by C. Dean (1958), reporting in the *Review of Scientific Instruments*. It is this type of instrument with which most NQR measurements have been made.

During most of the 26 years since the work of Dehmelt and Krüger, NQR has been regarded as a tool of the physicists in their effort to study condensed phase systems amenable to the method. A considerable data base has been accumulated on ^{35}Cl resonances, particularly through the efforts of P. J. Bray (1957-58), H. O. Hooper (1960), S. L. Segal, and others in the United States and of E. I. Fedin and G. K. Semin in Russia (1963). Bray and C. T. O'Konski have likewise provided basic data on ^{14}N resonances.

It was shown by M. Bloom and R. E. Norberg and by E. L. Hahn and B. Herzog, both in 1954, that pulse techniques, such as used in NMR, are applicable also to NQR, but very little use has been made of this observation.

NQR was brought to the attention of analytical chemists largely through articles in *Analytical Chemistry* by R. S. Drago (1966) and E. G. Brame, Jr., (1967). J. A. S. Smith, writing in the *Journal of Chemical Education* in 1971, lists a number of chemical applications, including studies of molecular point-symmetry in crystals of compounds containing Cl, N, or both; the use of NQR spectra as a "fingerprint" identification tool (it is less discriminating than proton NMR but applicable to different nuclei); and studies of inductive and mesomeric effects. Reports of NQR spectra for compounds containing ^{69}Ga, ^{59}Co, ^{55}Mn, and ^{185}Re nuclei are described.

NQR is a technique in its infancy with respect to analytical applications, comparable with NMR in the early 1950s. What its status will be 25 years from now is open to speculation.

MASS SPECTROMETRY

The discovery of positive rays in a discharge, by E. Goldstein in 1886, and the discovery by W. Wien in 1898 that these rays could be bent by electric or magnetic fields led to the thorough investigation of positive rays by Sir J. J. Thomson. His device for their analysis used ions with a wide range of velocities and produced parabolic curves on a photographic plate. From these plates came the first observation of the existence of isotopes, ^{20}Ne and ^{22}Ne. A. J. Dempster, at the University of Chicago, built an instrument in 1918, in which the energy of all ions was the same, leading to a sharp focus rather than a parabolic trace. This prototype of modern magnetic deflection instruments yields masses of ions according to the well-known formula:

$$\frac{m}{e} = \frac{H^2 r^2}{2V}$$

in which H and V refer respectively to the strength of the magnetic field and the applied accelerating potential, and r is the radius of the trajectory. (In this, as all other types of mass spectrometer discussed, the mass-to-charge ratio, m/e, is referred to as the "mass number" since in most ions the charge is unity, i.e., one electronic charge.)

Thomson's instrument had features in common with Classen's instrument used to determine the mass-to-charge ratio of the electron, described in 1907. It could resolve masses up to about 100 amu. In 1919 Francis W. Aston, who was Thomson's student, described an instrument in which ions were focused on a plane, irrespective of the fields employed, so that a photoplate could be used, not possible in the Dempster design. In describing the ion optics, Aston said, "Since it is a close analogue of the ordinary spectrograph, and gives a 'spectrum' depending upon mass alone, the instrument is called a 'mass-spectrograph,' and the spectrum it produces, a 'mass spectrum.'"

Aston's researches into the nuclides composing various elements led to his Nobel Prize in 1922. In his

FRANCIS WILLIAM ASTON, 1877-1945

    Educated at the University of Birmingham, Aston accepted an
invitation from J. J. Thomson to be his assistant at the Cavendish
Laboratory, Cambridge, where he remained for his entire career.
He was primarily an experimentalist, with little interest in theoretical matters or in teaching. He converted Thomson's mass
spectrograph into an instrument capable of the high precision
needed for isotope studies. He received the Nobel Prize for
Chemistry in 1922.

studies, he made use for the first time of fragment ions since he used methyl bromide to study the isotopes of bromine, sulfur dioxide to study sulfur, methyl iodide to study iodine, and the carbonyls of nickel and iron to study those metals. Little note was made outside of Aston's and Dempster's laboratories of the ability of the ionizing beam to rupture bonds in organic molecules. The first quantitative analysis of a mixture by mass spectrometry was performed in 1927 (published in 1931); it consisted in the determination of the components of a gaseous organic reaction mixture.

Around 1930 a number of developments profoundly changed the picture, paving the way for the measurement of isotope ratios. First, there was interest in measurements of ionization potentials and collision cross sections of gases bombarded by electrons of known energy; mass spectrometers and other instruments were developed for such measurements. At the University of Minnesota, the students of Professor J. T. Tate, particularly Walter Bleakney, Wallace Lozier, and Phillip T. Smith, developed ingenious instruments whose outstanding feature was the magnetically collimated beam of ionizing electrons perpendicular to the direction in which ions were drawn out. In contrast to high-voltage discharges or other modes of ionization, there was a simple quantitative relation between the intensity and energy of the electron beam and of the ions produced. Moreover, the ions had only a very small energy spread, so mass analysis was possible with a simple uniform magnetic field.

Other timely developments which influenced the technology were the use of improved high-vacuum techniques and the invention of the electrometer vacuum tube. In much of the early work in mass spectroscopy, waxed and greased joints were used, and vacuum conditions were poor. The new instruments, with all-Pyrex glass housings and properly trapped mercury diffusion pumps, could be thoroughly baked at high temperatures, eliminating impurities that could give spurious ion currents and minimizing stray electric fields caused by insulating coatings on electrodes of the instruments. The commercial availability of electrometer tubes revolutionized the quantitative measurement of small ion currents.

Finally, there was the new interest in nuclear physics, which made necessary an improved knowledge of relative abundances of stable isotopes and information on the existence or nonexistence of rare species. The more common ones had already been demonstrated by the early work of Aston and of Dempster.

A 180° magnetic deflection instrument designed by Bleakney at Princeton in 1932 set the basic pattern for the next two decades with respect to isotope abundance

measurements, electron impact studies, and gas analysis
by mass spectrometry. With this instrument Bleakney
accurately measured the ionization potential of molecular
hydrogen among other things, verified the existence of
the heavy isotope of hydrogen (deuterium), and measured
the relative abundances of the neon isotopes. Lozier
constructed a similar instrument at Columbia, subsequently used by Urey and his students and colleagues in
their pioneer studies on isotope separation by exchange
reactions. Another instrument constructed at Columbia
was used by Schoenheimer and Rittenberg and their associates in a variety of pioneering metabolism experiments
using ^{15}N as a tracer.

Meanwhile, at Minnesota, instruments patterned after
Bleakney's Princeton instrument were constructed in the
mid-1930s and used for electron impact studies to determine what would today still be regarded as remarkably
accurate measurements of isotope abundance ratios in
carbon, nitrogen, argon, and neon, and for ionization
studies of alkali metal vapors, krypton, and xenon. The
latter work utilized a spectrometer designed and constructed by P. T. Smith. Whereas the Bleakney-style
instruments were contained in a cylindrical glass enve-
lope which slid inside of a solenoid, the Smith version
had the 180° mass analyzer mounted in a horseshoe-shaped
glass appendage sealed at right angles to a glass tube
holding the ion source. This feature meant that larger,
and hence higher resolution, instruments could be constructed without sacrificing the bakeable feature so
important in ensuring cleanliness and integrity of the
performance.

A. O. Nier, as a new graduate student in physics
at Minnesota, copied the Smith design and in 1936 built
an enlarged instrument to fit into a 7-inch diameter
solenoid, able to resolve masses up to 100. He intended
to study fragmentation of relatively heavy hydrocarbons
by electron impact and indeed produced the first reliable
mass spectrum of benzene. The results were never published as it was a time when interest in electron impact
studies was waning and there was growing interest in
nuclear physics. With this instrument, he also established the existence of a rare isotope of potassium,
^{40}K, having an abundance of only 1/8300 that of ^{39}K,
the principal isotope.

The instrument was modified further when Nier went
to Harvard to work with K. T. Bainbridge as a post-doctoral fellow. The electron beam region was shortened
sufficiently that the entire ion source as well as the
ion analyzer section would fit in a simple horseshoe-
shaped glass tube that could be mounted between the poles
of an electromagnet. The stronger magnetic field of the

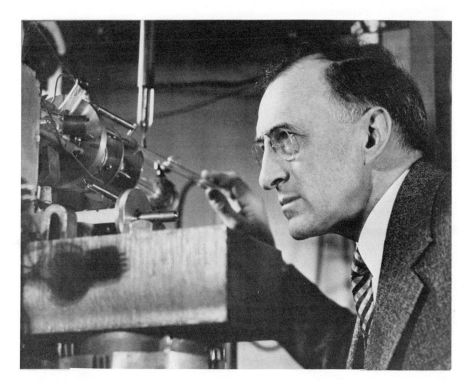

ARTHUR JEFFREY DEMPSTER, 1886–1950

Professor of Physics at the University of Chicago, Dempster
is shown here adjusting his mass spectrograph, the first to be
built in the United States.

electromagnet and the larger radius of curvature of the ion beam trajectory greatly increased the mass dispersion and resolution. As a result, masses above 200 amu could easily be resolved and the measurements could be extended to the entire atomic table without sacrificing the vacuum integrity which had proved so important for low mass studies. Precise determinations of lead and uranium isotope abundances, now possible, were of particular interest to those concerned with determining geological ages. The high performance of the instrument made it · an ideal model for mass spectrometers designed to analyze organic gas mixtures when such instruments were first produced commercially for the petroleum industry. The first such instrument in America was the CEC 21-101 (Consolidated Engineering Co.). It was used primarily for quantitative analysis of mixtures of light gases and of light hydrocarbons during World War II. A 90° magnetic deflection instrument was designed by J. A. Hipple, a former student of Bleakney's, at the Westinghouse Research Laboratory, and was produced commercially for isotope and gas analysis.

When America entered World War II there were, in effect, only a few laboratories in the world which could design and construct mass spectrometers suitable for rapid, accurate, gas or isotope analysis. All were located in the United States. While mass spectrographs and some types of mass spectrometers had been built in Europe and Japan, the American technology, so far as the use of advanced vacuum techniques and electronic circuitry was concerned, was far ahead.

When the decision was made to develop the atomic bomb in the United States, the need for isotopic analysis of uranium and hydrogen on a production scale became apparent. The Office of Scientific Research and Development (OSRD) awarded contracts to the University of Minnesota for the development and construction of a pilot number of instruments for uranium and hydrogen analysis and for a small, portable, unit for vacuum leak detection. Thus the helium leak detector was born. Samples from the various laboratories working on separation techniques were sent to Minnesota until the middle of 1942, when instruments built at Minnesota were sent to Columbia University and the University of Virginia, where subsequent measurements were made. The General Electric Co. received a contract to produce both uranium analysis mass spectrometers and helium leak detectors based on the Minnesota designs. By the end of the war, many of these instruments were in use in the Manhattan Project, particularly at Oak Ridge.

Fragmentation Patterns. In 1945 the first report

generalizing rules for aliphatic hydrocarbon fragmentation was published by H. W. Washburn, H. F. Wiley, S. M.
Rock, and C. E. Berry of Consolidated Engineering Co.
From such studies came the so-called "type analysis" of
various classes of organic compounds. These naturally
invited speculation about the chemistry involved in
breaking bonds. Following the introduction of the heated
inlet and reservoir by O'Neal and Weir in 1951, it became possible to examine the spectra of many classes of
compounds, not only the volatile hydrocarbons but also
more polar types. By 1956 F. W. McLafferty had pointed
out that concepts used to explain reaction mechanisms
of organic compounds in solution could also be applied
to fragmentation in the mass spectrometer and had set
the stage for qualitative analysis of organic compounds
by mass spectrometry. At the same time, the first applications of deuterium labeling were used to elucidate the
decomposition of organic ions; the classical studies in
this area encompass the work of S. Meyerson on the ring
expansion of ionized alkylbenzenes and derivatives to
give, frequently but not always, the seven-carbon tro-
pylium ion, $C_7H_7^+$. These "rules for fragmentation,"
along with organic chemical intuition, were used to
determine the structures of complex organic materials
by J. H. Beynon and were especially applied in natural
product chemistry by K. Biemann and by E. Stenhagen,
beginning in the late 1950s.

   <u>High Resolution</u>. Again, beginning in 1956, Beynon
began to popularize high-resolution mass spectroscopy
as a tool in organic structural determination. The
reason was that determination of the mass to a few ten-
thousandths of an atomic mass unit would allow determination of the empirical formula of the ion. For example, the only combination of ^{12}C (12.0000), ^1H
(1.007825), ^{16}O (15.9949), and ^{14}N (14.0031) which adds
to give 266.1995 is $C_{15}H_{26}O_2N_2$. For complex molecules
this approach greatly simplifies the interpretation of
the spectrum. It requires a significantly more expensive mass spectrometer because it is necessary to
define the energy of the ions very precisely to control
their orbits for accurate readings. Both the energy
and the paths of the ions must be properly focused.
This requirement gives rise to the inclusion of an electric sector to define the energy of a beam of ions
leaving its exit slit. Two different instrument geome-
tries have been developed to permit this focusing--one
by J. Mattauch and R. Herzog and the other by A. O. Nier
and E. G. Johnson. The first permits simultaneous
focusing of all ions in a plane, so that a photographic
plate can be used for detection; the other focuses the

ALFRED OTTO CARL NIER, 1911–

After pursuing his graduate education in physics at the University of Minnesota, Nier joined the faculty of his Alma Mater, and has been there almost continuously ever since. He has made many significant contributions in mass spectroscopy, where his name is best known in connection with the design of a widely used high-resolution instrument.

ions, one at a time, as the magnetic field is swept, thus requiring electrical detection. Most contemporary instruments for high-resolution organic analysis have adopted the latter method, although there are still times when simultaneous recording of all ions is desirable or necessary. In these cases the Mattauch-Herzog geometry must be used.

The generation of so much data when the masses of all ions are measured with high precision was a problem perceived by Biemann to be suitable for computer handling, and he made this point in 1964. This was not, however, the beginning of applications of computers to problems in mass spectrometry; that had occurred in 1951, when W. H. King and W. Priestley, Jr., described a punched-card calculator to solve the quantitative analysis of a mixture by deconvolution of the mass spectrum (or of the infrared spectrum) of the mixture into its components and showed that it required much less time than a desk calculator. Data acquisition by computers has been directed along two paths where large quantities of data are generated: the problem just stated with high-resolution mass spectra and the repeated sampling of gas chromatographic effluents with a moderate resolution mass spectrometer. More of that, later.

Sample Handling. To return to the early applications of mass spectrometry to organic analysis, a key step in organic sample analysis has always been taken whenever samples of lesser volatility have been brought within the scope of the technique. The introduction of a heated inlet system with a reservoir, in 1951, by M. J. O'Neal, Jr., and T. P. Wier, made it possible to obtain spectra of representative compounds from typical classes. The invention by Sites at Oak Ridge and by R. I. Reed of Glasgow of the direct introduction probe made it possible to examine much less volatile samples. In this device a small amount of the sample is mounted at the end of a heatable probe and is brought directly into the source of the mass spectrometer so that the sample ultimately sits only a few millimeters away from the ionizing beam of electrons. Anything exerting a vapor pressure of 10^{-7} torr without exceeding its decomposition temperature could be run if the probe could be heated high enough. For the first time many natural products could be studied. Cholesterol, which routinely suffered dehydration to cholestadiene if it were run through the heated inlet system, became a standard compound for comparison of different manufacturers' direct probes: the more intense the molecular ion of cholesterol, the better the probe.

A quite different method of introducing the sample,

which has become immensely popular, particularly in biochemical laboratories, has been the use of the effluent
from a gas chromatograph directly. Prior to this innovation, samples had to be collected in U-tubes from the
effluent for future mass spectrometric analysis via the
usual introduction techniques. The first direct coupling
of a gas chromatograph with a mass spectrometer was
reported by R. S. Gohlke in 1957. A difficulty came up
almost immediately: in order to have sufficient sample
to produce a usable spectrum, the helium carrier gas
pressure in the source was excessively high, so that a
simple stream splitter could not be applied. To circumvent this problem, devices were invented to enrich
the gas passing into the source of the mass spectrometer
in the desired organic compounds. The device of J. T.
Watson and K. Biemann was based on pumping the helium
away laterally through a glass frit; that of R. Ryhage,
upon a jet of gas through a nozzle in which the heavier
molecules are most likely to reach an orifice some
distance away in line with the nozzle opening; that of
Llewellyn, on differential migration through a membrane.
These were among the most popular devices although there
were others. More recently, with the use of larger
capacity vacuum pumps, a capillary gas chromatograph
effluent can be fed directly into the mass spectrometer;
when helium enters the source at only a few milliliters
per minute at atmospheric pressure, it can be pumped
away easily. There has also been some experimentation
with other carrier gases, suitable for chemical ionization purposes, which is discussed later. Here the presence of a carrier gas at a high pressure is desirable
since it controls the type of ionization which occurs.

Computer Applications. The application of computers
to handle the data from a gas chromatograph-mass spectrometer has been a powerful processing tool. The data
from one experiment may include hundreds of spectra;
processing it may include subtraction of background or
of other spectra, and the presentation of data may include the intensities of all ions per spectrum as a
function of spectrum number (and therefore time) to give
a regenerated gas chromatogram or the intensity of only
one key peak in each spectrum--which may be characteristic of a certain compound or class of compounds--an
idea of Biemann's. The result plotted against spectrum
number is variously called a mass chromatogram or a
mass fragmentogram.

The other major use of computers in mass spectrometry is the identification of compounds from their
spectra. Because mass spectra contain intensity information in discrete channels--integral mass units for low

resolution spectra--they are ideally suited for this kind of study. There have been two approaches. One has been to compare a spectrum with spectra retrieved from a large library; various algorithms for this comparison have been devised, of which the search systems of Biemann and Heller are the most widely used. Another approach has been derived from the methods of pattern recognition developed by computer scientists, in which the computer itself, by trial and error, may devise a procedure for identifying some feature of the compound by examining a number of spectra in a known set of compounds possessing this feature. T. L. Isenhour and P. C. Jurs have been at the front of these studies. McLafferty has taken the best features of the computer-training techniques and the information retrieval methods to produce a hybrid technique useful not only for matching a known compound but for identifying a new one. Libraries of spectra are deposited at several major installations around the world and include tens of thousands of spectra.

Ion Sources. We turn now to the ion sources developed for use in mass spectrometers. The most common in organic analysis is the electron-impact source, introduced by Dempster in 1921. In its present form a tungsten or rhenium ribbon serving as the cathode is heated to a high temperature by passing a current through it. Electrons are emitted, collimated by magnets so that they strike molecules of the sample and ionize them according to the reaction, $M + e^- \rightarrow M^+ + 2e^-$, in only a small volume out of the total source volume. The electrons that avoid collision are collected at an anode which is set about 70-80 volts more positive than the filament. Negative ions formed by attachment of electrons (or by attachment followed by dissociation) are formed, at this ionizing voltage, only about 10^{-4} times as frequently as positive ions. The lower sensitivity of the technique for negative ions has retarded their use in organic structural analysis. The greatest amount of structural interpretation of negative ions that has been reported has come from the laboratories of M. von Ardenne, C. Djerassi, and J. H. Bowie; they have generally worked at lower ionizing energies.

Compounds which cannot survive the heating necessary to vaporize them or which fragment so rapidly that no molecular ions remain for molecular weight determination severely limited mass spectrometry, when only the electron-impact mode of ionization was readily available. In 1953 E. W. Müller first observed ionization by the technique we now call field ionization and which has been commercially available for several years. A. J. B.

Robertson, H. D. Beckey, and others, developed the mass
spectrometric techniques related to the phenomenon.
Here the gas is ionized near a metal tip in a strong
electric field gradient; the electrons tunnel through
an energy barrier to the metal surface. An adaptation
in which the sample is actually adsorbed on the surface
from solution and then ionized and desorbed by a similar
mechanism is called field desorption and is only now
coming into use. The first successful experiments were
done by Beckey in 1969, although they had been postulated by Beynon in 1960. These devices have widened
the range of compounds studied by mass spectrometry to
unprotected sugars, nucleotides, organic salts, and the
like.

Chemical Ionization. A technique which slightly
preceded this last was that of chemical ionization mass
spectrometry. To trace its development, we must go back
to the earliest days of the studies of positive rays.
J. J. Thomson had observed the existence of a line at
$m/e = 3$ when he was studying hydrogen gas, as noted in
a 1913 publication. He took this to mean that there was
an allotropic form of hydrogen with the formula H_3, but
other workers concluded that because the intensity
varied as a function of the square of the pressure of
hydrogen in the mass spectrometer, the observed species
could not be a product of a simple ionizing event but
must result from a secondary process:

$$H_2 + e^- \rightarrow H_2^+ + 2e^-$$

$$H_2^+ + H_2 \rightarrow H_3^+ + H$$

This was the first observed ion-molecule reaction in the
gas phase.
Few reactions of other ions and molecules were
studied until about 1930, but then the advent of better
vacuum equipment caused interest to shift to studies of
unimolecular processes alone. In fact, in the common
electron-impact technique, used almost exclusively until
recently, it is undesirable to have such ion-molecule
products around, for if one mistakenly assigns the
molecular weight value to an ion-molecule product instead of to the correct ion, his interpretation of the
spectrum will be invalid. Consequently, vacua in most
mass spectrometers were maintained at around 10^{-6} to
10^{-7} torr to avoid ion-molecule peaks as much as possible. There was not much interest in studying these
reactions until the species CH_5^+ was discovered in the
spectrum of methane at higher pressures, in 1952,

independently by V. L. Tal'roze and A. L. Lyubimova, by
D. P. Stevenson and D. O. Schissler, and by F. H. Field,
J. L. Franklin, and F. W. Lampe. Such a curious species
(it has recently been observed in superacid solutions
by NMR studies) rekindled interest in ion-molecule reactions. In studying such reactions in methane over a
range of pressures up to several torr, M. S. B. Munson
and F. H. Field noticed (in 1966) that near 1 torr the
principal ions remaining in the mass spectrum were CH_5^+
and $C_2H_5^+$, which arise from the reactions:

$$CH_4^+ + CH_4 \rightarrow CH_5^+ + CH_3$$

$$CH_3^+ + CH_4 \rightarrow C_2H_5^+ + H_2$$

Each of these species is a Brønsted-Lowry acid, CH_5^+
being a stronger acid than almost any other organic ion
or neutral molecule. Thus, in a gas-phase collision, it
should be possible to transfer a proton to practically
any organic compound. The apparent exceptions might
arise if other more favorable reactions intervene or if
the rate of the reaction is too slow to allow detection
of the product. In fact, other reactions occur only in
certain instances (some alkylation instead of protona-
tion is observed, and there are some classes of compounds where hydride abstraction rather than proton
addition is found). The reaction of CH_5^+, generally
being exothermic by tens of kilocalories, occurs on
almost every collision in most cases. Early workers
had the insight to recognize that this could be another
from of ionization for molecules: instead of electron
removal, proton addition (or hydride loss) caused ionization and under conditions of low energy input into
the molecule, so that little fragmentation was observed.
They suggested that this general technique of ionizing
a few microtorr of sample in 1 torr of reagent gas such
as methane be known as chemical ionization-mass spectrometry. In chemical ionization, the reagent gas is
ionized by electron impact more often than the sample
molecules by a factor approaching the ratio of the partial pressures. The reagent ions collide with neutral
reagent molecules to form the acid species, which eventually find the sample molecules and ionize them.

Other reagent gases were later adopted, the nature
of the gas controlling the exothermicity of the proton-
transfer step. Among those examined were H_2, H_2O, iso-
butane, and NH_3, which produce the ions H_3^+, H_3O^+, $C_4H_9^+$,
and NH_4^+. In protonating other molecules, these ions
transfer less and less energy in the order shown above.
It is possible in this way to control the amount of

fragmentation of the ionized molecule.

Another ionization technique, called chemi-ionization, or Penning ionization, occurs when a metastable excited state of an atom has greater energy than the ground state ion of a molecule, so that the process: $G^* + M \rightarrow G + M^+ + e$ is exothermic. (Note that charge transfer from G^+ can also be called chemi-ionization.) This process was first observed in the early 1950s. Unlike chemical ionization, no heavy particle is transferred in chemi-ionization. With the excited states of some of the lighter rare gases as reactants, considerable energy may be received by the molecule, and a considerable amount of fragmentation may occur. This has led, on the one hand, to a search for gases whose excited states and ions are not so energetic--CO is a preferred molecule for obtaining only a small amount of fragmentation--and on the other, to studies involving the combination of reagent gases which act by chemi-ionization with those which act by the generally more gentle chemical ionization. An Ar/H_2O combination, among others, has been suggested by D. F. Hunt as one which provides both an ion near the molecular weight and also characteristic fragmentation peaks for a sample.

The subtleties of chemical ionization depend upon the chemistry involved and are still being explored. In addition to the conventional chemical ionization experiments described above, another technique for investigating the chemistry of these reactions is ion-cyclotron resonance spectrometry. This was first described by D. Wobschall in 1965, but applications to chemistry and chemical physics began only with the development of a commercial instrument following the design of P. M. Llewellyn and pioneering chemical studies by J. D. Baldeschwieler and his students in the late 1960s. Only a few applications to analysis have been described, but the development of Fourier transform ion-cyclotron resonance spectrometry may make this technique competitive with fast-scan magnetic deflection mass spectrometry for gas chromatographic work.

A theory of unimolecular fragmentation for the reactions occurring in the mass spectrometer after electron or photon impact, was developed by H. Eyring and his co-workers in the early 1950s. Termed the quasi-equilibrium theory, it assumes that the reactant species and the transition state for dissociation are in equilibrium with each other and allows rates to be calculated for each decomposition pathway as a function of the energy above the threshold. When one determines the energy distribution of the molecular ions (this has recently been approached through photoelectron spectroscopy) and the threshold energies for all competing and consecutive pathways, then one may use this theory to calculate the mass spectrum by statistical mechanics. The early applications suffered from the use of too poor an approximation for the dependence of the rate constant upon energy, but later calculations for simple hydrocarbons gave remarkably good predictions. In recent years, the theory has been applied to more complex molecules in an effort to understand fragmentation patterns more completely than the simple organic fragmentation rules allow. In this it has proved quite useful, but calculations are far from routine, and the experimentalist is in no danger of having his mass spectra produced routinely from first principles by a computer instead of a mass spectrometer.

The theory of bimolecular reactions--that is, ion-molecule collision--derives from early work on the collision of a point ion and a polarizable molecule in 1905 by P. Langevin, a student of Pierre Curie. After the renaissance of interest in ion-molecule reactions in the early 1950s, Stevenson and Gioumousis adapted this work to the determination of the rate constant for the collision of a point ion with a polarizable molecule and found good agreement for highly exothermic reactions of ion and molecules without dipole moments. Later it was found necessary to correct for molecules which have dipole moments; the orientation of the dipole by the ion provides another attractive interaction, and causes more rapid reaction, but the ion does not lock the dipole into a single orientation with respect to itself. As long as the molecule is fairly small, the ion is also small, and the reaction is fairly exothermic, this theory works very well. When these conditions are not met, the chemistry of the two species as they approach one another closely becomes more complex, and the theory has yet to be developed.

Spark Sources. Spark source mass spectrometry is a technique related to the organic methods described previously only in the configuration of the instrument; it is its own science with its own problems and solutions. It is interesting that again the concept goes back to Dempster, who pointed out in 1934 the utility of the spark source for elemental analysis. The first applications were in answer to the growth of solid-state physics after World War II, when a need for new analytical techniques arose. An instrument was designed in 1947, and demonstration of quantitative results was made by J. G. Gorman, E. J. Jones, and J. A. Hipple in 1951. General utility for trace analysis was shown by N. B. Hannay and A. J. Ahearn in 1954. Techniques involving focused radiation and ion bombardment were added

to the list of methods for vaporizing solids in the
1950s. Because it is necessary in trace work to analyze
for elements at low concentrations, an integrating
method of detection is routinely used--namely, photoplate rather than electrical recording. This requires
the use of Mattauch-Herzog geometry. Commercial instruments became available in 1958, and for standard spark
source work they all use the pulsed radio frequency
spark source.

Secondary ion mass spectrometry, which is extremely
sensitive, is becoming an important technique in surface
analysis and in three-dimensional analysis of solids.
This technique uses a beam of ions to sputter the surface of a sample; the small fraction of material sput-
tered as ions is drawn off into a mass spectrometer.
These instruments, first constructed in the early to
mid-1960s by several groups, include those providing
mass analysis without imaging capability, the "probe
imaging" ion microprobe mass spectrometer, and the
direct imaging mass analyzer.

Time-of-Flight Spectrometers. A disadvantage of
conventional mass spectrometers is the need for a heavy,
bulky, electromagnet, with its requirement of a well-
regulated direct current supply of some amperes. Several
methods have been developed to permit mass determinations
without a static magnetic field. One of these is the
time-of-flight (TOF) mass spectrometer, in which all
ions are given the same kinetic energy ($\frac{1}{2}mV^2$), so that
ions of differing masses assume corresponding velocities.
The ions are emitted from the source in short bursts,
and the times of arrival at a distant detector are measured. This principle originated with A. E. Cameron
and D. F. Eggers, Jr., in 1948 and was developed by
others in the early 1950s. However, it only became
practical with the design of a new ion source by W. C.
Wiley and I. H. McLaren of the Bendix Aviation Corp. in
1955. This led to a series of highly successful TOF
spectrometers by Bendix and other firms.

Quadrupole Spectrometers. Another type of non-mag-
netic spectrometer is based on the quadrupole mass
filter. The basic principle was initially worked out
for high-energy particle accelerators by N. C. Christo-
filos, a Greek electrical engineer whose hobby was
accelerators. It was adopted in 1952 by engineers at
Brookhaven National Laboratory for the Cosmostron accelerator. W. Paul and M. Räther in Germany first applied
the principle to mass spectroscopy in 1955. Ions are
separated by suitable radio frequency excitation combined with a direct potential, applied to an array of

four cylindrical metal rods symmetrically positioned
parallel to the center line of the instrument, down
which the ion beam is directed. For a given combination
of frequency and potential, only ions of a selected
mass-to-charge ratio succeed in reaching the exit orifice
and detector. In 1963 von Zahn showed that similar,
though not identical, results could be obtained with a
single rod and a parallel V-block, an arrangement called
a monopole mass filter. E. Fischer in 1959 devised a
system which is a three-dimensional analog of the monopole, the latter considered to be two-dimensional. This
device has been further refined by P. H. Dawson and
N. R. Whetten (1968), among others.

The quadrupole mass spectrometer and its derivative
types are marketed by several companies and are very
successful for mass numbers up to a few hundred. They
are also widely used in small versions as residual gas
analyzers in connection with vacuum production. Hewlett-
Packard has designed a unit called a dodecapole mass
spectrometer, using the basic quadrupole design with
the addition of eight additional field-shaping members.

NUCLEAR METHODS FOR CHEMICAL ANALYSIS

Radioactivity was discovered only about 75 years
ago (as long as an average man's life span). Since
then, rapid progress has been made in its use. This
brief account describes some of the more important applications of nuclear methods of chemical analysis. Most
of the significant advances have been the result of
major breakthroughs in instrumentation.

In 1896 Antoine-Henri Becquerel used the photographic plate to detect the presence of invisible rays
coming from uranium-bearing materials. The existence
of the electroscope and electrometer along with their
pertinent modifications established the necessary reproducibility of measurement that enabled Marie and Pierre
Curie, Ernest Rutherford, and others, to proceed in
unraveling the nature of radioactivity.

It should also be remembered that little progress
would have been made without considerable understanding
of chemical reactions. It was chemists such as Gustave
Bemont, André Debierne, Frederick Soddy, and Friederich
Giesel who performed many difficult chemical separations
of radioisotopes from uranium and thorium compounds.
In fact, it appears that the industrial chemist, Giesel,
had concentrated radium compounds prior to the scientific discovery of radium as an element, which was first
accomplished by the Curies in 1898.

Giesel and Sir William Crookes (better known for

his work on cathode rays) independently discovered that alpha particles caused scintillations in "Sidot's blende" (zinc sulfide). This discovery led to the Crookes spinthariscope, which greatly helped to identify radioactivity and its sources. Even though one had to stare through a microscope eyepiece and count the individual flashes of light, reliable counting could be done by two persons who checked each other by calling out simultaneously the occurrence of each flash. Radiochemists such as William Marckwald and Friederich von Lerch began to use electrochemical deposition and autoreduction onto metals (e.g., bismuth) as a means for separating radioisotopes. Others, including Otto Hahn, Kasimir Fajans, and Georg Hevesy played key roles in developing a fundamental understanding of the chemical and radioactive properties of the radioelements.

By the end of 1911 about 30 radioelements had been identified, and ingenious techniques had made possible the measurement of half-lives of less than one-hundredth of a second. At this point Hevesy, Fajans, F. Paneth, and Hahn first used radioelements as tracers to measure chemical properties such as solubilities, but still no applications were directed toward the analysis for the elements.

Important advances in the detection of alpha and beta particles were made when Hans Geiger, with Lord Rutherford, and later Otto Müller developed what was to become the Geiger-Müller counter. The proportional region, within which the signal changes with the energy of the ionizing particle, was also observed at this time. In 1911 C. T. R. Wilson developed the cloud chamber which allowed one to observe the path of a particle by virtue of its producing minute droplets of liquid in a supersaturated vapor. This device when used with a magnetic field greatly facilitated the determination of the energy and mass of an emitted nuclear particle.

In 1919 Rutherford observed artificial transmutation for the first time; he placed radium-C into a nitrogen atmosphere and detected energetic protons with a ZnS scintillation screen via the $^{14}N(\alpha,p)^{17}O$ reaction. During the next decade a deeper theoretical understanding of these phenomena was aided by the introduction of quantum mechanics and the nuclear-electronic structure of matter.

Of great significance was the development of the incandescent electric light, for Edison in 1883 had discovered that it is possible for an electric current to flow through a vacuum from a hot filament--a phenomenon which we now know is due to thermal electron emission. In 1904 Fleming invented the vacuum diode, and de Forest, in 1907, added a grid to produce a triode. The

development of the pentode and the concept of negative
feedback in the late 1920s made amplifier design feasible, and the stage was set for an infusion of renewed
activity into experimental nuclear research.

The electronic scaler, first described by C. E.
Wynn-Williams in 1932, greatly enlarged the scope of
application of radiation counters of the Geiger type
that had been developed some years earlier. Previously,
the maximum counting rate had been limited by the speed
of response of a mechanical counter operated through a
relay. A scaler of n stages permits each count on the
register to correspond to 2^n ionizing events, so that
the rate will be limited only by the properties of the
gas-discharge tube itself.

The availability of these radiation counters and
scalers greatly facilitated nuclear research. In 1934
Irène Curie and Frédéric Joliot caused a radioactive
species with a measurable half life to be produced arti-
ficially for the first time. The large quantities of
polonium separated from radium by the Curies years before made an intense enough source of alpha particles
for them to observe the $^{27}Al(\alpha,n)^{30}P$ reaction, producing
the radioactive isotope ^{30}P.

The neutron, whose existence had been postulated
earlier by Rutherford, was confirmed experimentally by
James Chadwick in 1932. In 1934 Enrico Fermi inadvert-
ently performed his first experiments in nuclear fission
by attempting to produce a transuranium element by neutron bombardment. He obtained a radioisotope which was,
as he anticipated it would be, "chemically homogeneous"
with manganese because it precipitated with MnO_2. It
was soon realized that many elements are carried down
from aqueous solution by manganese dioxide, and subsequent work by O. Hahn, F. Strassman, I. Curie, and
others (1939) verified the existence of elements produced by uranium fission.

The development of the electronic vacuum tube also
led to the major field of accelerator design. E. O.
Lawrence, at the University of California (Berkeley),
invented the cyclotron in 1930, and J. D. Cockroft and
E. T. S. Walton achieved the first nuclear transformation with a proton accelerator of the linear cascade
design in 1932. These instruments were followed by the
electrostatic generators of R. Herb and R. Van de Graaff
in 1939. At this point V. Veksler in the Soviet Union
and Edwin McMillan at Berkeley (1945) designed the syn-
chrotron, and high-energy nuclear research was under way.

The radium-beryllium neutron source and the cyclotron, coupled with the development of the proportional
radiation detector, made it possible to measure the
energy of alpha and beta particles and low-energy gamma-

and x-rays, which ushered in the development of activation analysis and the use of radioisotopes (about 190 had been identified). Hevesy was doing radioisotopic tracer work with ^{32}P using a Ra-Be neutron source, and ^{24}Na, ^{35}S, ^{55}Fe, ^{131}I, and ^2H (not ^3H) were also in use. The first recorded experiments using activation analysis were described by Hevesy and H. Levi in 1936, in which they analyzed mixtures of rare earths. Glenn T. Seaborg and J. T. Livingood (1938) were the first to use the cyclotron for activation analysis, by determining gallium (about 6 ppm) in iron.

The use and development of nuclear techniques in analytical chemistry can be considered negligible up to this time when compared with the developments during the 1940s. With the beginning of World War II, many scientists fled Europe, of these, Fermi demonstrated the first sustained fission reaction of uranium in January 1942 at the University of Chicago. This chain reaction confirmed theoretical predictions that related to power production and, of course, to the nuclear bomb. Many applications of nuclear techniques to analysis resulted from the work of the Manhattan Project. The early developments occurred largely at the University of Chicago, where Seaborg, M. Burton, C. D. Coryell, and G. E. Boyd headed respectively the plutonium, radiation effects, fission product, and analytical projects. The analytical laboratory under Boyd had a staff of 90. Several other laboratories throughout the nation were involved in the analytical chemistry of the Manhattan Project: Princeton (N. H. Furman), National Bureau of Standards (C. J. Rodden and J. I. Hoffman), and Iowa State University (F. H. Spedding).

An interesting nuclear technique was devised to establish the purity of the graphite used as a moderator in the first pile. Many conventional analytical techniques (e.g., spectroscopy) were not able to detect minute amounts of impurities. A neutron absorption technique was developed called the "Fermi shotgun procedure." A Ra-Be source provided neutrons which passed through the graphite to be analyzed into an indium foil, which was thereby rendered radioactive. The foil was wrapped around a special Geiger tube for counting. The count rate was highly sensitive to the number of neutrons taken out of the beam by the impurities in the graphite. So high was this sensitivity that once when Fermi wished to check the reliability of the technique, he spiked a sample of graphite with so much boron that the analysis blank increased to the point that it took days to clean up the laboratory to reduce it to usable levels.

The Clinton Laboratories (later to become the Oak Ridge National Laboratory) had its first reactor in

operation in November 1946, and R. T. Overman and G. E.
Boyd did some of the first reactor activational analyses
with it. Others in the group were W. Miller (now of
Pennsylvania State University), David Hume (MIT), and
L. B. Rogers (presently at the University of Georgia).
The other National Laboratories also made significant
contributions, as indicated below.

Radioisotopes from the Oak Ridge reactor were first
made available in 1946. Carbon-14 in the form of CH_3OH
ushered in the extensive use of tracers in the organic
and biochemical fields. In 1948 the Oak Ridge Institute
for Nuclear Studies was begun, and major declassification of nuclear techniques led to the widespread use of
such methods in analysis (about 800 radioisotopes were
known by this time).

The infusion of funds into the development of
nuclear technology in the 1940s and 1950s, and their
subsequent reallocation into the space program of the
1960s, has had an enormous effect on the development of
electronics. Prior to this time, the most common detectors were the G-M tube and the Lauritzen electrometer.
Much of the early work in designing counters for these
detectors was done by W. A. Higginbotham and E. Fair-
stein. The proportional counter became rather well
developed, especially for alpha-energy spectroscopy, and
a number of spectrometers were used at this time which
had individual preset energy discriminators whose out-
puts were scaled by vacuum-tube counting circuits. A
spectrometer consisted of an array of 20-40 of these
systems, where about five channels could be mounted in
a single 6-ft relay rack. Needless to say, power requirements were high, and only infrequently were all of
the channels operating correctly at the same time.

The electron-multiplier vacuum tube (ca. 1936) with
a photocathode as its first stage (called a multiplier
phototube or photomultiplier) was first used with a ZnS
coating for particle counting. Organic materials such
as anthracene were also used as scintillants. In 1945
P. J. Van Heerden discovered that nuclear radiation when
interacting with certain crystalline materials causes
emission of photons in the ultraviolet. R. Hofstadter
in 1948 showed that a gamma-ray energy spectrum could
be obtained by optically coupling a photomultiplier tube
to a thallium-doped single crystal of sodium iodide,
commonly referred to as a NaI(Tl) detector. The rate
of technological breakthrough in the electronics area
was now becoming rapid for in 1948 W. Shockley, J. Bardeen, and W. Brattain contributed the transistor, which
was to change completely the complexion of scientific
instrumentation. In 1949 K. McKay observed the effects
of radiation on germanium and silicon, and this had an

even greater impact on activation analysis than the transistor. In 1951 he noticed that "a shallow diffused p-n junction with reversed bias forms a space charge that functions as a fast solid-state ionization chamber."

The availability of the NaI(Tl)-photomultiplier gamma-ray detector spurred improvements in the speed and accuracy of production of gamma-ray energy spectra. The combination of the pulse height-to-time conversion circuit of D. H. Wilkinson (1951) with the magnetic core computer memory opened up the possibility of major improvement in nuclear radiation spectroscopy. Magnetic cores appeared in computers in the early 1950s, when the first transistorized computers were designed.

The first vacuum-tube pulse-height analyzers with 100 or 256 channels, including magnetic memories, became commercially available in late 1955 (J. McMahon, R. Schumann, C. Johnstone, G. Kelly, R. Chase, and others). There was some question regarding the use of transistor electronics for nuclear applications, in part because of the large temperature coefficients of the devices of that day. (The Harwell Instrumentation Conference in May 1954 reached no general agreement as to the part transistors would play in the future of nuclear instruments.) However, by 1959 fully transistorized pulse-height analyzers were commercially available, and some can still be found in routine operation today.

The first application of a semiconductor as the detector element itself was in the lithium-drifted silicon detector for alpha spectroscopy, reported by E. Pell (1960) and by J. McKenzie and G. Ewan (1961). Lithium-drifted germanium applications were described by A. Tavendale, G. Ewan, D. Bromely, H. Mann, E. Pell, and others in 1963.

While several laboratories demonstrated the possibility of using computers in doing nuclear experiments in the early 1960s, the cost was generally prohibitive. The development of integrated circuits for the space program, however, reduced the cost so substantially that minicomputers began to perform many functions of the conventional pulse-height analyzers. In fact, it is now common to use a computer both to control the lithium-drifted germanium gamma-ray detector and to process the resultant spectral data.

Activation Analysis. Upon declassification in 1949-50 of much of the work done in the Manhattan project, it became apparent that activation analysis can be a powerful analytical tool, especially for trace analysis. To conduct activation analysis in its simplest form, a sample is irradiated with some type of nuclear radiation, and the induced activity is measured and is compared

with that of a standard sample. Most samples are relatively sensitive to neutrons, and with the availability
of nuclear reactors, a highly accurate analytical technique was in the offing. However, availability of neutrons was then (and to some degree still is) a problem
in the convenient use of the technique.

The first practical applications of activation analysis were performed at Oak Ridge by G. W. Leddicotte and
W. S. Lyon in 1945. Reactors were also appearing at
this time in other countries. A. A. Smales (Harwell,
AERE) used the method to analyze geologic samples and
developed techniques for many other types of materials.
P. Albert (Vitry-Saclay, France) developed elaborate
analytical procedures for trace elements in ultra-pure
metals. This type of work was limited to those few
laboratories that had access to nuclear reactors. Even
though some analysts sent their samples for irradiation
to the National Laboratories, analysis was expensive and
safety regulations made sample handling and processing
difficult.

The U. S. Atomic Energy Act of 1954 resulted in a
significant increase in the availability of nuclear reactors. In 1956, the first university-owned "swimming-
pool" reactor went into operation at the University of
Michigan. With this reactor, W. W. Meinke and co-workers
explored the use of short-lived radioisotopes in activation analysis by using a system of pneumatic tubes to
transport samples from the reactor core to the laboratory for fast chemical processing, and from there to the
radiation detector for counting. Their NaI(Tl) detector
utilized the first dual-memory, 100-channel analyzer,
which allowed counting to commence during printout of
the previous cycle.

A few other research reactors were established in
this period (e.g., at the Naval Research Laboratory, at
Illinois Institute of Technology, the Battelle Research
Institute, and at MIT) as well as a few industrial facilities for the fledgeling electrical power field. Some
companies invested in Van de Graaff generators, and
significant work was accomplished by such workers as
V. P. Guinn at Shell Development Co. and O. U. Anders
at Dow Chemical Co., who independently evaluated the
potential of the fast neutron reactions for determining
such elements as oxygen. These systems were also used
for macro-constituent analysis of many elements. A
dramatic increase of the use of this technique occurred
when the relatively low-cost ($20,000) Cockroft-Walton
accelerator became available in the late 1950s. This
device, using the $^3H(d,n)^4He$ reaction, produced an exceptionally high yield of 14 MeV neutrons. It became
widely used for oxygen analysis via the $^{16}O(n,p)^{16}N$

process and short-lived nuclear products from other re-
actions which required similar rapid sample transport
for counting. Early developers of these techniques were
Anders, Guinn, Meinke, J. Hoste (University of Ghent),
J. Laverlochère (Grenoble, France), S. S. Nargolwalla
(NBS), F. E. Senftle (USGS), R. L. Caldwell (Mobil Oil
Co.), and R. E. Wainerdi (Texas A & M University).

The application of short-lived radionuclides to
activation analysis with accelerator or reactor-produced
neutrons opened the potential for multiple-sample automated activation analysis. Such a system was first
developed by Wainerdi in 1959-61. Samples were successively cycled through the irradiation and counting steps,
and the resultant data were stored on magnetic tape for
off-line computer processing. Others involved in this
area at an early stage were D. Gibbons (AERE, Wantage),
H. Yule (General Atomics), and Anders. It was soon
realized that activation analysis is a powerful analytical technique that can provide rapid, accurate analyses at reasonable cost. This very active period was
brought into focus by a first international symposium,
held at Texas A & M University in 1962.

This emphasis on automated activation analysis
coincided with the construction of an activation analysis
facility at the NBS. W. W. Meinke, at NBS in 1962,
cautioned the practitioners of the technique that verification of accuracy must involve radiochemical separations. Some analysts, particularly F. Girardi (Ispra,
Italy), and K. Samsahl (Srudivik, Sweden), responded to
this point by developing fully automated radiochemical
separation systems. This concern for chemical separation became less urgent with the introduction of the
lithium-drifted germanium detector, which in many cases
does not require elaborate separations. Early users of
these detectors were R. W. Perkins (Battelle N.W.), S.
Prussin (Berkeley), and Girardi. During the 1960s a
number of special coincidence techniques were devised
to improve selectivity of the gamma-ray spectrometer.
Many of these developments centered in J. Hoste's laboratory. Signal-to-Compton background ratio in the Ge(Li)
detectors was improved by coincidence shielding techniques developed by Perkins. Today the large size of
Ge(Li) detectors has minimized the need for coincidence
shielding, but radiochemical separations from highly
active matrices still may be required.

During the late 1960s many special purpose activation analysis techniques were developed. For example,
S. Amiel (Israel Atomic Energy Commission) used the
nuclear reaction $^{18}O(\alpha,n)^{21}Ne$ to determine oxygen-18 by
detecting the emitted neutrons. The needs for increased
neutron flux at a variety of energies and the breadth of

nuclear reactions that can be obtained from charged
particles renewed interest in the cyclotron. (Today
there are no more than 50 reactors available for high-
sensitivity neutron activation analysis throughout the
world. The fact that there are this many is mostly
attributable to the Triga reactor, first demonstrated
by Guinn at General Atomic.) Charged particles (^{1}H, ^{2}H,
^{3}He, ^{4}He nuclei) provide sensitive analyses, but coulomb
interactions with the sample must be carefully measured,
and the production of neutron deficient radionuclides
(particularly for the light elements) tends to impair
selectivity in gamma-ray spectroscopy. Nevertheless,
excellent results have been obtained by E. Ricci (Oak
Ridge), M. Peisach (SUNI, South Africa), E. Schweikert
(Texas A & M University), and T. B. Pierce (Harwell).
Photon activation provides analyses for certain elements
that are difficult to detect with neutrons, and many
applicable methods have been developed by C. Engleman
(Saclay), and G. Lutz (NBS).

Many aspects of activation analysis were discussed
in great detail at the 1965 international conference at
Texas A & M. Over half the conference was devoted to a
description of the applications of this by now quite
sophisticated general technique which claimed to be
accurate to within a few per cent for multi-element analysis in the parts-per-billion concentration range. The
problem of having sufficient neutron flux for this type
of analysis continued, of course, and this led several
companies to offer to analyze samples for a fee. Considerable emphasis was placed upon the utility of the
14-MeV Cockroft-Walton neutron generator. Activation
analysis was subsequently shown to be highly competitive
with vacuum-fusion techniques for estimating oxygen in
certain metals. It was only marginally competitive for
determining macro constituents even though it attained
in the best laboratories, such as those of Nargolwalla
(NBS), and D. DeSoete (University of Ghent), about 0.1%
relative accuracy.

The 1968 and 1972 international conferences were
centered about applications of the "newly" available
Ge(Li) detector, but few truly innovative ideas were
described. Activation analysis had reached a level of
maturity wherein most of the studies were centered about
the measurement of random and systematic errors in the
various steps of the technique.

Activation analysis has been applied to problems
in the biomedical and botanical fields. Pioneers in
these areas were J. M. A. Lenihan (Glasgow), D. Comar
(Orsay, France), and M. Rakovič (Prague). An important
part of this activity was in the production of reference
materials. In this area, a dried kale was made available

by H. J. M. Bowen (University of Reading), and dried,
homogenized samples of orchard leaves and of liver by
P. D. LaFleur (NBS). The use of neutron activation
analysis in the geological and cosmochemical fields was
pioneered by A. A. Smales and W. D. Ehmann (University
of Kentucky), F. E. Sentfle (USGS), R. A. Schmitt (Oregon State University), G. H. Morrison (Cornell University), and J. W. Morgan (University of Melbourne).
Activation analysis has been very useful in the forensic
sciences, extending from the examination of evidence in
criminal cases to the authentication of archeological
artifacts. Leaders in these areas were R. E. Jervis
(University of Toronto), Guinn, R. F. Coleman (AERE,
Aldermaston), and M. J. Pro (U. S. Treasury Department).
In the environmental and oceanographic fields were J. W.
Winchester (Florida State University), Glen Gordon
(University of Maryland), and L. A. Rancitelli (Battelle
N.W.). Very active workers in several areas of appli-
cations were D. Brune (Studsviks), H. Hamaguchi (Uni-
versity of Tokyo), E. M. Lobanov (Tashkent, USSR), and
E. Steinnes (Institute of Atomic Energy, Kjeller, Norway).

Radioisotopic Tracers in Analysis. As noted previously, only a few radioisotopes were available before
the development of the radium-beryllium neutron source.
These sources produced isotopes of limited usefulness
because of their low specific activity. However, after
the cyclotron was developed in the 1930s, a number of
radioisotopes with quite high specific activity were
produced. Finally, when the nuclear reactor was made
available for applications of radiation, it was only a
matter of a year or two until a large number of active
isotopes were introduced.

By 1945 over 400 radioisotopes were known, and this
number increased to more than 800 by 1949. The most
useful for analytical purposes were those that could be
used to tag molecules for studies of biological systems.
Carbon-14, tritium, phosphorus-32, and iodine-131 were
used routinely to follow the pathways of biochemical
reactions. The following paragraphs mention only those
who provided major contributions to the use of radioisotopes in quantitative chemical analysis.

In a great deal of the early work, radioisotopes
were used to evaluate the efficiency of a chemical separation. Before World War I, G. Hevesy developed with
F. Paneth a means of tagging lead salts to measure their
solubilities. Others have contributed to separation
chemistry through the use of radioisotopes--e.g., K. A.
Kraus and E. Nelson (Oak Ridge), in ion-exchange applications; H. Freiser (now at the University of Arizona),
G. H. Morrison (Cornell University), and H. Finston

(Brookhaven) in solvent-extraction techniques; M. Haissinsky (Laboratoire Curie, Paris) in electrochemistry; J. F. Duncan (University of Wellington) and G. B. Cook (IAEA) in the field of precipitation.

The two most important applications of radioisotopes to quantitative chemical analysis were provided by isotope dilution and radiometric analysis. The first radioisotope dilution experiment was performed by O. Hahn, who used ^{231}Pa to determine the separation yield of ^{234}Pa. In 1932 Hevesy used ^{210}Pb to measure the amount of lead separated from minerals. This work led to a variety of techniques using radioactive indicators. (Professor Hevesy was awarded the Nobel Prize for these studies.)

The power of isotope dilution as an analytical technique was realized by Rittenberg in 1940 when he applied it to complex biochemicals. However, the growth in the use of isotope dilution was accentuated by the ready availability of suitable isotopes after 1945. A number of special tricks to circumvent some of the difficulties encountered in the classical technique were developed during these years. One of these was the so-called inverse radioisotope dilution, used to determine the mass of a radioactive material.

A recent contribution to isotope dilution analysis came when J. Ruzicka (1958) suggested that quantitative measurement of the separated and purified material need not be done if one can be assured that the *same* amount of material is separated from the sample both before and after dilution. This simple modification made it possible for the first time to use isotope dilution for trace analysis.

The first application of a radiometric analytical technique was described by A. Langer at Westinghouse in 1940. However, much of the activity in this field has taken place in Hungary (T. Braun), and Czechoslovakia (J. Tölgyessy). An interesting application was introduced by D. J. Chleck (Tracerlab, Inc.) who used organic clathrates to trap ^{85}Kr. Various gaseous pollutants will displace the krypton from the clathrate, and the amount of released isotope can be measured. Extremely high sensitivity can be realized.

The very important application of a radiometric technique, called radioimmunoassay, whereby a labeled hormone competes with unlabeled hormone for antibody, was introduced in the 1950s by S. A. Berson and R. S. Yalow.

Mössbauer Spectroscopy. Resonance fluorescence of electronic levels in molecular species has been known for decades, but nuclear gamma-ray resonant scattering was experimentally difficult because the recoil energy imparted to the absorbing nucleus was sufficient to shift it considerably off resonance. In 1959 Rudolph Mössbauer was investigating gamma-ray resonant scattering in iridium-191 under conditions where at room temperature the recoil energy happened to be less than the temperature-broadened linewidth of the 129-keV nuclear energy level. Reducing the temperature of both source and absorber removes some of the Doppler broadening, and the resonant scattering should decrease due to less overlap of the lines. Just the opposite occurred, and this led to the development of the field of recoilless nuclear gamma-ray resonant scattering. The effect is called the Mössbauer effect, for which Mössbauer was awarded the Nobel prize only three years later. (He still apparently refuses to call the effect by his own name. Consequently, computer searches on key words often omit his current papers.) By moving the source mechanically, relative to the absorber, one can Doppler-shift to an off-resonance condition; this discovery paved the way to instrumental Mössbauer spectroscopy.

The Mössbauer effect received immediate attention from physicists, and its application to chemical structure analysis came very quickly. Analytical chemists were being asked with increasing frequency to determine quantitatively the different chemical forms of an element in a material, and it appeared that Mössbauer spectroscopy might be a useful technique. The extremely narrow linewidth of the radiation enabled one to measure directly the electronic (chemical) interaction on the nuclear energy levels (called hyperfine interaction). This meant that internal magnetic and electric fields could be measured, and solid-state physics was the first discipline to reap the benefits.

Although it appeared in the early 1960s that a number of elements could be measured, the available half-lives of radioisotopic sources limited the Mössbauer technique to a few elements including particularly iron, tin, iodine, some of the rare earths, and heavy elements.

The difficulty in making an accurate spectrometer lay in the device for producing smooth motion; motion with random deviations of only 1 μm/sec was barely tolerable for iron and tin work. The most successful drive mechanism was the electromagnetic coil driven in a permanent magnetic field, introduced by G. K. Wertheim and R. L. Cohen (Bell Laboratories, 1963). An optical interferometric pickup with electronic feedback was added by J. J. Spijkerman (NBS, 1966). Multichannel scalers were used to time-average the spectra, and measurement times varied from 1 to 10 hours, depending on the type of sample.

Calibration of the Doppler velocity scale became a
problem. Iron foil along with sodium nitroprusside were
often used as calibration standards (J. J. Spijkerman
and J. R. DeVoe, NBS, 1967).

The study of ferrous materials initiated by Wertheim
became the single most important Mössbauer activity because it was the simplest to perform. Various types of
iron oxides were identified, and the development of the
conversion electron surface detector resulted in the
nondestructive measurement of the relative amounts of
corrosion products of iron-bearing materials (Spijkerman,
1969). Organoiron and -tin compounds were studied by
R. H. Herber (Rutgers University, 1965-70). He demonstrated that organotins showed a continuous distribution
of chemical shifts, and this discovery caused significant advances in the understanding of the structure of
these compounds. Tin compounds were further studied by
V. I. Goldanskii in the USSR and by others.

The possibility of quantitative analysis was investigated by using tin oxide. However, the cross section for resonant scattering is a function of the properties of the solid state; consequently each sample requires a cross section determination. Alternatively,
one can chemically transform the tin into a pure known
material whose tin cross section is established or can
be calibrated. DeVoe and P. A. Pella (1970) have shown
this to be possible; however, information on the relative amounts of the various oxidation states in the sample is lost. If one is dealing with a material in which
the solid-state properties that determine the Mössbauer
cross section depend weakly on the relative amounts of
the oxidation states, a ratio of these states can be
measured. The Mössbauer technique today still cannot
be considered truly quantitative. It can, in carefully
studied samples, be used to measure the relative abundances of the oxidation states of a few elements. New
techniques for producing more nuclides that emit radiation useful for the Mössbauer effect may be forthcoming,
but it remains for the solid-state physicist to determine how one might predict the resonant scattering cross
section for an unknown sample.

LASERS IN ANALYTICAL CHEMISTRY

C. H. Townes and A. L. Schawlow in 1958 and T. H.
Maiman in 1960 deserve recognition for their respective
roles in creating the first laser. However, it wasn't
until F. J. McClung and R. W. Hellwarth in 1962 created
the giant pulse technique and P. P. Sorokin and J. R.
Lankard in 1966 and F. P. Schafer, W. Schmidt, and

J. Volze in 1966 achieved laser action in dyes pumped
by giant-pulse lasers that the greatest analytical usefulness of lasers resulted.

The first use of any laser (fixed frequency) device
in analytical chemistry was as an atomizer-exciter in
laser microprobe analysis. F. Brech and L. Cross were
the first to realize the potential analytical usefulness
of the laser microprobe utilizing a high-power pulsed
laser.

S. P. S. Porto and D. L. Wood are credited with the
first use of a laser (pulsed ruby at 6943 Å) in Raman
spectrometry to examine condensed phase samples; they
used a photographic detector with a grating spectrometer.
Since their work in 1962, numerous other workers have
utilized fixed frequency lasers (pulsed ruby, He-Ne, Ar,
and others). Many commercial concerns have jumped on
the bandwagon with laser Raman spectrometers, but only
a few firms remain. The use of lasers rejuvenated the
little-used technique of conventional spontaneous Raman
spectrometry for both qualitative and quantitative analysis of gases, inorganic compounds, organic compounds,
and single crystals. Lasers have further been applied
to resonance Raman spectrometry to improve sensitivity
of analysis. Considerable gains in sensitivity are also
possible by using intense lasers in conjunction with the
non-linear properties of matter, resulting in such interesting phenomena as the inverse Raman effect, the
hyper-Raman effect, the Raman-induced Kerr effect (RIK),
and coherent anti-Stokes Raman spectroscopy (CARS). Of
these phenomena, only CARS, discovered by R. W. Terhune
in 1963, has been utilized for anything remotely analytical, being used to measure spatial H_2 concentrations
in flames. However, because of the many-orders-of-mag-
nitude increase in sensitivity of analysis over conventional Raman spectrometry, the possible analytical
applications and uses of CARS and possibly RIK for trace
analysis of atoms and molecules in the gas phase as well
as in the condensed phase seem rather large at this time.

In 1971 N. C. Peterson, M. J. Kurylo, W. Braun,
A. M. Bass, and R. A. Keller reported on absorption enhancement when absorption cells containing Na and I_2
were placed inside the cavity of a rhodamine 6G dye laser
pumped by a xenon flash lamp. By this means the high
sensitivity inherent in laser induced absorption was
realized for the first time. Also in 1971 M. B. Denton
and H. V. Malmstadt, using a Q-switched ruby laser with
frequency doubling and a dye laser, and L. M. Fraser and
J. D. Winefordner, using a pulsed N_2-tunable dye laser,
independently showed the analytical benefits of pulsed
laser atomic fluorescence flame spectrometry. Although
the detection limits are lower and the analytical

calibration curves are longer with laser excited atomic
fluorescence flame spectrometry than with intracavity
flame atomic absorption spectrometry, this technique,
as well as the latter one, have not yet found widespread
analytical utility, presumably because of the high equipment cost, the complexity of dye lasers, and the marginal improvements in analytical figures of merit compared with simpler atomic spectrometric methods.

One of the most exotic uses of lasers is in remote
sensing, made possible because of the small divergence
over long distances and the large power per pulse. Remote sensing approaches utilize methods involving either
direct absorption over a long path through the atmosphere
or backscattered light, resulting from the Raman effect,
fluorescence, Rayleigh or Mie scattering. R. T. Menzies
in 1971 seems to have first realized the potential of
fixed frequency lasers for long path absorption monitoring of the atmosphere. Numerous workers have utilized
lasers (fixed and variable frequency) in backscatter
methods for remote sensing, particularly for pollution
monitoring in the atmosphere and monitoring of oil slicks
on bodies of water.

Lasers have also been used to detect spots of
materials at picogram levels on thin layer chromatograms,
to detect small areas of biological material in microscopy via fluorescence assay, to detect by means of absorption spectrometry effluents in chromatographic columns, to detect isotopes of elements in molecules and in
atoms, to separate isotopes of atoms, and to obtain both
spatial and temporal resolution of temperatures and concentrations of species in flames and other plasmas. The
use of semiconductor lasers for infrared absorption spectroscopy is likely in the near future to have as large
an impact, if not greater, on infrared absorption spectroscopy as the laser had on Raman spectroscopy. The
extremely narrow line widths (of the order of 10^{-4} cm^{-1})
and the relatively high (1 mW) tunable radiant powers
result in excellent signal-to-noise ratio and a higher
quality infrared spectra than ever attained in the past
with conventional IR spectrometers or Fourier transform
IR spectrometers. In December 1976, in *Chemical & Engineering News*, a group of Oak Ridge National Laboratory
scientists (S. Hurst, M. H. Nayfeh, and J. P. Young)
announced the use of a laser to ionize selectively cesium
atoms in an environment containing 10^{19} argon atoms and
10^{18} methane molecules; these workers were able to detect
one cesium atom in this environment.

It is apparent that lasers have already created
significant changes in analytical spectrometry and are
destined to account for even more substantial, and in
some cases, amazing changes in analytical instrumentation
and methodology.

CHAPTER IV

ELECTROANALYTICAL CHEMISTRY

     This section deals with the developments in elec-
troanalytical chemistry in the United States as seen
from the viewpoint of contemporary U. S. scientists.
The main thrust of electroanalytical chemistry in this
country has been in the area of technique development,
and it is from that point of view that this history is
presented. Probably the classical background for the
development of modern electroanalytical techniques--and
here we mean to consider dynamic rather than static
methods--lay in the comprehension of the classical potentiometric methods. Material on the development of
early aspects of potentiometry and the more recent development of ion-selective electrodes has been supplied
by Professor Roger Bates of the University of Florida,
who was for many years at the National Bureau of Standards. Bates has written:

          Modern potentiometric methods have their
     roots in basic discoveries concerning the theory
     of electrode behavior and the properties of elec-
     trolytic solutions. The foundations of electro-
     chemistry were fashioned largely in Europe during
     the 19th century and the first quarter of the
     20th century. The architects were such giants
     of scientific discovery as Arrhenius, Bjerrum,
     Brønsted, Debye, Faraday, Haber, Nernst, and Ost-
     wald. In America, the major contributions of the
     California school headed by G. N. Lewis were com-
     plemented by the precise and extensive experi-
     mental studies of Harned and his associates. The
     theory of acid and alkali titrations was set
     forth in detail by Michaelis, and the use of po-
     tentiometric endpoint detection was greatly stim-
     ulated by the appearance in 1931 of I. M. Kolthoff

and N. H. Furman's book "Potentiometric Titrations."

The hydrogen electrode with palladium and platinum as catalysts was shown by the work of Nernst, Böttger, Bjerrum, Joel Hildebrand and others to be highly reproducible when properly formed. It was applied by S. P. L. Sørensen in 1909 to the experimental realization of his newly defined scale of pH. A monograph by W. M. Clark (1920) brought the Sørensen pH to the attention of American science.

Although the electrochemical properties of thin membranes of certain glasses had been discovered as early as 1906 in the experiments of Cremer and Haber, it remained for Duncan MacInnes and Malcolm Dole in 1930 to select the glass composition known as Corning 015 as having the most suitable pH response. Commercial glass electrodes soon followed. The book of Dole, appearing in 1941, brought the glass electrode to the attention of scientists in many fields and led to an enormous increase in the use of this new tool for measuring the acidity of a wide range of media.

The availability of these high resistance sensors stimulated the development of electrometers based on dc amplification of the electrode signal. Advances in measurement techniques continued, and the developments in electronic instrumentation that were the outgrowth of World War II led to the highly stable and precise pH meters of the present day.

The alkaline error of the 015 electrode proved to be a serious limitation to the accuracy of pH measurements in solutions containing appreciable concentrations of both Na^+ and OH^-, and it was not long before new pH-responsive glasses containing Li^+ as the alkali ion constituent replaced the soda-lime glasses earlier in routine use. Purposeful enhancement of sodium error produced electrodes responding in Nernstian fashion to sodium ion. Glass electrode technologists have been able to fabricate electrodes with chemical resistances adequate to withstand prolonged use at temperatures of 100°C and above. In conjunction with pressurized reference electrodes, these make possible the industrial process control of pH at high temperatures.

B. P. Nicolsky of the U. S. S. R., and George Eisenman, of the University of California at Los Angeles, among others, are to be credited with major contributions to the theory of glass electrode behavior. The monograph (1967) prepared

under the editorship of Eisenman summarized in
admirable fashion the intricate relationships between glass composition and electrode response.
The nature of ion selectivity was clarified, and
a definition of the selectivity factor was formulated.

The liquid-junction potential is a persistent
and as yet unsolved problem in direct potentiometry. Early attempts by P. Henderson and M.
Planck to calculate the diffusion potential across
junctions of certain structures were moderately
successful but required information, not usually
available, concerning ionic mobilities at moderate and high concentrations. In 1926 H. S.
Harned showed that an exact solution of these
equations would require a knowledge of the activities, rather than the concentrations, of each of
the diffusing ionic species. The impossibility
of measuring these quantities by thermodynamic
methods was emphasized by Guggenheim, P. B. Taylor,
Harned, and others. Emphasis was subsequently
placed on assuring constancy of the junction potential and on its elimination. The approximate
equivalence of the transference numbers of K^+ and
Cl^- in solutions of potassium chloride led Bjerrum,
MacInnes, Guggenheim, and others to recognize the
advantages of concentrated KCl solutions as a
bridge between reference electrodes and the test
solutions under analysis. The saturated calomel
electrode is a common reference in the United
States today, while the $3.5M$ KCl bridge is often
used in Europe.

Constant ionic media such as $1M$ $NaClO_4$, seawater, and the like were shown by Sillén, Irving,
Bates, Schwarzenbach, and others to stabilize the
liquid-junction potential to the extent that
meaningful relative hydrogen ion concentrations
could be derived from the emf of glass-calomel
cells with liquid junction. This procedure was
used extensively in determining the stability
constants of metal-ligand coordination complexes.
Rapid and convenient procedures for determining
pK values using the glass electrode and silver-
silver halide electrodes in cells without liquid
junction were also devised.

Cells without liquid junction were chosen at
the National Bureau of Standards to provide a
means of establishing reference standard buffer
solutions for a national scale of pH. This scale
was endorsed by the International Union of Pure
and Applied Chemistry and, with minor modifications,

adopted in most industrialized countries of the world. A monograph by Bates, first appearing in 1954, clarified *inter alia*, the nature of this quasi-thermodynamic pH scale based on "conventional activities."

Determination of metal ions by direct potentiometry or by titrations has proved successful in those cases where stable electrodes reversible to the metal ion are available. Thus, cadmium, zinc, lead, silver, mercury, thallium, and occasionally copper ions have been determined with indicator electrodes consisting of the pure metal or (more often) an amalgam. Although selective for a single ionic species, the potentials of these electrodes may be subject to disturbances and side reactions from the presence of oxygen, oxidizing or reducing agents and the like.

As early as 1937 Kolthoff and Sanders demonstrated that pellets of the silver halides and thiocyanates and of thallous iodide respond in a theoretical manner to the ions of which these salts are composed. Nevertheless, efforts to develop practical membrane electrodes specific for a wide variety of ions--both cations and anions--did not bear fruit until the 1950s and 1960s. Pungor achieved a useful degree of selectivity with heterogeneous membrane electrodes formed by impregnating a silicone rubber matrix with an insoluble salt of the selected ion. M. S. Frant and James Ross (1966) introduced "solid-state" membranes composed of a single crystal of a slightly soluble salt of the ion for which specificity was sought. Their fluoride electrode, utilizing a crystal of lanthanum fluoride, displayed a high degree of selectivity.

When suitable crystals could not be found, selectivity could be achieved by use of a complexing agent or ion exchanger confined, by means of an ion-permeable film, between the exterior test solution and the inner electrode element. The applicability of this type of electrode design was extended by the development of "neutral carriers," such as the crown ethers, selective for the alkali and alkaline earth ions. For example, W. Simon devised a successful potassium electrode based on the preference of the antibiotic valinomycin for complexation with potassium rather than with sodium or other ions. The versatility of solid-state electrodes was greatly enhanced by the development of mixed crystal membranes. A crystal of Ag_2S, highly selective for sulfide ion, was made to respond, for example, to Cu^{2+} or Pb^{2+} by incorporating CuS or PbS as well as Ag_2S in the membrane.

New designs of useful electrodes came from the Orion and Beckman companies and from many laboratories, including those of Gary Rechnitz, George Guilbault, and W. Simon and from the Copenhagen laboratory of J. Růzicka and E. H. Hansen. The glass electrode was sometimes coupled with an immobilized enzyme or suitable substrate. An electrode responsive to ammonium ion, for example, could measure urea when coupled with a film of urease. Similarly, the work of Rechnitz, Guilbault, and others provided electrodes for the determination of enzymes and other biologically important compounds which, through highly specific interactions, produce electroactive ions. Ionic selectivity was achieved by Růzicka and Hansen and by H. Freiser through direct contact coupling of an electroactive substance with an electrode of graphite or other conducting material. Hydrophobic membranes permitting the passage of CO_2 or NH_3 into a film of aqueous buffer solution in contact with a pH glass electrode were successful in measuring the concentrations of these substances in solution, and the methods were extended to include amines, SO_2, HCN and other gases. In the mid-1970s electrodes for the determination of more than 20 ions and other species were available commercially.

Rechnitz and his associates identified factors influencing the time response of ion-selective electrodes, and the mechanisms of operation of these electrodes were further clarified by R. P. Buck. A monograph edited by R. A. Durst summarized the state of the art at the beginning of 1969, and later developments were described at a 1973 symposium of the Internation Union of Pure and Applied Chemistry.

Both theory and experiment confirmed that ion-selective electrodes respond to some function of the ionic activity. In constant ionic media, however, they can often be standardized to measure ion concentrations, and the ionic strengths of test solutions were sometimes adjusted to achieve this objective. For many other applications, ionic activity standards must be used. To avoid large errors due to residual liquid-junction potentials, scales of ionic activity covering a wide range of ionic strengths were devised. These were based on conventional average

ionic hydration numbers. For the measurement of
very low concentrations of free metal ions, reference buffers composed of the metal ion and a suitable ligand were shown to be useful standards.

Even here, in the discussion of potentiometry, it
is of interest to note the importance of instrumentation
to the area. Electronic developments during World War II
influenced not only pH meters but, as will be seen later,
almost all aspects of electroanalytical chemistry. Further, the most recent electronics revolution, inspired
by the Nobel prize-winning work of Shockley, Brattain,
and Bardeen, has led to a host of modern-day instrumentation developments. As will be seen, most of the advances and developments in methodology emerged from
universities, but the major work on instrumentation has
come from industrial laboratories, as was the case with
the transistor, which was invented at Bell Laboratories.

It is also worth pointing out, in a historical
sense, that the collaboration of Professors N. Howell
Furman and I. M. Kolthoff, referred to above in connection with their book on potentiometric titrations, is an
early indication of the influence they had on the development of modern electroanalysis. While many others
have contributed to this area, clearly the work carried
out by Furman at Princeton and Kolthoff at Minnesota and
their academic descendents represents the major thrust
in this area.

While one who has not lived through an era cannot
readily understand its problems, perhaps the view of
analytical chemists that prevailed in the 1920s can be
recalled by some recollections of Professor I. M. Kolthoff, who discusses some of his early problems while
still in Holland:

> Before 1920 the concept of pH and its signifi-
> cance were far from recognized by biochemists,
> physiologists, bacteriologists, etc. Frequently I
> gave lectures before these and other medical groups
> and was generally referred to as "the pH-er" (pro-
> nounced in Dutch "payha-er", with a like in "haha").
>
> The professor of physical-inorganic chemistry
> (the first Baker Lecturer at Cornell University*)
> looked down on any chemical contribution made by a
> pharmacist (I was the only one). It happened sev-
> eral times that some of the students in chemistry
> would come to tell me that the professor in his
> lecture had told them not to read any of the junk
> which K. published in the (Dutch) *Chemisch Weekblad*.
> This happened again when in 1917 I had published

---

*Ernst Cohen.--ed. note.

three papers on the "Estimation of Solids in
Potable Water from the Electrical Conductance."
I had done quite a bit of work on conductance of
mixtures of electrolytes and was pretty sore. I
went to the professor and--in short--made him
retract all his criticism. When leaving I told
him that the only honorable thing for him to do
was to make a clear statement at his next lecture.
Instead, he went to my boss and teacher, N.
Schoorl, and complained bitterly that I had been
disrespectful.

In 1924, when I had been invited to give some
lectures in the United States, I went to say good-
bye to "the professor," who had just returned
from Cornell, and he said: "Kolthoff, remember
that the Dutch have an excellent name in the U. S.
and you could easily spoil it."

The professor of organic chemistry complained
several times before the 1920s to my boss that he,
Schoorl, should prevent me from publishing such
papers as "the calculation of the equivalence potential in redox titrations" (this was entirely
original work) and on my work on acid-base indicators. [After publication of my first book in
1920, "Der Gebrauch von Farbindikatoren," my name
was well established in Germany. The attitude of
the professors in Chemistry at Utrecht University
changed enough to allow me to become a "lecturer
in electrochemistry" (without salary).]

Quite generally, professors in chemistry looked
down--with reason--on analytical chemists. These
were the maid-servants of other chemists (Ostwald,
1894). This was also the situation in the United
States when I started at Minnesota in 1927. After
receiving the Ph.D., my students got positions as
"analysts" or glorified technicians in industry.
In the early 1930s I made an agreement with the
late Professor F. H. MacDougall, head of physical
chemistry, that my students could major with me
in physical and minor in analytical chemistry.
(They had to take all required courses in, and the
thesis topic had to be approved by, physical
chemistry.)

The background that Kolthoff brought to the United
States is shown by another of his recollections:

In the early 1920s I used to attend the annual
meetings of the Deutsche Bunsengesellschaft. The
1924 meeting was held in Göttingen and was at-
tended--among others--by young Hückel. It was
soon after the publication of the Debye-Hückel
theory of strong electrolytes. Walther Nernst,

NATHANIEL HOWELL FURMAN, 1892-1965

Professor Furman was associated with Princeton University
from 1909 until his death, first as a student, then as teacher,
finally becoming Russell Wellman Moore Professor. He was an outstanding teacher and analytical chemist, specializing in electroanalytical methods. He was co-author of many widely used textbooks, and was ACS President in 1951.

who was in his early sixties, gave the first lecture and opposed this theory. The late Kasimir Fajans (University of Munich, since 1938 at the University of Michigan) had arrived at the opposite conclusion. The discussion was not enlightening and was terminated by Nernst by saying: "Glauben Sie mir doch, mein lieber Kollege, wenn ich sage, dass es so ist, dann ist es so." The meeting was also attended by Svante Arrhenius, then 65 years of age, who died less than three years later. I had the privilege of being introduced to him (also to Haber) and was deeply impressed with his modesty. I spent much time with Hückel who told me that Arrhenius was vitally interested in the new theory which he considered as a welcome extension of his theory. It is quite well known that his Ph.D. thesis (1883), "Recherches sur la conductibilité galvanique des electrolytes," met with serious objections by the science faculty of the University of Uppsala, who finally granted him the degree "non sine laude approbatur." Wilhelm Ostwald was one of the first to recognize the importance of the Arrhenius theory: ". . . dessen Arbeiten zu dem Bedeutendsten gehören was über die Affinitätstheory veröffentlicht ist."

It is obvious that the development of potentiometry, and the understanding of that area, did contribute to the changes that took place in the electroanalytical area in the 1930s. Perhaps further insight into this relationship can be seen by some comments of Professor H. A. Laitinen, now of the University of Florida, who has written:

> An important modification of the potentio-metric titration, involving the use of two identical indicator electrodes, across which was passed a small polarizing current from an external source, was introduced as early as 1922 by H. H. Willard and F. Fenwick and described in more detail by R. G. Van Name and Fenwick. The principles underlying this method were clearly set forth in 1951 by C. N. Reilley, W. D. Cooke and N. H. Furman, who considered the current-voltage curves at various stages of the titration and pointed out that the response corresponded to the slope of the steady state current-voltage curve at the zero current axis. Accordingly, they introduced the name "derivative polarographic titrations," which however has not survived. The amperometric titration can be traced back in principle to 1897 when E. Salomon,

working in Nernst's laboratory, titrated chloride with silver using a pair of polarized electrodes and measured the limiting current, proportional to silver ion concentration. Even the rotating indicator electrode dates back to 1905, when Nernst and E. S. Merriam performed the same titration, as well as acid-base titrations using two indicator electrodes. The method was not fully developed until polarography and voltammetry had become established in analytical methodology. Kolthoff has described Nernst as "the father of potentiometry, potentiometric titrations, voltammetry and biamperometric titrations." He himself has introduced the names of the last three of these techniques, as well as of conductometric titrations. The modern era of the use of rotated microelectrodes dates back to 1941. Since that time a great many variations in cell and electrode geometry, mode of stirring and addition of reagents have been devised. The dead-stop endpoint of C. W. Foulk and A. T. Bawden recognized a close relationship between their work and that of Willard and Fenwick and Van Name and Fenwick, but evidently they did not fully understand the mechanism of the electrode polarization beyond the endpoint, because they spoke of polarization "presumably due to an adsorbed oxygen layer at the anode and an adsorbed hydrogen layer at the cathode" even though the applied potential difference was only 10-15 mV. The most important distinction, however, between the early work and later work is that Foulk and Bowden did not extrapolate mass transport limited currents back to an endpoint but merely used the current as a qualitative indication as to when the endpoint had just been passed.

In 1933 a photograph of Professor Jaroslav Heyrovský appeared in the *New York Times*. The caption of that photograph follows:

The polarograph, here shown with its designer, Professor Jaroslav Heyrovský of Charles University, Prague, automatically analyzes complex chemical solutions and thus saves hours of laboratory work. The solution is contained in a small vessel in which it is electrolytically decomposed. Since the decomposition is electrical its progress can be read off in the form of a current, the intensity of which is recorded on a strip of paper wound on a drum. The curves obtained give both the relationship between the

current which travels through the solution and
the magnitude of the applied electromotive force.
With this instrument, Professor Heyrovský finds
it possible to analyze both qualitatively and
quantitatively the numerous complex alcohols as
well as the still more complicated compounds of
which the lower forms of life are composed.

The invention of the polarograph by Professor
Heyrovský was certainly the key to the development of
the modern era of electroanalytical chemistry. Although
a considerable amount of work on techniques of electrodeposition had been done, going back as far as Faraday,
concepts of mass transport as mentioned earlier, were
not well understood. The development of polarography
and its understanding, by Heyrovský, Ilkovič, and later
by Brdička, Koutecký, and many others in Czechoslovakia
triggered a large amount of work in the United States.
The importance of polarography is best indicated by the
fact that Jaroslav Heyrovský received the Nobel prize
in chemistry for this work.

The impetus for polarography in America appears to
have stemmed from the visit Heyrovský made to this
country in 1933. We may perhaps appreciate the moment
by the recollections of two individuals, first Professor
Kolthoff and then Professor P. J. Elving of the University of Michigan.

First, from Professor Kolthoff:

My acquaintance and friendship with the late
Jaroslav Heyrovský dates back to 1926. It was
at the end of 1924 that O. Tomiček, later professor of analytical chemistry at Charles University, Prague, Czechoslovakia, came to work
with me for a year in Utrecht. He studied the
applications of titanium(III) chloride to potentiometric redox titrations. I visited him in
1926 in Prague and met Heyrovský for the first
time. After that I visited every two years,
except during the war, but thereafter again.
My last visit there was when the Communists had
taken over. My first scheduled lecture was
postponed for a day because of the funeral of
ex-President Benesch. I vividly recall that I
started my lecture by paying tribute to Benesch
and ended up by saying: "In 1940 Lingane and I
dedicated our book on Polarography to you, Professor Heyrovský, with the motto of my Alma
Mater (Utrecht): 'Sol justitiae illustrate
nos.'" (I then added: "May the sun of justice
soon shine on you again.") You could hear a
pin drop, until some ten per cent of the audi-
ence (Communists) left and reported me to the

police. I breathed more freely the next day
when I left the country by plane after delivering a second lecture.

In 1933 both Heyrovský and Otto Hahn visited
me in the same week. Heyrovský gave us two
lectures on polarography; Hahn lectured on
adsorption on precipitates. At that time I had
been lucky to have had Lingane as a temporary
research assistant. Although I had visited
Heyrovský a few times, I never had studied the
analytical possibilities of polarography. Soon
after Heyrovský's visit, Lingane started research for his doctor's thesis. Meloche in
Wisconsin had published a paper in which he
described the polarographic determination of
alkali ions in lake water. To my knowledge
Meloche was the only one in the United States
who had a polarograph from Prague. When Lingane started his experimental work in 1934, he
very skillfully built his own polarograph
(polaroscope) with which all the fundamentals
of the field were studied. (Wisconsin had a
beautiful instrumental lab. One of my serious
limitations has been--and still is--my lack of
interest in instrumentation. Before my retirement we purchased only the most essential equipment for our research. In my early days in
Utrecht I used a slide wire and a rheostat as
a potentiometer and a Lippmann capillary electrometer as nullpoint instrument.) Lingane's
precise work is equally fundamental now as it
was at that time. It was in 1936 that H. A.
Laitinen started to work for his doctor's degree.
I was very lucky, as he had declined an assist-
antship at the University of Illinois and had
decided to stay at Minnesota. We discussed the
electrochemical and, more specifically, the
electroanalytical possibilities of platinum
electrodes. Laitinen did very fundamental work
on diffusion to a platinum disk electrode. He
also originated the analytical use of the rotated platinum electrode. We coined the words
"voltammetry" and "amperometric titrations,"
which are now common terminology.

While Professor V. W. Meloche of the University of
Wisconsin appears to have had the first polarograph in
the United States, the detailed study of polarography
was to be carried out at Minnesota and Princeton. Professor Elving, who was a student at Princeton, has
written about his recollections. In describing the
caption of the article from the *New York Times*,

JAROSLAV HEYROVSKÝ, 1890-1967

Educated in Czechoslovakia and England, Heyrovský spent his professional career in Prague, initially at the Charles University, later as head of the Heyrovský Institute of Polarography. He received the Nobel Prize in Chemistry in 1959, in recognition of his work in polarography.

reproduced above, he stated that:

The *Times* managed to describe polarography well at a time when most chemists would have been likely to confuse polarography with polarimetry. The reason for my saving the item was that either Professor N. Howell Furman or Professor Earle R. Caley mentioned to some of the students in the undergraduate quant lab at Princeton that there was to be a lecture by a Professor Jaroslav Heyrovský from Prague who was spending six months at the University of California and who was lecturing at American universities about a novel analytical technique which he had developed. I have no specific recollection of the lecture, but it evidently made an impression on me since in 1940, when I was teaching at Purdue University, I was interested to learn that my colleague Bryant Bachman had purchased a Fisher Elecdropode (a manual polarograph). As part of some studies on nonaqueous media as solvents for analytical and general purposes, I borrowed the polarograph and ran polarograms of some metal ions in formamide. The results were quite interesting in indicating analytically useful separation of half-wave potentials, but I did not pursue them further since I was then mainly involved in starting research on organic elemental analysis.

As had been indicated, Heyrovský used his 1933 stay in the United States as the opportunity for a program of "consciousness raising" concerning the utility of the polarized micro dropping mercury electrode. In 1934, Heyrovský lectured on polarography at the Mendelyeev Centennial in Moscow. In 1936, a volume of Böttger's famous treatise on physical methods of analysis appeared with a chapter on polarography by Heyrovský. These three events helped to trigger the tremendous activity in polarographic investigations and techniques which began in the late 1930s.

An important factor in the development of polarography was the foreigners who came to Prague as students and visitors. These, infected by Heyrovský's enthusiasm, initiated activity in polarography throughout the world. The first was Shikata from Japan, who developed the recording polarograph, which was also one of the first recording devices to be used in analytical chemistry. From the United States there came Otto Müller as student and I. M. Kolthoff as visitor; articles in *Chemical Reviews* in 1939 by

Kolthoff and James J. Lingane on principles and analytical applicability of polarography and by Müller on organic polarography, followed in 1941 by Müller's series of articles in the *Journal of Chemical Education* and by Kolthoff and Lingane's book, served to acquaint American chemists with the potentialities inherent in polarography. Among the other noteworthy visitors to Prague were G. Semerano from Italy, who published a book on polarography in 1932, Wiktur Kemula from Poland, who later developed the hanging mercury drop electrode, and Bruno Breyer from Australia, who developed alternating current polarography. In Prague, Heyrovský collected an exciting, able group of collaborators; one need only mention Brdička, Ilkovič, Koryta, Kůta, Vlček, and Zuman.

It is well to emphasize that Heyrovský's discovery of polarography is an interesting example of that important process in science: the accident that may result from a minor change in procedure, and, most importantly, that is followed up by the curious and receptive mind.

A view of the factors that brought electroanalytical chemistry to the forefront at Princeton can be considered by some remembrances of Professor Clark Bricker, now at the University of Kansas. As Bricker points out, the number of students actually engaged in such studies at Princeton was small, but their contributions were significant. Bricker provides an historical viewpoint:

In 1795, John Maclean was the first professor of chemistry appointed at the College of New Jersey (Princeton). Professor Maclean continued in this position until 1812 when he accepted an appointment at the College of William and Mary. The chemistry department at the College of New Jersey grew slowly during the 19th century, and it was not until 1883 that LeRoy Wiley McCay was appointed an assistant in analytical chemistry. McCay had received his undergraduate degree at Princeton in 1878 and then studied for four years in Germany at Freiburg and Heidelberg. McCay progressed through the ranks of instructor, assistant professor, and finally was appointed professor of inorganic chemistry at Princeton in 1892. He was interested in determining arsenic, the sulfo and sulfoxy compounds of arsenic, the separation of tin and antimony, the use of hydrofluoric acid in ordinary and in electro-chemical analysis and in mercury as a reducing agent. In the 45 years that McCay was a faculty

member at Princeton University, his only graduate student was N. Howell Furman who completed
his undergraduate work in 1913 and his Ph.D. in
1917. After two years as an instructor at Stanford University, Furman returned to Princeton
in 1919 and remained a faculty member at the
institution until his retirement in 1960.

Furman in his autobiography wrote concerning
his years as a student at Princeton, "At Princeton University the professors so adorned their
profession that while I admired the life they
led, I never dreamed that I might some day enter
the charmed circle. While pretty much all of
the elder statesmen became acquaintances and
some of them fast friends, Professor LeRoy W.
McCay became an outstanding influence and naturally being his special assistant in quantitative
analysis, I elected to do thesis work in that
area." Furman became interested in electroanalytical chemistry during his research for his
doctoral thesis. The first paper to be published
jointly by Furman and McCay was entitled "The
Use of Hydrofluoric Acid in the Separation of
Some Heavy Metals from Tin, Antimony, Tungsten,
Molybdenum, by Means of the Electric Current."
It would appear that Furman's first publication
in the field of potentiometry was a paper that
appeared in 1932 entitled, "Electrotitration
with the Aid of the Air Electrode." There is no
question that the visit of I. M. Kolthoff to the
United States in 1924 greatly stimulated Furman's interest in potentiometric titrations and
related subjects. The association of Kolthoff
and Furman led to the co-authorship of "Potentiometric Titrations" which was first published
in 1926 and later revised in 1931. In addition,
Furman translated two other books that Kolthoff
had written, "Volumetric Analysis" and "Acid-
Base Indicators."

Furman continued to be a leader in the field
of potentiometric titration by publishing reviews
of this subject in *Industrial and Engineering
Chemistry* and by publishing articles with students during the 1930s. The use of the concentration cell in quantitative analysis, more
specifically, the estimation of small amounts
of chloride in salts, was first proposed by
Furman and George W. Low, Jr.

In the 1930s, Professor Jaroslav Heyrovský
visited the United States and spent a short time
at Princeton. This visit stimulated Furman to

enter the field of polarography and after a
Heyrovský-type polarograph was constructed in
the machine shop at Princeton, Furman directed
the theses of several students, including Clark
Bricker, Kenneth G. Stone, and William C. Cooper,
in the field of polarographic analysis.

In the early 1950s, the analytical group at
Princeton made significant contributions to the
field of electroanalytical chemistry through the
work of W. D. Cooke, C. N. Reilley and R. N.
Adams. It was through this group that a thorough
understanding of the principles of voltammetry
was realized, and this led to a complete understanding of derivative polarographic titrations
(potentiometric titrations at constant current).
It was with this same group that coulometric
analysis and titrations also obtained a solid
foundation which sparked the development of many
studies in this general field throughout the
United States and the world.

During his 41 years on the faculty at Princeton, Furman supervised the doctoral dissertations
of 26 students in addition to collaborating with
two post-doctoral research associates. In addition, it is important to point out that Furman
supervised the independent work of many under-
graduates during his tenure on the Princeton
faculty and also had a profound and lasting
impact on all the analytical graduate students.

The importance of electroanalytical chemistry
was clearly demonstrated during the early days
of World War II and the development of the Manhattan Project. In late 1941, Furman and Bricker
were asked to attend a meeting at the lamp
division of Westinghouse in Bloomfield, N.J.
It was at this meeting that the first request
of an industrial organization was made to produce commercial quantities of uranium metal.
The purity of the uranium had to be higher than
that of any metal that had been produced to
that date. The question was how to analyze for
trace impurities in uranium metal. Furman and
Bricker developed an electrolytic method using
a mercury cathode to separate the trace metals
from the dissolved uranium metal. After the
mercury was removed by distillation, the metal
residue was dissolved and analyzed by a polarographic technique. While in 1976 this method
may seem quite antiquated, it is important to
realize that in 1942 it was the only reliable
method to identify the metal impurities in

uranium and other strategic materials.

The name of Furman is certainly associated with electroanalytical chemistry and Princeton University. It is important to realize, however, that Furman was not interested only in electroanalytical chemistry. His contributions to the broad field of analytical chemistry included his investigation of ceric oxidimetry, his study of organic reagents, and his broad interest in spectrographic, chromatographic and extraction techniques. The work performed by Roy Mundy and Furman on the extraction of uranium nitrate solutions led to an efficient industrial method for the preparation of pure uranium salts.

In 1976, electroanalytical chemistry is no longer playing a major role at Princeton but the heritage of that institution and more specifically, that of N. Howell Furman is still very much alive through the research efforts of the first and second generation students.

We have seen above Professor Kolthoff's view concerning the requirements of instrumentation. A slightly different view of the importance of instrumentation in the polarographic area has been provided by Professor John Stock of the University of Connecticut. Writing about the work of Heyrovský, and the development of polarography, Stock has written:

Heyrovský and his co-workers vigorously developed his invention. Although current-voltage curves can be constructed by point-by-point plotting, this procedure is obviously slow. In 1925, Heyrovský and Shikata invented the polarograph, which automatically records these curves. Although polarographic methods had spread well beyond the boundaries of Czechoslovakia by the mid-1930s, such methods had by then attracted but little attention in the United States. The first extensive American research program in polarography appears to be that of V. W. Meloche and his co-workers at the University of Wisconsin. Their 1937 paper on the polarographic determination of ketones describes methods for measuring polarograms obtained by plotting and by automatic recording. The latter was carried out with an instrument made by the Leeds and Northrup Co. This instrument appears to be one of the first of the pen-recording type to be manufactured in the United States. Photographically reading polarographs, produced under Heyrovský's supervision, were imported until

Germany occupied Czechoslovakia in 1940. The
Sargent-Heyrovský model XI, introduced in 1941,
was the first American instrument of this type.

Although polarographic literature had become quite extensive by the end of 1940, no
English-language monograph on the subject then
existed. This situation was remedied in 1941
by the appearance of Kolthoff and Lingane's
"Polarography." This work, doubtless springing
from a far-reaching research program initiated
by I. M. Kolthoff at the University of Minnesota, and its 1952 second edition were major
factors in popularizing polarography throughout
the world. A bibliography, included in the
special issue of *Talanta* to honor the 70th
birthday of Professor Kolthoff, provides an
overview of the massive contributions made by
this scientist and his co-workers during some
25 years of this program.

Along with the direct analytical utility of polarography, the development of amperometric titrations must
be considered. Both the dropping mercury electrode and
the rotating platinum electrode, as pioneered by Kolthoff
and Laitinen, have found application. Further comments
by Professor Stock regarding developments in the amperometric area are of interest:

Various precipitation reactions were studied
polarographically by Heyrovský and S. Berezicky
in 1929. For example, potassium sulfate was
progressively added to a solution of barium
chloride. This was polarographed after each
addition, and the decrease in the barium ion reduction current (or "wave height") was noted.
In fact, a polarographic titration of this type
can be performed by maintaining the indicator
electrode (here the DME) at fixed potential.
This is chosen to lie on the plateau, or "limiting current region" of the titrand. The current then decreases linearly as the electroactive material is removed, becoming small and
essentially constant when the titrant is in
excess. This L-type titration curve changes to
one of V shape if both titrand and titrant are
electroactive at the chosen potential. Other
types of curves are possible and the technique
can be applied to certain acid-base and redox
titrations, as well as to those involving precipitation or other "combination" reactions.
The general principles were investigated in the
1930s, principally by Czechoslovakian workers.

The term "amperometric titration," now used

almost universally, was proposed by Kolthoff
and Y. D. Pan in 1939. During the next two
decades, Kolthoff and his associates made extensive contributions, one of the most important being their introduction of the rotating
platinum electrode. This is particularly
suited to measurements that are made at constant potential, as in amperometric titrimetry.
When the chemistry is favorable, titrand concentrations down to the micromolar region can
be handled.

Biamperometric titration involves the use
of two essentially identical electrodes, instead of one "indicator" microelectrode and a
reference electrode. The roots of the techniques go back to 1897, when Salomon, working
in Nernst's laboratory, used two silver electrodes to follow the argentometric titration
of chloride. In 1926, C. W. Foulk and A. T.
Bawden, at the Ohio State University, showed
that precise iodine-thiosulfate titrations
could be carried out at two platinum electrodes, between which a small fixed potential
was maintained. These workers introduced the
term "dead-stop endpoint titrations." Although
still occasionally encountered, this term has
been essentially supplanted by "biamperometric
titration," as proposed by Kolthoff in 1954.

In 1943 G. Wernimont and F. J. Hopkinson,
of the Eastman Kodak Co., showed that moisture
could be simply and accurately titrated with
Karl Fischer reagent to a "dead-stop" endpoint.
It is from this time that the real potentialities of biamperometric titration began to be
realized.

Instead of maintaining a constant potential
between the two identical electrodes, a small
but constant current may be forced to flow between them. Certain titrations may then be monitored by observing the potential developed between the electrodes. This technique was developed in 1951 by C. N. Reilley, W. D. Cooke,
and N. H. Furman, at Princeton University, under
the name "derivative polarographic titration."
The work at Minnesota, initiated by Kolthoff with
J. J. Lingane, soon involved among others, H. A. Laitinen,
D. N. Hume, W. E. Harris, E. F. Orlemann, and later,
T. S. Lee, S. Bruckenstein, E. P. Parry, and many others.
At Princeton, Furman's work with C. N. Reilley, Clark
Bricker, R. N. Adams, and others was to increase the
understanding of electroanalytical principles. All of

the individuals referred to as having started with Kolthoff or Furman continued in the electroanalytical area,
and at present many of their academic great-great grand-
children continue in the same tradition.

The direction electroanalytical chemistry has taken
has been strongly influenced by advances in theory that
came about some 20 years after the work initiated at
Minnesota. Probably the individual most responsible was
Professor Paul Delahay, now at New York University.
Delahay came to this country shortly after the end of
World War II to work with Professor P. Van Rysselberghe
at the University of Oregon. Since Delahay's work
stemmed most directly from the advances in polarography
that had come about just prior to the 1950s, some of his
comments may be of interest.

Before recounting the part I took in the
development of electroanalytical chemistry after
the Second World War, I should like to recapture
the atmosphere prevailing in analytical chemistry at that time. Electrochemical methods
then occupied a central position in analytical
chemistry, and polarography was in the front
rank among these methods. Kolthoff was the
acknowledged master of the field, and his book
(with Lingane) on "Polarography" (1941) was the
bible. I had obtained a copy of it in Brussels
in 1946, and I kept studying it during the
voyage on the *Ile de France* in October 1946 when
I crossed over to the United States.

Instrumentation was primitive at that time,
and the photographic recording polarograph was
still in use. I had already worked with this
instrument (a German version from Leybold) at
the University of Brussels where I was instructor
in 1945 and 1946. Commercial polarographs with
pen-and-ink recorders were not yet available.

I had met Van Rysselberghe in Brussels in
1946, and he invited me to the University of
Oregon in Eugene. I was associated with him
for three years. He had at that time a contract
(with the recently created Office of Naval Research) for the study of metallic corrosion by
polarography. Van Rysselberghe's interests
were primarily in thermodynamics and particularly in the approach advocated by DeDonder and
his school at Brussels. Prigogine had published his thesis on irreversible thermodynamics in 1947, and Van Rysselberghe was attempting to apply this new approach to electrode processes--a problem which he pursued
for many years. I did not share his interest

in this problem, but we often discussed electrode processes which could not be accounted for by the ubiquitous Nernst equation. The idea of my studying "irreversible" polarographic waves was born then, but I did nothing of significance on this problem at the time. I was learning my trade and completing the transition from electrical engineering to chemistry.

After having settled down at Louisiana State University, where I arrived in December 1949, I soon began to think about this problem in a fresh way. In a paper published in 1951, I proposed a theory of irreversible waves based on control by semi-infinite linear diffusion and the kinetics of charge transfer.

This work was not well received by some of the well-established investigators in polarography when I presented it at a couple of meetings. This adverse reception was easy to understand: the polarographic theory, as expounded in the book of Kolthoff and Lingane, was a neat package to which irreversible waves did not belong. The prevailing attitude was, it would seem, "One does not talk about such things in good families!" The thermodynamic interpretation of electrochemical methods of analysis was still dominant, and I suppose it was not pleasant to see this neat world shattered by subversive ideas.

Kolthoff took a more enlightened attitude and suggested in early 1952 that I write a book on the emerging newer aspects of electrochemical methods of analysis. Although we communicated only by letters for the most part, he took a strong interest in the project and guided my initial faltering steps. In fact, I would have given up the writing of the book, at least at that time, had he not insisted that I go ahead.

In the meantime, I was developing in collaboration with a very gifted student, Telivaldis Berzins, what I later called chronopotentiometry. This work was begun after I had read a paper by L. Gierst and A. L. Juliard in which they revived the work on constant current that had been done at the turn of the century by H. J. S. Sand and others. By that time, I knew how to analyze such problems correctly by using Laplace (and on one occasion Fourier) transforms, as I had studied in detail the 1947 fundamental paper of Koutecký and Brdička on polarographic currents with partial control by a chemical reaction. The work on chronopotentiometry proceeded swiftly and was reported in four papers (in 1953 and 1954), covering the essential points of this theory and supporting experimental results.

The manuscript of the book on new instrumental methods was completed before the summer of 1953. I then went to Europe for two months, and upon my return to Baton Rouge I rewrote most of the text in the fall of 1953. The text was completed during the Christmas vacation of 1953. It covered not only the newer aspects of polarography but also voltammetry with linear sweep of potential, alternating current methods, chronopotentiometry, the rotating disk electrode, and miscellaneous other topics (including a chapter by Reilley on high-frequency methods).

The book went far beyond classical polarography, and it opened up new approaches which soon were explored by an increasingly wider group of electroanalytical chemists. A new "style" was born, and, I suppose, I was chronologically the first of a new breed of electroanalytical chemists. The book was well received, and, much to my surprise, it still is being published regularly each year some 20 years after its publication. It was reprinted several times by the publishers as they did not expect such a long life for a research monograph. The book was soon translated into Russian.

I attended the famous 1954 Discussion of the Faraday Society on fast reactions and was fascinated by these new developments and particularly by Eigen's work on relaxation processes in solution. Thus, I began to study fast electrode processes and initially opted for a method involving relaxation following the application of a constant current--in line with our previous work on chronopotentiometry. The 1955 paper I wrote with Berzins on this subject became, I suppose, a classic in the field.

Professor Delahay's mention of the electrical double layer prompts the thought that an understanding of the double layer is a prerequisite for research in electroanalytical chemistry. Although modern theories of the electrical double layer derive from Stern and Gouy and Chapman's original work, a considerable debt is owed to the late Professor David C. Grahame at Amherst, whose detailed studies of double layer phenomena, as evidenced

by his classical paper in the 1947 *Chemical Reviews*, are
still read by many in the electroanalytical area. Considerable theoretical insight into many a problem in the
electroanalytical area was provided by work in the late
1950s and 1960s by W. Reinmuth of Columbia. Detailed
quantum mechanical aspects of electron transfer processes were provided by many workers, although the chief
contributor in the United States was certainly Professor
Rudolph A. Marcus of the University of Illinois. Although we are primarily concerned with the historical
aspects of electroanalytical chemistry, to some extent
it is impossible to separate the more theoretical aspects
of electrochemistry from the electroanalytical area.

Professor Delahay's comments indicate the impact
that the work on classical polarography had on his scientific career and accomplishments. As he indicates,
electroanalytical methods did indeed occupy a central
position in analytical chemistry. Most of the major
universities where analytical chemistry existed, in
fact, appeared dominated by those in the electroanalytical area in the late 1930s and through the 1940s and
1950s. An explanation of why this is so may be provided
by some comments of Professor P. J. Elving:

It is interesting to speculate why research
in polarography suddenly became so important in
analytical chemistry, especially in the United
States where it dominated academic analytical
chemistry during the 1940s and 1950s and is still
going strong. This happened in spite of the
relatively small fraction of actual analyses
which involve polarographic measurement.

In the 1930s there was increasing emphasis
on the use of theory and explication in chemistry as evidenced, for example, by the development of physical organic chemistry. Analytical
chemists felt this pressure, and there were
conscious attempts at an in-depth explanation
of the phenomena and techniques involved in
analytical chemistry as it was then practiced.
This is seen, for example, in the classical
areas of gravimetric and volumetric (titrimetric) analysis in the studies of the kinetics
and mechanisms of precipitation, e.g., nuclea-
tion phenomena, and the more sophisticated investigations of titrimetric reactions, e.g.,
use of standard potentials and complexation to
explain the variation in efficiency of Ce(IV)
as an oxidizing agent with the nature of the
mineral acid used. However, many of the main
and developing areas of analysis were either
largely preempted in respect to theory by

physicists, e.g., emission spectroscopy and radioactivity, or seemed to offer only little opportunity for virtuoso theoretical development, e.g., the bit of chromatography then known. There was some activity, largely empirical, in visible absorption spectroscopy. Feigl had developed the concept of specific groupings in complexation, but the theory, which was then available, was restricted and had to be applied in a non-mathematical form.

Then, in the mid-1930s, polarography in the form of the polarized dropping mercury electrode came to the attention of analytical chemists. Experimentally, polarography was close enough to both potentiometry and electrolysis to make analytical chemists comfortable with its use. Theoretically, the Czechs--Heyrovský, Brdička, Ilkovič, Herasymenko--were developing a series of mathematical formulations, based on fundamental considerations, which American academic analytical chemists found attractive and which stimulated investigation both of additional theory and of variations in technique. In addition, it should be stressed, polarography had an analytical attractiveness in respect to specificity and sensitivity.

Polarography attracted many able academic analytical chemists, which resulted in a great volume of good research, especially from the viewpoint of introducing graduate students to the methodology of research and to the approaches of analytical chemistry. There also began to be a moderately extensive use of polarography for actual analysis, e.g., the routine determination of lead in large numbers of samples connected with the demands of industrial hygiene and toxicology.

The rest of the story is familiar. Academic activity in polarography became less and less concerned with analytical applicability and more and more with the mechanisms and mathematical theory involved. At the same time, there was extensive development in the United States and abroad of techniques and methodologies based on polarography, e.g., chronopotentiometry, chronocoulometry, a.c. polarography, tensammetry, cyclic voltammetry, square-wave polarography, pulse polarography, controlled potential coulometry, coulometric titration, and stripping analysis.

Unfortunately, the separation of basic

research from practice became to some extent self-defeating. Developments of techniques and methodologies tended to become ends in themselves. This was typified by the sad complaint of a speaker at a Gordon Conference on electrochemistry in the early 1960s, that he had a marvelous way of answering questions with his electroanalytical approach but nobody showed any interest in asking these questions. Thus, after considerable use in both inorganic and organic analysis in the 1940s and 1950s, polarography showed a slow, steady decline as other techniques took over, e.g., atomic absorption for inorganic applications and gas chromatography for organic applications. However, in more recent years there has been a reversal with a slow increase in the use of polarographic techniques due to the high sensitivity inherent in electrochemical current measurement, especially as the background represented by the capacity current can be minimized. At the present time we see the increasing application of stripping analysis, largely for inorganic applications, and of pulse polarography for both organic and inorganic analysis.

In addition there has been in the past decade or two a steadily increasing interest in using polarography as a primary research tool, e.g., the development of perturbation techniques for investigating the individual steps in the overall electrode process has resulted in being able to measure the rates of rapid chemical reactions coupled to charge-transfer processes, such as free radical dimerization rates. In addition, there has been increasing use of characteristic potentials, e.g., $E_{\frac{1}{2}}$, as indices to the chemical, physical, and biological properties and behavior of organic compounds and increasing elucidation of electrode reaction paths or mechanisms as a guide to methods of synthesis and to chemical and biological reaction paths. For example, there is increasing reference to the use of polarographic behavior, particularly $E_{\frac{1}{2}}$ values, to characterize organic, metallo-organic and metal-organic ligand complexes.

In the last few years there has been a significant coalescence of techniques in the area of bioelectrochemistry, which involves the focussing of electrochemical methodologies on the investigation of biologically significant compounds, phenomena and problems.

As the techniques alluded to by Professor Elving have developed, their utility which was initially considered to be totally analytically oriented has become well recognized by other chemists. Thus, we presently see organic and inorganic chemists using electroanalytical techniques--polarography and its descendents--in a wide variety of experimental work where analysis per se is not the goal. The electroanalytical methods have proved to be powerful tools in elucidating complex chemical reactions.

Certain aspects of electrolysis and electroanalytical separations can be attributed to Michael Faraday. However, in the United States, at the turn of the century, considerable work was already being carried out in the area of electrolytic determinations and separations. In the 1880s, Wolcott Gibbs used a mercury cathode, calling attention to the use of mercury as a negative electrode, the positive electrode being a plate of platinum. "...It was found possible to separate iron, cobalt, nickel, zinc, cadmium and copper so completely from solutions of the respective sulphates that entrance of metal could be detected in the liquid...." In the 1900s, a large amount of work on electroanalysis was performed by Edgar Fahs Smith of the University of Pennsylvania. This resulted in a number of editions of his book, "Electro-Analysis," being published by Blakiston in the first 20 years of the 20th century. This book, which discusses research by Smith and others, has a considerable amount of material on separation of metals, largely using chemical masking. Rotating electrodes, surprisingly, are discussed from the point of view of speeding up the time required for electrolysis. Although some control of potential (electrolytic voltage) was recognized, the systems used only two electrodes--an anode and a cathode.

Modern techniques of controlled potential electrolysis and electrolytic separations owe a great deal to the development of the potentiostat by A. Hickling in England in 1942. This device permitted the potential of one electrode to be controlled electronically with respect to a reference electrode; current then passed between the electrode whose potential was controlled and another, non-controlled, electrode. Thus, the focus was in the control of the potential of the electrode where the reaction of interest took place rather than on the total electrolysis potential applied across the cell. Considerable development was carried out on potentiostats by Lingane, H. Diehl at Iowa State and others. The development of this instrumentation permitted considerable work in electrodeposition and electroseparation to be performed in the 1940s and 1950s by Lingane,

OLIVER WOLCOTT GIBBS, 1822-1908

   Professor of Chemistry at the College of the City of New York
for 14 years, then Rumford Professor at Harvard University, Gibbs
was subsequently head of the Chemical Institute at Harvard.   He
was editor of *The American Journal of Sciences* and pne of the
founders of the National Academy of Sciences.   His greatest
scientific achievement was the discovery of electrogravimetry.

Furman, Louis Meités, (initially at Yale, then at Brooklyn Polytechnic Institute, and now at Clarkson), and
L. B. Rogers, (initially at Oak Ridge, then at MIT, Purdue, and now at Georgia). The latter's work on underpotential, for instance, is a classic in its field. In the 1940s, a good deal of useful information was published by the G. F. Smith Chemical Co., and one of its booklets, written by Harvey Diehl, did much to publicize constant potential electrolysis.

The development of the potentiostat did a great deal for the instrumentation in this and other electroanalytical areas. However, probably the most significant change in electroanalytical instrumentation over the past 50 years came about as a result of the development of operational amplifiers and associated electronic circuitry. Probably the earliest to recognize the importance of this electronic development was Professor D. D. DeFord of Northwestern University. DeFord's unpublished but widely circulated notes on operational amplifiers in the late 1950s were certainly used by many electroanalytical chemists as an introduction to this new area. In 1959 the Ph.D. thesis of C. G. Enke, working with Laitinen at Illinois, credited DeFord for the circuit of a stabilized voltage follower and included operational amplifier circuits for a chopper-stabilized potentiostat and a current integrator.

Constant potential coulometry, introduced by Hickling in England, was refined and developed in the United States by J. J. Lingane and co-workers at Harvard, W. M. MacNevin and co-workers at Ohio State University, and by Glen Booman of Phillips Petroleum Co. Booman's work, a direct result of the desire of nuclear workers to perform remote and highly accurate analyses of uranium, represents an excellent combination of electroanalytical chemistry and instrumentation.

Constant current coulometry and coulometric titrations appear to have developed as a result of work by two Hungarian scientists, L. Szebelledy and Z. Somogyi, in 1938. Their work was expanded and refined by Lingane at Harvard with a number of students, including R. Iwomoto, F. C. Anson, J. Kennedy, A. J. Bard, and D. Davis. The use of externally generated coulometric reagents was introduced by DeFord and co-workers, and again contributions were made by Furman at Princeton, together with C. N. Reilley, W. D. Cooke, and R. N. Adams. One of the earlier workers in this area was Professor Ernest Swift of the California Institute of Technology. Some of his remembrances follow:

> Obviously, if an electrolytic process is to
> be used for the quantitative determination of a
> constituent, one of the electrode reactions must

be capable of yielding 100% current efficiency;
and as many significant figures as are required
can be used. Work that was done in the latter
part of the last century in connection with
various types of coulometers, or voltammeters
as they were then called, demonstrated that
there were a considerable number of electrode
reactions that could be made to proceed with
100% current efficiency. Although this work had
as its primary objective the determination of
the value of the faraday, the principles underlying coulometry were clearly established. Analytical chemists are entitled to a certain amount
of humility arising from the fact that the analytical implications of this work were not exploited to a significant extent until after about
40 years of this century had passed.

In 1917 Grower estimated the thickness of a
plating of tin on a copper wire by making the
wire the anode in an electrolytic process and
measuring the quantity of electricity required
to dissolve the tin anodically. Here was a
clear demonstration of the principles of coulometry. But, except for a few similar applications, over 20 years elapsed before this pioneering work was generally exploited. Then in
1942 Hickling devised an electronic instrument
which he called a potentiostat, whereby the
potential applied to the working electrode could
be controlled. By use of this device he demonstrated that 100% current efficiency could be
obtained in the reduction of cupric copper to
the metal at a platinum cathode and in the oxidation of iodide to iodine at a platinum anode.
In 1945 Lingane made use of a mercury cathode
for the determination of copper. He later used
a silver anode at which the various halides were
precipitated as the corresponding silver salts.

There are certain characteristic features
in these procedures which are used as a means of
classifying coulometric processes. First, in
all cases the substance to be determined is
involved in the half-cell reaction taking place
at one of the electrodes--that is, the cupric
copper is reduced at the cathode and the halide
is either oxidized or precipitated at the anode.
As a result such procedures have become known
as primary or direct coulometric methods. In
order to obtain 100% current efficiency in such
primary processes, the potential applied to the
working electrode must be controlled, and,

ERNEST HAYWOOD SWIFT, 1897–

After undergraduate work in Virginia, Swift migrated west and received his graduate education at the California Institute of Technology. He was on the Cal Tech faculty from 1920 to 1967, and is presently Professor Emeritus. He has made many contributions to analytical chemistry, particularly in coulometric titrimetry and related fields.

accordingly, such procedures are also designated as controlled potential processes. Choice as to which of the above terms is used is dictated by whether the predominant interest is in the external circuitry or in the reactions taking place within the electrolytic cell. The limits within which the potential control must be maintained will depend, first, upon the accuracy of the determination being made, and second upon the presence of other electrode reactive substances in the solution.

A chronological deviation of a few years has been made in order to present the above examples of primary processes because in 1938 a series of seven articles titled "Coulometric Analysis as a Precision Method," was published by Szebelledy and Somogyi. This title appears to have been the first use of the term coulometric analysis.

Rather than describe their work in general terms, a specific example can be used to illustrate the principles involved. They were interested in the determination of thiocyanate. They added a relatively high concentration of a soluble bromide to an acid solution containing the thiocyanate, anodically produced bromine, and allowed this bromine to diffuse into the solution and to oxidize the thiocyanate. By working with relatively large samples of thiocyanate and by measuring the quantity of electricity involved by means of a chemical coulometer, they demonstrated that an accuracy of within 1 ppt could be attained. Szebelledy and Somogyi used chemical indicators for determining the endpoint of these titrations. Such a process as this has subsequently been termed a coulometric titration.

Because of wartime restrictions on scientific communications prevailing in Europe at that time, these articles did not become generally available until after termination of World War II. Prior to the entry of the United States into that war, and at the request of the National Defense Research Committee, a project was initiated at the California Institute of Technology having as its general objective the detection and analysis of toxic agents. A specific problem concerned the determination of the vapor phase concentration of mustard gas (dichlorodiethyl sulfide) produced during field tests. In the method then used the agent was absorbed in bubblers and

titrated with standard bromine solutions with
methyl orange as indicator. When used with microgram quantities of the agent, this method involved various limitations. One of these was
the instability of dilute solutions of bromine,
while another was difficulty with the endpoints.
After considerable effort, two modifications were
developed. First, titration with the bromine
solution was replaced by the electrolytic generation of bromine with a constant, known current
and measurement of the time required. Second,
the endpoint was obtained by an amperometric method.

Although independently developed, there are
interesting similarities between this method and
that of Szebelledy and Somogyi. First, the
titrant is electrolytically generated bromine.
Second, the constituent of interest is measured
by the quantity of electricity used and the
process can be termed a coulometric titration.
There appears support for the adage that when
conditions are propitious, similar developments
are likely to occur in more than one location.

Two fundamental differences exist between
these two latter processes and those described
previously. First, in the previous ones, the
substance being determined was directly involved
in the electrode reaction; in these latter processes a half-cell reaction is used to generate
an active compound, called an intermediate, which
then reacts with the substance being determined.
For this reason, such processes are called secondary or indirect coulometric methods. Second,
such processes can be caused to take place at a
constant current and, in such cases, are called
constant current methods.

By taking advantage of those intermediate
half-cell reactions which can be made to proceed
with 100% current efficiency, the coulometric
principle can be applied to many substances
which are not reversibly oxidized or reduced at
conventional electrodes.

Because an electric current is so much more
amenable to automatic control than is a stopcock or other mechanical device, coulometry
offers various advantages in the ever-developing
field of automation. Methods and instruments
for automatic control of titrations have been
developed, as have methods for obtaining a continuous record of the concentration of a constituent in solutions or in a gas phase.
Another technique which utilizes a constant current

is chronopotentiometry; while analytical utility of the
various forms of coulometry has been amply demonstrated,
that is not true of chronopotentiometry. Nevertheless,
it merits discussion because it did cause considerable
flurry and also because as a method it is experimentally
quite simple. The Sand equation, which is the basis for
chronopotentiometry, dates back to 1901. A constant
current is applied between two electrodes, and the
potential of the working electrode is measured against a
reference electrode. The potential at the electrode
moves initially from its zero current equilibrium potential (or the electrode can be pre-biased) to a potential
characteristic of the material undergoing reaction at
the electrode surface. After a significant elapsed time,
the potential shifts sharply to another value where another reaction can take place. The time required to
cause this jump, from the onset of current application,
is called the transition time, and the square-root of the
transition time is directly proportional to the concentration of material undergoing reaction and is inversely
proportional to the current being applied. The concept
was described by Sand in his 1901 paper but lay dormant
until resurrected in 1953 by Gierst and Juliard in Belgium and, at about the same time in this country, by
Delahay and co-workers, who worked out the theory for a
number of complicated electrochemical situations. Also
at about the same time, C. N. Reilley at North Carolina
had been working on the analytical utilization of the
procedure. A considerable amount of theoretical insight
was furnished by Reinmuth at Columbia as well. The advantage of chronopotentiometry lies amost exclusively in
the simplicity of the instrumentation required; a battery
connected to a cell through a large resistance can be
used as a constant current source, and an X-Y recorder
suffices for a readout device. However, transition times
are difficult to measure accurately, and hence the analytical sensitivity is not great. The technique still
finds application as a qualitative diagnostic tool for
certain types of electrochemical processes. One particularly useful application of chronopotentiometry was in
studies of the adsorption of electroactive material at an
electrode surface. Although the theory for this was put
forth by W. Lorenz in Germany, interpretation of results
depended on a preconceived model of the reaction pathway.

One technique that developed as an outgrowth of
polarography and which enjoys widespread use is that of
cyclic voltammetry. The original work, by J. E. B.
Randles in England and A. Sevčik in Czechoslovakia, was
modified in a major way by Irving Shain and collaborators
at the University of Wisconsin. The classical work by
Shain and Richard Nicholson, now at the National Science

Foundation, is perhaps one of the most frequently cited papers in the electroanalytical literature. Nicholson continued work in this area when he began his academic career at Michigan State University. The popularity of cyclic voltammetry stems in part from the ease with which significant and substantial information on complex electrochemical mechanisms can be obtained. Particularly due to Shain, Nicholson, and co-workers, the quantitative interpretation of cyclic voltammetric data has become a reasonable task. Experimentally, the technique, in which a linear voltage scan is applied to the electrode, is useful at both mercury and solid electrodes. It is this latter feature which has made use of the method of interest to both organic and inorganic chemists. While analytical work can be carried out at the 10^{-5} to $10^{-6}M$ levels, this technique, except as used in stripping analysis, is probably less widely used in the purely analytical mode than in the diagnostic.

A good many of the workers referred to above can trace academic geneology back to the influence of Kolthoff or Furman. Shain, however, received his Ph.D. from the University of Washington with Professor L. Crittenden. Crittenden was an Illinois graduate in analytical spectroscopy whose interest in the electroanalytical area was kindled by Professor H. A. Laitinen.

As Professor Elving's remarks cited above have indicated, the past few years have shown a large increase in the analytical use of polarographic methods. One particular reason for this is the development of the technique of pulse polarography and the availability of reliable, low-cost instrumentation. While conventional dc polarography is useful in the $10^{-5}M$ region or so, pulse polarography finds application in the $10^{-7}M$ region. This technique was devised by G. Barker in England as an outgrowth of his work on square-wave polarography. In the early 1960s E. P. Parry and R. A. Osteryoung, then at the North American Rockwell Science Center in California, constructed an instrument and carried out work clearly demonstrating the analytical usefulness of the technique. Along with K. B. Oldham and later J. H. Christie, they demonstrated the utility of the pulse polarographic method and developed additional theory and methodology. The instrument developed by Barker was available from England for about $25,000! In the early 1960s North American sold the plans for the instrument that Parry and Osteryoung had constructed to Beckman Instruments; although prototypes were constructed, Beckman elected not to market the instrument. A bit later a commercial instrument was marketed by Melabs in Menlo Park, Calif., but it was not until Jud Flato at Princeton Applied Research Corp. (PARC) developed the model 170,

then the model 174 polarographic analyzer, that the use
of pulse polarography became widespread in this country.

A method's utilization needs commercial instrumentation for success, regardless of the method's inherent
capabilities. Barker, Parry, and Osteryoung had demonstrated the capability. It remained, however, for Flato
to bring widespread utilization to fruition by developing reliable, low-cost instrumentation. Flato's comments regarding his entry into the area are particularly
of interest:

> Our entry into analytical polarography, and
> specifically into differential pulse polaro-
> graphy, came about at least partially by acci-
> dent. When I joined Princeton Applied Research
> Corp., a consultant to the company had been
> working with phase-sensitive ac polarography
> using a PARC lock-in amplifier and a home-made
> polarograph. As the company's first chemist,
> I was asked to visit this gentleman and see if
> the work he had done had produced any possi-
> bility of a commercial instrument. I saw some
> results which were interesting, but the com-
> plexity of the instrument, built up over several
> laboratory benches, did not impress me as some-
> thing which could be commercially feasible.
>
> Seeing one of these "kluges,"* however, re-
> minded me that I had seen similar systems in a
> large number of laboratories and read of them
> in many papers. I thus decided that a multi-
> purpose instrument capable of performing many
> of these functions might give the company the
> desired entry into the chemistry lab instru-
> ment market.
>
> At the time in question, the company had
> no specific chemical products, and we were
> seeking an entry into the marketplace. We had
> no thoughts at the time of expanding into the
> routine analytical market, as a matter of cor-
> porate policy, although I thought that this was
> where the road to greatest growth and profits
> might lie.
>
> It seemed to me that an instrument which
> incorporated most of the capabilities mentioned
> in the literature, without requiring the user
> to tie together a lot of electronic equipment
> and know what he was doing, would have a worth-
> while market. When you attempt to do this--

---

*Something wherein the "whole" is equal to far less
than the sum of the parts.

design something with capabilities published by many different people--you find yourself asking over and over again, exactly what features, what ranges, what sensitivities, what functions to include. In retrospect, I see where many of the features included in the instrument should never have been put in and where some other important ones were left out. At the time of the original effort, however, and with the resources at hand, this information was unavailable.

Market research in the instrument industry, especially when you are trying to develop a product for a market that has not been previously addressed, with capabilities kept a secret until announcement, is neither an art nor a science--it's pure magic. Unlike the peanut-butter and eye-shadow markets, you cannot select 500 or 1000 appropriately placed people and ask them questions without having the rest of the world find out. The people one needs to ask about the capabilities desired in a research instrument are the people who are at the forefront of research in that field. Their comments are extremely important, but the chances that they will keep the inference that the company is about to develop such an instrument a secret are near zero. This is especially true if you are a new company trying to get into the business without attracting the attention or prodding the product development departments of larger and more well established competitors.

Under the circumstances, I was reluctant to leave out any possible feature which might increase the saleability of the product. We built in everything we could think of, up to and partially including the "food preparation-center hydrostatic process-module." This, of course, led to the accusation that the model 170 was the world's only $10,000 pH meter or that it obviously was designed by a musician because only a piano player could handle it, etc., etc.

The initial design team consisted of myself and a very able and experienced assistant engineer, Frank Eckert. Originally, I had been asked to do the design work alone since the engineering management of the company didn't really see where any great difficulty would be encountered in hanging together a bunch of op-amps. I prevailed upon them to give me someone

to work with, but we still thought we could
simply figure out a wiring diagram, build and
test the various circuits, hang them together,
and have something that worked. In fact, when
we began the design effort in September of 1967,
we felt quite certain that we could show an
instrument, fully working, at the Pittsburgh
Conference in 1968 with no difficulty. We did
in fact meet that deadline by working 38 hours
a day for the entire period, enlisting a large
number of additional people, and having several
nervous breakdowns, but the initial estimates
were that there would be no major difficulties
and we could do the thing very rapidly with
just two guys.

Examining the difference between this development and previous Princeton Applied Research
Corp. products is instructive in explaining
this underestimate. Previous products for the
company--lock-in amplifiers, box car integra-
tors, etc.--required circuit design innovations
to make them work. Innovation was the key, and
it was thought that this innovation took time
and effort while circuits were breadboarded,
tested, etc. In contrast, the design of the
170 involved no complicated circuit design
problems and no major innovations. It was thus
felt that it could proceed very routinely down
a straight and narrow path. This turned out to
be totally wrong because the complexity of the
switching and harnessing networks was such as
to provide major problems.

We managed to show an instrument at the
Pittsburgh Conference in 1968 which seemed to
be working although many of the actual circuits
were not complete, but we were a long way from
production. Many of the circuits which seemed
to be working in March of 1968 really had severe
second-order problems which could not be solved
for many months. Circuits which worked very
well on simple low ionic strength solutions blew
up entirely when dealing with high ionic strength
systems, and at the same time, circuits which
worked well on high concentration solutions were
far too noisy at low levels, etc. In any event,
an additional year of work was necessary before
we could ship instruments.

The model 170 was revolutionary for its
time in that it permitted the electrochemist to
perform a wide variety of different measurements
on the same solution simply by changing some

front panel controls, and in that it could be operated by someone who had no knowledge of electronics and no ability to hang together op amps in appropriate configurations. This opened electrochemistry research to many people who had the necessary chemistry or physics background but had never been able to acquire the electronic expertise required to work successfully with only home-made instrumentation.

We had what could be described as an immediate marketing success and soon found ourselves struggling to fulfill the initial demand. Over the first two years of shipment of the instrument, a substantial number were sold, and we began to acquire a taste for the market and to see new similar products. Our market feedback then led us to investigate making a low cost potentiostat for the man who didn't wish to spend $10,000 or $12,000 for a 170, and/or a low cost polarograph.

We knew that the model 170 was being used in a fairly large number of analytical laboratories, most prominently in the drug industry, to perform analyses of trace levels of organic compounds with great success. We had had many requests to develop a lower cost instrument so that the techniques developed in the research laboratories could be employed on the production floor.

Our first attempt at a low-cost instrument, using the same basic circuit approaches as in the 170, was actually constructed in our laboratories in the spring of 1970. This device differed from the 170 in that it was designed strictly for polarography and had none of the additional features for other techniques. It had a much lower output power capacity and much simpler switching, and it used integrated circuit operational amplifiers as its basic building block. The use of I.C. op amps and the elimination of much of the complex switching yielded an instrument whose cost was quite a great deal lower than that of the 170. However, we felt that the only way we could really exploit the potential market for differential pulse polarography, in light of previous unfavorable polarographic experiences, was to make an instrument so cheap that people would take a flyer in the technique even though they had previously been disillusioned with polarography.

When we showed the original breadboard of
the model 174 to our production people and
asked them for an estimate, they came up with
a number which we considered far too high in
light of these factors. We thus went back into
the instrument and began to look for ways to
cut costs by improving production design and by
deleting features. In the 170, a wire harness
had 400 wires and was approximately one inch in
diameter. Examining the 174 circuitry, we saw
that the switching was simple enough to handle
with a single wafer since, in every case where
components were required to be associated with
a switch, one side of each component was tied
to a common bus. This led us to a design for
the instrument where the switch wafers were
mounted directly on the printed circuit board
and where all the components which would normally be on the switches were also mounted on
the printed circuit board. The use of this
design technique permitted assembly labor costs
to be brought way way down since the cost of
inserting a component into a pc board is far
lower than the cost of hanging it on a switch
and since the wiring harness and its relatively
difficult installation was eliminated.

During the design process, we also were
facing the new requirement of relatively extensive applications--marketing efforts. We
knew that successful analytical instrument
marketing required a great deal of application
support, published "cook book" sheets with
methods written up and all pitfalls and interferences described, etc. We had to review our
costing structure and our profit margins to some
extent so as to provide sufficient money to support this effort within cost of the instrument
and still keep its price low enough.

Fortunately, the design techniques discussed
produced a sufficiently cheap instrument, and
we were able to announce the model 174 at the
Pittsburgh Conference in 1971 with an initial
selling price of $1,925 complete with drop
timer.

Even though, in 1976, the cost of the model 174 is
about $1,000 higher than when it was introduced, it still
represents an excellent example of the fact that widespread use of a technique, particularly by non-experts,
demands appropriate instrumentation.

The discussion of the development of electroanalytical instrumentation above indicates the importance

of instrumentation in analytical chemistry in general.
Although the topic of instrumentation will be covered
elsewhere in this history, an exchange of views between
two eminent electrochemists regarding the importance of
instrumentation may be of interest.

The importance of instrumentation, as viewed by
H. A. Laitinen, currently editor of *Analytical Chemistry*,
may be seen in excerpts of a letter he recently wrote
to Professor I. M. Kolthoff. As Kolthoff's words above
indicated, Professor Kolthoff never had much interest
in instrumentation. In fact, Laitinen's letter is in
response to a letter from Kolthoff in which he, Kolthoff,
wonders why instrumentation has become a part of analytical chemistry. Portions of Laitinen's words follow:

> Your letter, especially your puzzlement as
> to why instrumentation has become part of ana-
> lytical, has stimulated some memories and thoughts.
>
> You recall, I am sure, the visit to Minne-
> sota by Ralph Müller in late 1930s, when he was
> still at NYU. He advocated a curriculum in in-
> strumentation at the undergraduate level, and
> we gave him a hard time. I still doubt that at
> that level the curriculum makes much sense, but
> at the graduate level I believe instrumentation
> has a logical place as a part of analytical chem-
> istry. It also is a part of physics, of elec-
> trical engineering, and a number of other applied
> sciences.
>
> With regard to its incorporation into the
> analytical science, I think one factor was the
> influence of Walter Murphy and Larry Hallett
> during the emergence of the present *Analytical
> Chemistry* from its predecessor during the early
> post-war period. Instrument makers provided a
> source of advertising revenue, and analysts
> were a logical market. But just as war is "too
> important to be left to the generals," instru-
> ment design became too important to be left to
> commercial manufacturers. Larry Hallett brought
> Ralph Müller in as corresponding editor, and
> over the years, Ralph surely influenced the
> thinking of many analytical practitioners and
> research workers. When I became editor, I felt
> that Ralph's special contribution should be
> continued. Along the way, I came to feel that
> the subject had become much too broad for any
> individual to handle, and with Ralph's full
> cooperation, initiated the present system of
> an Instrumentation Panel, who work with an
> associate editor to suggest contributors,
> approach authors, internally review the first

drafts and edit the revised articles.

Turning to the more basic question of why instrumentation should be a part of graduate education and research in analytical, I can trace our experience at Illinois during my 34 years there. Illinois was relatively well equipped with commercial instrumentation in 1940. Thanks largely to the efforts of G. L. Clark they had among other things an extensive collection of x-ray equipment, a large Littrow prism spectrograph, a Cenco Spectrophotelometer, and by 1941 even an electron microscope, all in analytical. I borrowed a Fisher Elecdropode from G. F. Smith (he had given up on it because the electrode plugged up), and in 1942 was able to get a Sargent polarograph with the help of C. S. (Speed) Marvel who wanted to encourage my work with Stan Wawzonek on hydrocarbon polarography. Most of my first work at Illinois, as at Minnesota, was done with primitive manual equipment.

I have often told my students that I felt the development of polarography was distorted, and the fundamental aspects probably delayed, by the early invention of the Heyrovský-Shikata polarograph in 1925. Many of the basic phenomena, especially the detailed current-time behavior, were hidden due to over-damping to get time-average currents. I still recall the amazement of Paul Sherrick, at Sargent, at the complicated curves they recorded on the model XX, and later model XXI, which still lagged behind the true variations of current.

Nevertheless, it was modern electronic instrumentation which broadened polarography to the modern-day battery of techniques. I did not use an oscilloscope in research until about 1950, and this was really not stable or sensitive enough for accurate measurements. The Tektronix scope really revolutionized current-time measurements by making reliable and accurate dc measurements available to non-specialists. I still recall, during my sabbatical with Randles in 1953, the effort he had gone through to make stable dc amplifiers for his cathode-ray tube.

In my own experience the need for such measurements was dramatized by the thesis work of Chris Enke, who was studying fractional monolayers of oxides on platinum electrodes. He used operational amplifiers for constant

current coulometry and integration of current-
time curves. In the meantime, Howard Malmstadt
had come to Illinois (in 1951) with an extensive
background in electronics from the navy. I had
tried, through seminars, to introduce electronics
into the graduate analytical program in 1949-51,
without much success. Ralph Johnson, for example,
arranged a series on this subject, and later a
graduate student of G. L. Clark, E. P. Bertin
(now at RCA) conducted a semester's seminar.
Unfortunately, these did not give the students
any lab experience, yet, the alternative paths,
through physics and electrical engineering, both
proved inefficient because of prerequisites to
advanced courses. A student could, and several
did, minor in these fields, but to the detriment
of advanced courses in other branches in chemistry. Howard Malmstadt, first alone and soon
with the collaboration of Chris Enke, developed
a practical lab approach that avoided the traditional soldering and bread-board system. This
approach, of course, has tremendously influenced
the teaching of electronic instrumentation,
often by past students of these two. Many universities are using this system in departments
other than chemistry, including physics and
electrical engineering. The question remains,
outside of the historical accident that it
started in analytical, "does it belong there?"
I maintain that it does although it also belongs
in other disciplines.

A good example I like to cite is the use of
automated rate measurements for trace phosphate
determination (Malmstadt, Javier, and Crouch)
through either the yellow 12-molybdophosphate
or molybdenum blue procedures. The first, in
particular, uses the initial reaction rate of
a reversible reaction, via the faint color of
the yellow complex, for determinations more
sensitive, more accurate and far more rapid than
the classical photometric procedures. Only
through specific research, first to set up the
special instrumentation, then to study the reactions, could such procedures evolve.

The point is that analytical, just like
the other branches of chemistry, is in a constant state of evolution, borrowing from and in
turn contributing to its sister sciences as
you have so often pointed out yourself.

While the discussion above applies not just to
electroanalytical chemistry, the viewpoint of two

distinguished practioners in the electroanalytical area
reflects the changes that have occurred over the past
five decades; the academic electroanalytical chemists
in particular have made much use of homemade equipment
in recent years.

Many other techniques have been applied to electroanalysis or used by electroanalysts to study a variety
of electrochemical reactions. One of the most interesting is the use of rotating disc, and rotating ring-
disc, electrodes. Theoretically treated from a hydro-
dynamic view by the classical work of V. G. Levich in
the Soviet Union, the technique was brought to the
United States by the efforts of Professor Stanley Bruckenstein, then at the University of Minnesota, and his
collaborative efforts with John Albery of Oxford and
Barry Miller of Bell Laboratories. The fact that all
science is not necessarily based on deliberate decision,
but may have a high degree of chance, is well illustrated
by Professor Bruckenstein's remembrance of his initiation
into the rotating disc area:

> I became interested in rotating disk elec-
> trodes as a result of reading the proofs of the
> English translation of Levich's book "Physical
> Chemical Hydrodynamics." Skip Scriven, then an
> associate professor of chemical engineering at
> the University of Minnesota, was involved in
> editing this book for its *Scripta Technica* and
> asked if I would convert into "electrochemistry"
> the translation of Levich's chapter dealing with
> maxima at the dropping mercury electrode. This
> I did, learning a considerable amount during
> this effort.
>
> I had been aware of the rotating disk elec-
> trode in a peripheral fashion but on reading
> Levich's book became convinced that there was
> much that could be done with it and the rotating
> ring-disk electrode.
>
> Soon after that A. N. Frumkin visited Minne-
> sota as a guest of Kolthoff, and my conversations
> with him led to my ultimately spending six months
> in Moscow. Before I went to Moscow I had already
> started ring-disk work at Minnesota, which
> accelerated greatly after my return from Moscow.
>
> In Moscow I was technically at the Electro-
> chemical Institute since my visit had been
> arranged through the National Academy of Sci-
> ences. As a matter of fact, I spent more than
> 95% of my time in the Chair of Electrochemistry
> at the University. There my main interaction
> was with Lev Nekrassov. I had regular inter-
> action with Frumkin and Levich too.

The original purpose of my work was to investigate ac impedence. Unfortunately, the apparatus which had been ordered by Frumkin about a year before never arrived during my six months stay in Moscow. I was therefore left pretty much on my own and began to read the rotating disk and ring-disk theory that Levich had done. Not being an especially good mathematician, I looked at a table of integrals for a particular integral that appeared in ring-disk theory and found it expressed in explicit form. It was some months later that I learned that the Russians were evaluating it numerically, as was Levich. I pointed out the integral to him in this American table, and he muttered "that's what comes of leaving mathematics to graduate students." Anyway, this integral appears as a footnote in a paper by G. A. Feldman and myself, dealing with transit times at rotating ring-disk electrodes.

During my stay in Moscow I also realized the value of shielding techniques at a rotating ring-disk electrode and wrote my one paper which resulted from my stay in Moscow, dealing with shielding theory. This paper appeared in *Electrokhemya* and was translated from English into Russian by Lev Nekrassov as I wrote the English version. His constant complaint was "you cannot write it that way in English because there is no way to translate that into Russian." After my return to the United States, this particular paper was translated from Russian back into English by a commercial publisher, and they had the audacity to send me their translation with a request that I check it for accuracy (no fee offered). I have my original manuscript which was translated into Russian and their translation of the Russian back into English. All I can say is--never trust a translation (I don't know if I mean by that Nevrassov or the American translator).

I should mention that on my way to Russia, I visited Oxford, primarily for the purpose of seeing R. P. Bell whom I had met at Minnesota and also to pass on greetings to John Albery from Maury Kreevoy, a physical organic chemist still at Minnesota, who knew him. While I was there I spoke to John about his research, he showed me his Ph.D. thesis, and I recognized a real talent for mathematics. Having some money lined up for the summer following my return from

Moscow, I convinced him to come to Minneapolis
with a purpose of tackling some ring-disk
mathematics.

As you know, while John was with me that
10-week period, the basis for seven papers was
written, a substantial amount of this occurring
in a Kosher delicatessen known as "Bernie's."

The only reasonable conclusion that can be
reached from the above recital is that mustard,
dill pickles, corned beef, pastrami, and coincidence can lead to good electrochemistry.

Another very useful technique, which in the past
few years in particular has seen widespread use and investigation, is anodic stripping voltammetry. In its
simplest form, a metal ion is reduced from solution into
a mercury drop; since the volumes of the solution and
drop are markedly different, the metal amalgam is much
more concentrated than the metal ion in solution. Application of a suitable wave form--linear scan, differential
pulse, staircase--oxidizes, or strips, the metal from
the mercury drop. Under appropriate conditions of
cleanliness, it is possible to work in the sub-parts-
per-billion range. The earliest work in the United
States appears to have been carried out by L. B. Rogers
and co-workers, then at the Massachusetts Institute of
Technology. Other workers in the 1950s and 1960s included Irving Shain at Wisconsin and W. D. Cooke at
Cornell. Mercury pools, silver electrodes, and finally
mercury drops were employed. A bit later, Professor
D. K. Roe, then also at MIT, and his graduate student,
Wayne Mattson, carried out work on a mercury plated
thin-film electrode which proved particularly advantageous for anodic stripping applications. While Mattson then went to the University of Michigan as a faculty
member in environmental engineering, his interest in the
thin-film anodic stripping work ultimately led to the
establishment of Environmental Science Associates (ESA),
which both manufactures anodic stripping apparatus and
performs routine stripping analysis.

On occasion, serendipity plays an important role
in the discovery process. This is probably nowhere
better illustrated than in the happenings at the California Institute of Technology which lead to the discovery of thin-layer electrochemistry. Fred Anson was
studying the apparent adsorption of ferric iron from
concentrated solutions at platinum electrodes. The
technique employed was chronopotentiometry. Experimentally, it was observed that a platinum electrode,
dipped into a concentrated ferric solution, rinsed, and
then dipped into another solution not containing iron
showed chronopotentiograms with approximately equal

forward and reverse transition times. This was interpreted as indicating ferric adsorption. In one experiment, C. R. Christensen, the graduate student doing the
work, cut the electrode off, and the effect remained.
What was happening was that the platinum electrode,
sealed into glass which was dipped into the solution,
played no part in what was observed. Instead, minute
cracks at the point where the platinum wire was sealed
into glass resulted in its being filled with ferric solution which was effectively trapped in a thin layer
about the electrode. This discovery prompted Anson and
then student Arthur Hubbard, now at the University of
California at Santa Barbara, to exploit electrochemistry
in thin layers of solution. A considerable amount of
theoretical and experimental work was carried out by
Anson and Hubbard as well as by C. N. Reilley and co-
workers at the University of North Carolina. (It is an
interesting, and understandable, sidelight that Christensen, who had discovered the problem originally, carried
on the latter portions of his Ph.D. research in a non-
electroanalytical area.) The advantage of the thin-layer
approach is that the experiments are coulometric in
nature; while a variety of cells have been fabricated,
the simplest to envision consists of a micrometer with
platinum pole pieces electrically insulated from one
another. A drop of solution is placed between the pole
pieces, the micrometer gap is closed to some small value,
and external connection, via a drop of liquid on the
side of the micrometer, is made to auxiliary and reference electrodes. The pole pieces of the micrometer can
be adjusted to different potentials. Under conditions
where the electrochemical perturbation is not too rapid,
diffusion may be ignored since the space between the
electrodes is very small and the system functions in a
coulometric mode. A good deal of extremely clever experimentation is possible with this system.

The technique of chronocoulometry arose out of a
collaborative effort between R. Osteryoung and F. C.
Anson with the aid of J. H. Christie, again in the mid-
1960s. This technique, in which a potential step is
applied to an electrode and the charge(coulombs)-time
behavior is observed, has been used to study the adsorption of electroactive species. The technique depends on
its ability to distinguish between charge which arises
from material which must diffuse to the electrode to
react and charge which is present at the interface as
the step is applied. Double potential step chronocoulometry permits one to separate the coulombs arising from
double layer charging; hence, the charge due to the reaction of adsorbed material may be determined. This
technique has been applied extensively by Anson and

co-workers and by Royce Murray at the University of North Carolina to study a number of systems in which the presence of an anion in solution, which is adsorbed at the mercury-solution interface, induces the adsorption of a cation which would not normally adsorb. The method also has application to the study of electrode kinetics.

Another technique which has been studied rather extensively is that of ac polarography. Much credit must be given to the work of the late Professor B. Breyer in Australia, who carried out pioneering work with this technique. In the United States, however, the work of Professor Donald Smith and co-workers at Northwestern University has resulted in extensive theoretical and experimental publications over the past 15 years or so. This technique has widespread application to analysis as well as to the study of complex electrochemical kinetic problems. As mentioned in the remarks of Flato, given above, ac techniques tend to be complicated; even though they have not found widespread acceptance, the work of Smith and others, especially A. M. Bond in Melbourne, has been significant in demonstrating the capabilities of the approach.

A recent innovation, combining developments in both mathematics and electroanalytical chemistry, has been that of semi-integral methods, as devised by K. B. Oldham, initially at Rockwell International Science Center in California, now at Trent University in Canada. Arising in 1969 from Oldham's interest in the mathematics of Fick's Law problems, it has culminated in Oldham's devising electronics capable of performing semi-integration procedures experimentally in electrochemical systems. The distinguishing feature of the method appears to be that the signal of analytical interest-- the semi-integral of the current--ultimately assumes a nearly constant value, proportional to the concentration of electroactive material but independent of the shape of the exciting potential function. While the method is of some interest, its use in practical analysis at this time is small. Its greatest promise may be in field units where the constant signal obtained, independent of the exciting signal, could be used in certain monitoring functions.

One of the most recently developed and widely used of the techniques applied by electroanalytical chemists is spectroelectrochemistry. Utilizing various forms of transparent electrodes--tin oxide, thin films of platinum, or gold grids--the work performed initially by T. Kuwana, starting in about 1968, initially at the University of California at Riverside, then at Case-Western Reserve and now at Ohio State, has resulted in a combination of electrochemistry and spectroscopy which has

permitted the elucidation of a number of complex electrochemical processes. The intent here is not primarily
analytical in nature but is aimed at mechanistic studies.
The interest in studying electrode surfaces, coupled with
the recently developed area of photoelectron spectroscopy,
has caused a number of workers, including N. Winograd at
Purdue, Murray and Hubbard at Hawaii, and E. Yeager at
Case-Western Reserve, to investigate the use of ESCA and
other related techniques to observe the electrode surface in some detail. Since electrode processes are
obviously heterogeneous, studies of heterogeneous catalysis, particularly by G. Somorjai at the University of
California at Berkeley, have had important impact on
attempts to understand the detail of electrode processes.

Potentiometry used solid electrodes and polarography,
as originally developed, used dropping mercury electrodes.
However, as time passed, the limitations of the mercury
electrodes prompted a good deal of work which employed
various forms of solid electrodes for analytical and
mechanistic work. Perhaps the individual whose work is
most closely associated with the developments in this
area is Professor R. N. Adams of the University of
Kansas. His book on solid electrodes is a well-recog-
nized summary of work in that area. Some of his comments on the development of solid electrodes may be of
interest:

> Although solid electrode voltammetry began
> in Europe before the turn of the century, much
> of the modern practice began in the post-World
> War II period. Zlotowski apparently reported
> the first recorded solid electrode voltammograms
> working in Poland in 1934. Not much further
> activity appeared in the literature until L. B.
> Rogers and co-workers, working on the Manhattan
> Project, showed their recorded solid electrode
> voltammograms of manganese and other inorganic
> species. These recordings showed the essence
> of what has plagued workers in the field ever
> since--namely, the difficulty of dealing with
> previous electrode history and unknown or un-
> controllable surface effects. I can well re-
> member Buck Rogers on a visit at Princeton
> giving me some fatherly advice when I told him
> my plans were to dig deeply into solid electrode
> techniques. "Stay away from them, Buzz," he
> said, "they're too miserable for a young man to
> deal with." (Looking back, I sometimes wish I
> had taken that advice and stuck to flying or
> beachcombing!) However, within the next 10-
> 15 years, a variety of diverse inputs developed
> electroanalytical techniques at solid electrodes

to a highly respectable state. While we still cannot always control the history and surface effects, we know much more about them and can intelligently interpret the solution electrochemistry we're attempting to measure.

As mentioned above, a wide variety of influences impinged on the development of solid electrode voltammetry. When I came to N. Howell Furman's lab at Princeton in 1953, the outstanding team of W. D. Cooke and C. N. Reilley was already in gear. During the next few years Cooke's genius at the lab bench and Reilley's broad overview of electroanalytical approaches, together with Professor Furman's tremendous background in potentiometry and oxidation-reduction methods, set the stage for an outpouring of electroanalytical research. This was especially directed toward constant current and coulometric titrations. Almost all of this work utilized solid electrodes, and we became intrigued with their vagaries and effects on solution electrochemistry. This was in 1951-53, and one must remember that the now commonplace theoretical background of electroanalytical chemistry was just being put together. The work of Charlot, Gauguin, and the European school was appearing, but the bible, Paul Delahay's monograph, was not published until 1954. Some of the earlier coulometry by Swift and co-workers was available, but, in general, there were lots of things still buried in the secrecy of the Manhattan Project.

Platinum was the electrode of choice for much of the early coulometric work. J. K. Lee, working with Clark Bricker and me, began some of the first platinum oxide electroanalytical studies at Princeton. Anson and Lingane at Harvard were also examining platinum surface effects and provided definitive chemical identification of oxidized surfaces. Contributions in this general period from Kolthoff and Tanaka, Shain's group, and others began to provide a unified picture of the effects of surface oxidation upon recorded voltammograms. Breiter, Giner, Anson, Enke, Feldberg, and many others, including much input from the Russian school, clarified many of the problems. By the late 1950s and early 1960s those of us with perseverance enough felt that at least we knew how to live with solid electrodes, even if we

couldn't make them behave the way we wanted.
Electrode surfaces other than noble metals
received increasing attention. The early
studies of wax-impregnated graphite by Gaylor,
Conrad and Landerl, Joe Morris, and others
indicated the usefulness of carbon for anodic
oxidations. In our laboratory at the University of Kansas it was my fond hope to
develop electrodes that would not undergo
surface oxidation. We never really succeeded,
but, instead, found a very useful modification
of carbon--the so-called carbon paste electrode. To this day we are still trying to
understand how it works. However, it usually
works so well that we have been relatively
happy in our ignorance. Other forms of carbon, like pyrolytic and glassy carbon, have
taken their places in the electrode storeroom.

At the present time it seems safe to say
that the entire spectrum of electroanalytical
techniques is practiced at solid electrodes.
Even a new area, spectroelectrochemistry, as
practiced by Kuwana, Osteryoung, Murray,
Heineman, and others, employs mainly solid
electrode surfaces. The widespread usage of
cyclic voltammetry by organic, inorganic, and
even physical chemists primarily involves solid
electrodes, especially in non-aqueous media.
The most exciting new developments come from
the second generation of electroanalytical
chemists like Hubbard, Winograd, Murray, and
others, who have pointed modern instrumentation and theory at solid electrodes and are
showing the way for us to tailor the surfaces
to our needs.

An outgrowth of efforts to understand the varieties
of surface phenomenon at electrodes has lead to the currently active area of electrode surface modification.
As practiced by Larry Miller, in 1975, initially at
Colorado State University, now at the University of
Minnesota, Murray at North Carolina, Kuwana at Ohio
State and Anson at Cal Tech, efforts are being made to
bond material covalently to electrode surfaces to alter
or to catalyze the course of an electrode reaction.
While this area is still in its infancy, it is clear
that significant work will be carried out.

Many other individuals, procedures, and theories
have had an impact on modern electroanalytical chemistry
and have contributed to its historical development.
Developments in theoretical concepts contributed by R.
A. Marcus; electrochemical engineering, by Charles Tobias

and John Newman at Berkeley; the application of digital
simulation by S. Feldberg at Brookhaven; a vast amount
of work in the application of ESR to electrochemistry
by D. Geske and A. Maki, then of Harvard and later by
A. J. Bard at Texas; electrochemiluminescence work, by
Chandross and Visco at Bell Labs, Bard, and others. At
times it is hard to distinguish what is electroanalytical. The performance of any electrochemical procedure--
fundamentally or analytically oriented--requires an
understanding of the principles underlying the procedure.
In the material presented above an effort has been made
to hit certain highlights and to focus on the last 40
years or so since it is in that time period that what
we now consider electroanalytical chemistry really came
of age.

CHAPTER V

ANALYTICAL SEPARATIONS

DISTILLATION

Distillation by itself is never a method of analysis but is merely an important method of separation. It is always necessary to observe or to measure some property of consecutive portions of the distillate in order to obtain an analysis. The first primitive distillation analysis probably occurred accidentally when prehistoric man noticed that the liquid drippings from the cooler part of some kind of heated container of liquid were different in color, odor, or taste from the starting material. Indeed, at some point in history it was noted that the drippings from the heating of fermented grains or fruits had amazing physiological effects. Somewhat similar observations about various properties of the drippings from heated liquids must have occurred in the winning of essential oils and of fresh water from salt water. The early understanding of distillation therefore included heating the material (vaporization) and a cool surface from which distillate of different composition could be obtained (condensation). All subsequent apparatus and explanatory theory have been developed from this primary requirement.

As the infant chemical industry and experimentation grew, this crude apparatus evolved into the alembics of the alchemists and the glass stills of the early organic chemists. Then in 1794 the first big advance came in the form of the Liebig condenser, which used a counter-current cooling stream of water, and should actually be attributed to von Weigel. By the 1800s industrial continuous distillation equipment was developed which was capable of good separations in a single multiplate distillation column. This development was particularly sparked by whiskey production. For almost a century the theory of this industrial equipment lagged behind practice, until the work of Sorel (1889-1899) and W. K. Lewis at MIT (1909) laid the foundation for the mathematics of continuous distillation.

This work did not directly benefit small-scale laboratory distillation, where it was desirable to use batch distillation on samples of limited size. Nevertheless, for materials which were easily separated, simple distillation methods were developed and standardized. Two of many of these were the Kjeldahl method for nitrogen initiated in the 1880s and the official method for determining the alcohol content of liquids published in 1916 in the "U. S. Pharmacopoeia."

Although simple batch distillation was used widely, it was incapable of separating mixtures of similar materials. The difficult but practical problem of separating the components of petroleum gave tremendous impetus to the development of distillation in general. In order to study the individual chemical components, it was necessary to isolate them. One of the first major steps was the insertion of a thermometer into the head of the distillation apparatus. Curves of boiling point vs. quantity of distillate could then be obtained, and Engler-type apparatus and procedures began to be used. The first ASTM method for analyzing gasoline by distillation was published in 1927 and utilized the volume of distillate collected in successive 25°F intervals.

As early as 1811 small one- or two-inch diameter columns had been fitted with perforated plates, but any real progress toward their use in batch distillation did not come until the 1930s. Bruun, at NBS, described an essentially all glass two-inch diameter column in 1933. It was a miniature version of the bubble cap-plate columns widely used industrially. Its chief limitation was a lack of flexibility for different fluid conditions and operating conditions.

Also, beginning in the 1930s, Fenske and co-workers published many papers describing several advances. Many of these papers were published under the triumvirate of M. R. Fenske, D. Quiggle, and C. O. Tongberg and were known colloquially as the "Figgleberg papers." The key ideas were the use of column packings to increase the vapor-liquid contact area, the use of column insulation to obtain adiabatic conditions, the use of controlled reflux, and the use of vapor-liquid equilibrium relations. This work made possible the precise analysis of gasoline samples of modest size.

Similar work in 1930s and 1940s was pursued by F. D. Rossini and his colleagues (Mair, Streiff, Glasgow, and Willingham) at NBS. They developed remarkably efficient stills for their investigations of complex mixtures of petroleum homologs. Even later, J. Feldman, M. Orchin, and others at the Bureau of Mines were able to characterize a variety of natural and synthetic fuels.

Many variations in distillation equipment were tried, and ideas proliferated widely so that it is difficult to assign priorities. However, by the 1950s packed distillation columns capable of 50-plate separations were common, and units capable of 200- or more plate separations were operated for special purposes. Especially noteworthy is the spinning-band column capable of separations of several hundred plates and characterized by a low pressure drop due to the nearly empty column. Because of its capabilities it is nearly the sole survivor of sophisticated laboratory distillation apparatus. In this same period of proliferation, apparatus and procedures were perfected and standardized by many workers, especially by Walter Podbielniak who developed several distillation systems adapted to the analysis of many kinds of liquid mixtures. Many of these were almost completely automated.

Distillation theory, particularly that pertaining to batch distillations, was developed during the first part of the 20th century. The first significant contribution came in 1902 when Lord Rayleigh devised a differential equation and integrated it into the practical form known by his name. It described theoretically the course of a single plate simple batch distillation by a graph of distillate composition vs. the fraction of charge remaining in the still pot. The fact that Rayleigh's equation applied only to one-plate distillations limited its practical use.

In the interim before Rayleigh's equation was developed further, K. Peters introduced the very useful concept of the HETP (height equivalent to a theoretical plate) in 1922. This allowed comparison of the efficiencies (of separation) of the various permutations of distillation systems. Then by 1932 Fenske had developed an equation which allowed convenient calculation of the HETP from equilibrium data obtained during a distillation of a binary mixture at total reflux. As useful as this concept was, and is today, it did not describe the progress of a multi-plate distillation. By about 1940 A. Rose and also E. H. Smoker made the first of a series of advances in batch fractionation theory. The Rayleigh equation derivation was extended to the case for any number of plates. The mathematical solution was simple for the case of total reflux since the Fenske equation related the charge and the distillate composition for any number of plates.

Gradually the complex interrelationships of reflux

ratio, vapor-liquid equilibrium, number of theoretical
plates, column holdup, varying composition, and multiple
component mixtures were clarified. This elucidation was
more or less completed by the early 1950s with the advent
of computers which made it possible to obtain solutions
for the complex differential equations involved. However, at this point gas-liquid partition chromatography
came into being and essentially replaced distillation
for analysis because of its convenience and accuracy.
Still, as a primary method of separation or enrichment,
distillation will always have an important role in
analysis.

SOLVENT EXTRACTION

Liquid-liquid extraction has been used on the laboratory scale from the earliest times, especially in the
preparation of dyes, perfumes, and other early preparations. An early example of the use of liquid-liquid
extraction in analytical chemistry is the fire assay for
gold, silver, and platinum metals. The sample is fused
with a mixture of flux, reducing agent, and lead oxide.
The noble metal is extracted by the molten lead, in
which it is more soluble than in the molten slag.
The history of solvent extraction has been marked
by a number of equipment improvements. For example, the
design of the Soxhlet extractor by Franz Soxhlet has
been important in the analysis of foods. A continuous
liquid-liquid extractor for solvents lighter than water
was designed by Kutscher and Stendel in 1903. Somewhat
later, this extractor was adapted by Wehrli for the continuous extraction with solvents heavier than water.
In 1941 A. J. P. Martin and R. L. M. Synge used the
countercurrent principle in designing the first effective
"mixer-settler" extractor, which was designed to separate mixtures of amino acids by partition between an
aqueous and an organic phase. Mechanical difficulties
with the apparatus led them to abandon this approach and
instead to develop the related technique of liquid-
liquid chromatography. Perhaps the most important advance in apparatus design was the invention of the Craig
apparatus by L. C. Craig of the Rockefeller Institute.
This ingenious apparatus, which replaces the battery of
separatory funnels, allows the operations to be carried
out systematically and automatically. The original apparatus was equivalent to a set of 25 separatory funnels.
Today it is not unusual to work with 100-400 units,
allowing satisfactory separations of complex mixtures
to be achieved.
Liquid-liquid extraction in inorganic chemistry has

been characterized by the observation of unexpected
chemical behavior rather than by developments in apparatus. In 1842 E. Péligot noticed the extraction of
uranyl nitrate from aqueous nitric acid solutions by
ether. This extraction was important almost a century
later in the atomic energy project. W. Skey (1867)
observed the solubility and extractability of various
thiocyanates and metal chlorides in ether. He proposed
a number of metal separations based on these observations, but his idea was not pursued until 1892, when
J. W. Rothe showed that large amounts of ferric iron
could be separated from many other elements by extracting
ferric chloride with ether. Since then Rothe's method
has been a standard one for removing large quantities of
iron that might interfere in other determinations. However, the most important development was the introduction
by H. Fischer in 1925 of the organic reagent dithizone,
which allows for the quantitative extraction and determination of a number of elements. Since Fischer's work,
many organic reagents have been introduced. One of the
more important is thenoyltrifluoroacetone (TTA), which
was introduced by M. Calvin and his co-workers and which
made a large contribution to the analytical chemistry
of the transuranium elements. Recently, there has not
only been a continuing interest in new organic chelating
agents but also in ion pair association in liquid-liquid
extraction.

The theoretical description of liquid-liquid extraction has tended to lag behind its practice. The
first quantitative studies of liquid-liquid extraction
were carried out by M. Berthelot and J. Jungfleisch in
1872. In 1891 W. Nernst gave the first thorough statement of the partition isotherm. More recently a number
of authors have discussed the quantitative aspects of
solvent extraction of metal chelates and ion pairs.

GAS CHROMATOGRAPHY

Gas Adsorption Chromatography. The origin of selective adsorption of vapors began before World War I, and
the first important use of this technique was in the gas
mask. After the war, commercial applications were developed such as for the recovery of gasoline from
natural gas. In the 1920s the charcoal test for light
hydrocarbons in natural gas was widely used. Basically,
adsorption was done at a low temperature, and the
adsorbate was desorbed at a higher temperature while
purging with a vapor. A. Eucken and H. Knick improved
this technique in 1936 by using an external oven which
was slowly moved along the adsorbent tube. In 1943

N. C. Turner combined these techniques and introduced the measurement of the thermal conductivity of the effluent. P. Schuftan had previously introduced the interferometer as a detector. These early techniques developed into the frontal and displacement methods which were thoroughly studied in the 1940s by Claesson and others at the Institute of Tiselius in Uppsala, Sweden, and by C. S. G. Phillips and his co-workers at Oxford University in the early 1950s.

During the early 1940s other work was being done which laid the actual foundation of modern gas adsorption chromatography. At the University of Marburg/Lahn in Germany Dr. Gerhard Hesse and his co-workers were using gas adsorption to separate volatile organic acids. This method developed into the new technique of gas adsorption chromatography. In 1941 Hesse, H. Eilbracht, and F. Reicheneder described their new technique as a variation of Tswett's liquid adsorption chromatography and correctly interpreted the technique. Hesse and B. Tschachotin in 1942 described the technique in more detail. Unfortunately, further activities in Dr. Hesse's laboratory were interrupted by World War II.

G. Damköhler, one of Eucken's students, and H. Theile were also associated with the early gas adsorption chromatography development. However, again World War II prevented dissemination of their publications and sub-sequent impact on future developments. In England E. Glueckauf was also working with this new technique, and by 1946 he had developed a method for determining helium and neon in air. This method developed into gas chromatography by 1951 but was not published earlier since it was associated with classified atomic energy research.

The first modern gas adsorption chromatography was done by Erika Cremer at the University of Innsbruck. Dr. Cremer moved to Innsbruck in 1940 and began to work with a group on the hydrogenation of acetylene and ethylene. She postulated in 1944 that these compounds could be separated by a chromatographic process in the gas phase and that the adsorption energies could be calculated from the elution times. The collapse of Germany pre-vented publication of a theoretical discussion of the idea. However, by 1946 Dr. Cremer with F. Prior had demonstrated the validity of her idea. Acetylene-ethylene mixtures were separated using a column filled with silica gel, with hydrogen as a carrier gas and a thermal conductivity detector. The work was continued in Dr. Cremer's laboratory by R. Müller as part of his doctoral thesis in 1950.

During this time Dr. Cremer and her associates developed their technique for separation and analysis

as well as for the determination of heats of adsorption.
They also introduced the idea of relative retention
times, the difference between the retention time and the
adjusted retention time, the determination of peak area
from the product of peak height and peak width at half-
height and they demonstrated the importance of the logarithm of the adjusted retention time and its relationship to the absolute column temperature.

In 1952 the organizers of the ACHEMA, the world's
largest chemical exhibition in Frankfurt am Main, invited university laboratories to participate for the
first time. One of those to participate was Dr. Cremer
who exhibited the first modern gas adsorption chromatograph that she had developed. At the time, little
notice was given to the device but times change, and by
the 1961 ACHEMA exhibition, 27 companies exhibited over
50 commercially available chromatographs.

Part of this change was due to the work of Jaroslav
Janák in Czechoslovakia. Dr. Janák started as a chemical engineer at the West Bohemian Chemical Works at
Most. One of his duties involved the laboratory where
gas samples were analyzed. The company ordered a Podbielniak "Hyperrobot" analyzer, but trade restrictions
prevented its import. Janák was then forced to develop
his own analyzer and began his first experiments in
1949. By 1952 he had developed a chromatograph utilizing carbon dioxide as the carrier gas and a nitrometer
as a detector. He published several papers on the principles and applications of his device over the next few
years and even obtained a patent in 1955 on his apparatus.

Janák introduced a two-column system in parallel
and in series, and in 1955 he demonstrated the use of
zeolites as adsorbents. His nitrometer system as a detector had been used for many years, probably because
the gas volumes of the fractions could be measured directly. However, it required constant attention and
eventually was replaced by commercial automatic recording
devices.

During this time, 1950-1953, Turkel'taub, Zhukho-
vitskii and associates developed a technique--chroma-
thermography--which utilized a heater moving along the
chromatograph column. This method was widely used in
the USSR, but any impact on analytical chemistry in the
West was small.

With the rapid development of gas-liquid partition
chromatography in the 1950s, gas adsorption chromatography was relegated to the analysis of the inorganic
and light hydrocarbon gases. However, the introduction
of new adsorbents has led to renewed interest in the
technique for larger molecular weight organics. The
new phases include: the macroporous polymers introduced

by O. L. Hollis in 1966, graphitized carbon by I. Halász and C. Horvath, and A. V. Kiselev and others, the carbon molecular sieve by R. Kaiser in 1969, and Tenax by R. van Wijk.

Gas-Liquid Partition Chromatography. One of the most significant advances in chromatography was the introduction of the use of liquid-liquid partition as the basis of chromatographic separation by A. J. P. Martin and R. L. M. Synge in 1941. Their achievement was duly recognized with the awarding of the 1952 Nobel prize for chemistry.

The development of this technique had its roots in Martin's work at Cambridge University. Here he had developed a complex liquid-liquid countercurrent apparatus which utilized the partitioning of a solute between two liquid phases. He continued to utilize this technique when he moved to the Wool Industries Research Association in 1938 where he was joined by Synge. The key to the development of modern partition chromatography came in 1940 when Martin realized that it was not necessary to move both phases simultaneously. If only one phase moved past a second stationary phase, the required conditions would be attained. Within a day a simple column was constructed and tested. It was soon realized that this simple arrangement could accomplish a separation better and faster than previous devices by many fold. Within a year Martin and Synge published their landmark paper describing this new technique. In this paper they also proposed that a gas could be used as the mobile phase instead of a liquid.

Although the idea of gas-liquid partition chromatography had thus been proposed to the world in 1941, no one picked it up for experimental verification; however, gas adsorption chromatography continued rapid development during the 1940s. This delay can best be explained by the events of World War II which interrupted scientific communication. A large part of Europe was excluded from the circulation of the English *Biochemical Journal*, in which their paper appeared. Thus this fertile idea lay for almost 10 years until Martin himself initiated its development.

By 1948 Martin had moved to the National Institute for Medical Research where A. T. James joined him. Together they were working on a project which was going badly. Whatever was tried turned sour, and James became so discouraged that Martin suggested that they drop the project and instead work on his 1941 proposal. Their work immediately progressed smoothly and rapidly, and in a short time experimental verification of their new technique of gas-liquid partition chromatography was

submitted for publication on June 5, 1951. This paper
and three more in 1952 initiated the exponential growth
of one of the most valuable separation techniques.

The original technique utilized columns of 1 to 3
meters with 4 mm id which were filled with inert porous
particles coated with the liquid phase. The sample was
added by pipette, and the eluted fractions were determined by titration, and the process was quite tedious.
D. H. Desty, N. H. Ray, and R. P. W. Scott each immediately contacted Martin about applications of his technique. Improvements, such as the adoption of the thermal
conductivity detector used widely in gas adsorption,
came rapidly as these and other workers adopted this
technique in their laboratories. By 1955, application
to a number of problems was demonstrated, and the first
commercial instruments were introduced. Over the next
20 years an explosion of growth in gas chromatography
occurred, which led to its becoming the most widely used
analytical technique today. Hardly a laboratory exists
where this technique is not practiced. Complex multicomponent mixtures can be separated in minutes and the
concentration of the constituents obtained. It is difficult to realize that weeks of tedious work would be
required to accomplish the same analysis without the
help of gas chromatography. Hundreds of workers and
thousands of publications have made history since 1951,
and only some of the more important contributions can
be discussed.

The first work of Martin and James was done with
packed columns, and most of the columns used today are
of this type; however, their efficiency is limited. By
1958 Scott had essentially reached the limit with a 15-
meter column which had an efficiency of about 30,000
theoretical plates.

The major problem to be overcome in using packed
columns was producing or obtaining a useful and reliable
support material. Most of this work was done by the
chromatographer himself, using material originally produced for other purposes. Of considerable merit were
the efforts of several companies that developed and made
available several inert supports of a narrow size range
as well as pure stationary phases. Some of these companies were May and Baker in Great Britain and Johns-
Manville Corp., Applied Science Laboratory, Analabs, Inc.,
and Supelco in the United States.

In 1959 the introduction of silanization of the
support material aided greatly in the preparation of an
inert support. Also the use of low liquid loading introduced by E. C. Horning and co-workers in 1960 opened
the way for steroid and pesticide analysis.

Meanwhile, M. J. E. Golay made a breakthrough in

ARCHER JOHN PORTER MARTIN, 1910-

    Following his doctorate at Cambridge University (1936), Mar-
tin joined the Wool Industries Research Association (1938-1946),
then became head of biochemical research for Boots Pure Drug Co.
From 1948 to 1959 he was on the staff of the (British) Medical
Research Council.   In 1959 he became director of Abbotsbury Laboratories, Ltd.   He shared the 1952 Nobel Prize in Chemistry with
R. L. M. Synge, for their joint development of partition chromatography.   He also did pioneering work with A. T. James in gas
chromatography.

column development. He reasoned that a packed column was essentially a bundle of capillary tubes coated on the inside surface with the liquid phase. To test this idea, a long, small-diameter tube was coated and tried. Surprisingly, the theoretical and actual performances of this column were nearly identical. This result was quite unlike that with packed columns which fell quite short of theory. Golay presented his results in 1957 at the Lansing Symposium and a full theoretical discussion the following year at the Amsterdam Symposium. Dijkstra and DeGoey also presented results from similar columns at this meeting.

This capillary column revolutionized high-resolution chromatography, and columns of several hundred thousand theoretical plates were quickly produced. By 1959 D. H. Desty and co-workers at British Petroleum, Scott at Benzole Producers, R. D. Condon at Perkin-Elmer, as well as A. Zlatkis at the University of Houston and S. R. Lipsky at Yale, both in cooperation with Lovelock, had shown many practical applications in several fields. Fortunately, at this time two ionization detectors which had the sensitivity necessary for the small sample sizes required by the capillary columns had just been developed. Further development and optimization of these columns also involved I. Halász and his group at Frankfurt University, R. C. Teranishi and co-workers at the Western Regional Laboratory of the U. S. Department of Agriculture, and Schomburg at the Max-Planck Institute für Kohlenforschung.

The next step in the development of the capillary column was based on a proposal by Golay to prepare a porous surface on the inside of the column. This should increase the sample capacity while decreasing the thickness of the liquid layer. C. Horvath put this idea into practice in 1963 by developing the support-coated open-tubular column.

D. H. Desty and A. Drezenbull had described the production of glass capillary tubing in 1960. During the next several years much work was done by several groups before surface preparation and coating techniques were fully understood. Contributors included Grab in Zürich, Bruner, Cartoni, and Liberti in Rome, Tesarik and Novotny in Czechoslovakia, Novatny continuing work in the United States, Guiochon in Paris, Keulemans in Eindhoven, Horning in Texas, and Schomburg in Mülheim.

Theory. The theory of chromatography was slow to develop because of the extremely complex interaction of thermodynamics, mass transfer, and kinetics which occurs in the chromatographic process. Also in this development process the interaction of the different

chromatographic methods is evident. In fact the theoretical plate model for column efficiency introduced by
Martin and James in 1941 was adopted from the concept
of the theoretical plate introduced by Peters in 1922
as a measure of system efficiency in distillation. Although the HETP (height equivalent of a theoretical
plate) introduced to chromatography by Martin did not
explain band spreading, it did give a practical means
of determining column efficiency and consequently had a
strong impact on the development of chromatography.

Until 1940 chromatography was essentially an art,
but in this year J. N. Wilson published the first theoretical treatment of a model to describe quantitatively
the chromatographic process based on complete equilibrium. Although this early treatment provided remarkable
insight into the chromatographic process, it neglected
the dynamic effects of a continuous system and consequently did not take into account the actual causes of
band spreading.

In 1943 D. DeVault developed a fundamental relationship between the retention volume of a solute, the
equilibrium constant (partition coefficient), and the
volumes of the mobile and stationary phases. His treatment was the first to describe the concentration profiles for linear and nonlinear isotherms and constant
flow rates. In addition, by relating the thermodynamic
equilibrium constant and the retention volume, he opened
the possibility of a convenient means of making physio-
chemical measurements.

Still, the recognized existence of nonequilibrium
conditions had not been taken into account until H. C.
Thomas put forth his theoretical treatments from 1944
to 1948. He was able to linearize the equations of
chromatography so that nonequilibrium conditions could
be treated. This allowed the determination of adsorption and desorption rates from the experimentally
obtained concentration profile.

Thomas' treatment and the plate theory from distillation assumed that the flow was relatively slow and
that consequently near-equilibrium conditions prevailed
and that thus Gaussian profiles would be obtained where
linear isotherms were involved. In 1954 using this same
key assumption, E. Glueckauf developed the relationship
between the HETP, particle size, and diffusion through
the film on the particle for ion exchange chromatography.

Still to be accounted for were the effects of mass
transfer and longitudinal diffusion of the solute. L.
Lapidus and N. R. Amundson presented an exact theoretical
treatment of these influences in 1952, but because the
treatment was rigorous, it was not directly useful. In
1956 J. J. van Deemter, F. J. Zuiderweg, and

A. Klinkenberg simplified the formulas of Lapidus and Amundson to the Gaussian profile and combined this with Glueckauf's treatment. The result related the HETP to the flow velocity, particle diameter, and solute diffusivity in a simple and directly usable form. What is now known as the "van Deemter plot" is a graphical expression of his equation which greatly facilitated the optimization of chromatographic conditions.

Further attempts to explain chromatographic behavior with more precise models led J. C. Giddings and H. Eyring to the random walk theory of chromatography in 1958. This was followed by Giddings' generalized nonequilibrium theory of chromatography the following year. A simultaneous attempt was made by M. J. E. Golay, who investigated the separation process using the mathematics of communications engineering. This developed into a mathematical theory of the chromatographic column in 1957, which in turn led to the development of the theory and practice of coated open-tubular columns in 1958. Also in 1958, E. Kováts proposed a retention index system to express column retention. With this system the retention of a substance can be predicted and the selectivity of the various liquid phases can be characterized. A. Wehrli worked with Kováts on the index system, and the work of L. Rohrschneider proceeded along the same lines; W. O. McReynolds further developed Rohrschneider's work as a basis for characterizing the liquid phase.

Instrumentation. In 1955 the first commercial gas chromatographs appeared in Europe and in the United States. The instrument companies played a vital role in disseminating information for educating new chromatographers and for solving applications problems through data sheets, newsletters, and manuals. They also provided reliable instruments which quickly incorporated new developments. Griffin and George (London) and Metropolitan Vickers Electrical Co. (Manchester) were two of the earliest in Europe. The instrument companies in the United States generally had the greatest impact on the overall development of the technique. The first two to introduce gas chromatographs were the Burrell Corp. (the Kromo-Tog) and Perkin-Elmer Corp. (the model 154 Vapor Fractometer) in the spring of 1955. A few weeks later Podbielniak introduced the Chromacons. In 1956 the GC-1 from Beckman Instruments, the Fisher-Gulf Partitioner from Fisher Scientific, and a model from Consolidated Electrodynamics were introduced. In the ensuing years other companies also developed instruments with the latest advances. Some of these companies became almost totally oriented about gas chromatography.

The F and M Scientific Glassware Co., the Wilkens Instrument and Research Co., and the Hamilton Co. were three of these. The first two companies developed and marketed instruments while the Hamilton Co., founded around 1958 by C. H. Hamilton in California, wrestled with the general problem of introducing very small samples in a small time period into the chromatograph, and they developed the high-precision microsyringe.

Numerous detector systems have been developed since the use of the automatic titrator by James and Martin. N. H. Ray applied a katharometer (thermal conductivity detector) previously used in gas adsorption chromatography, in 1954. C. S. G. Phillips' group at Oxford University developed several detectors based on various parameters, but these did not gain wide acceptance. Martin developed a gas density balance detector in 1954, but this was also not widely accepted.

A simple and selective detector was developed in 1955 by R. P. W. Scott. This was the hydrogen flame temperature detector, and it was just gaining acceptance when the more sensitive hydrogen flame ionization detector came into being. This detector was described by two groups in 1958: J. Harley, W. Nel, and V. Pretorius in the Republic of South Africa, and I. G. McWilliams and R. A. Dewar at I.C.I. of Australia and New Zealand. It gained rapid application and is one of the most widely used detectors today.

Another very sensitive detector was the result of J. E. Lovelock who introduced the argon ionization detector in 1958. This detector competed with the flame ionization detector, which eventually won out due to its wider linear range. Modification of the argon detector by Lovelock et al. led to the electron capture detector for selective detection of trace impurities.

Three other important detectors were developed. D. M. Coulson and L. A. Cavanagh in 1960 developed a coulometric detector selective for chlorine-containing organic compounds. Cremer et al. introduced the thermionic detector in 1961. It was based on a flame ionization detector whose flame contained alkali metal ions which selectively interacted with heteroatoms present in the eluting compound. A widely used version of this detector, selective for phosphorus and halogen, was based on the work of A. Karman and L. Giuffride. A further development by a group at the University of Missouri led to a nitrogen-sensitive thermionic detector in 1967. The third detector was introduced by S. S. Brody and J. E. Chaney in 1966. This was the flame photometric detector which viewed the flame of a flame ionization detector through optical filters to isolate the emission wavelengths of phosphorus and sulfur.

Even with the introduction of selective detectors, chromatography still could not identify the components of a sample unequivocally. An obvious approach to overcome this disadvantage would be the examination of the eluting components with a qualitative technique. Initial work by A. E. Martin and J. Smart in 1955 demonstrated the feasibility of identifying the chromatographic effluent by infrared spectroscopy. Their technique was to oxidize the effluent catalytically to CO_2, which was then passed through an infrared cell where absorption by CO_2 was monitored at an appropriate wavelength. Although this system did not identify the components, it was a good qualitative detector and it demonstrated the feasibility of real-time infrared monitoring at one wavelength. The technique in use during the next few years called for trapping and subsequent examination by infrared for identification. Finally, in 1964 A. M. Bartz and H. D. Ruhl and, independently, P. A. Wilks and R. A. Brown demonstrated the possibility of obtaining an infrared spectrum of a compound on stream, as it was eluted from the column. Thus the separation capabilities of chromatography were combined with the identification capabilities of the infrared without any tedious sample collection.

The concept of using a qualitative detector was also realized with a mass spectrometer. In fact, the combination of gas chromatography with effluent monitoring by a mass spectrometer was demonstrated earlier than the infrared technique, in 1957, by J. C. Holmes and F. A. Morrell, and also by W. Donner, T. Johns and W. S. Gallaway. The effluent from the chromatograph was introduced into the mass spectrometer, and the mass spectrum of the effluent was repeatedly scanned and displayed on an oscilloscope. The mass spectrometer technique was inherently much more powerful than the infrared because its sharp line spectrum lent itself to more definite identification through digital data processing and because of its much greater sensitivity. In its original form it was also more expensive.

The demands of analysis stimulated widespread use of the gas chromatography/mass spectrometry technique, and literally hundreds of workers developed this method further. Modern instruments are generally combined with a dedicated computer system. These systems are capable of separating and identifying complex mixtures in a matter of hours and certainly represent one of the most powerful analytical tools in existence.

Isothermal operation of a chromatograph has its shortcomings when one is dealing with a wide boiling-range mixture. The conditions are optimized for a relatively small region of the boiling range of the mixtures components. Hence, for low-boiling components the temperature is too high, and for high-boiling components it is too low.

James and Martin attempted to solve this problem by changing the column temperature during the experiment to reduce the elution times of the high-boiling components. Another approach was to connect two or three columns in series with each at a different temperature.

The first actually to program the temperature rise during a separation was the group of C. S. G. Phillips in 1952. A few other scattered reports of using this technique can be found during the 1950s. With the advent of the 1960s temperature programming became an accepted technique due to the fundamental work of S. Dal Nogare and co-workers and the efforts of F and M Scientific Co. At this time Habgood and Harris, Giddings, Said, and Rowan almost simultaneously presented the theoretical background of the technique.

The major problem of the bleeding of the liquid phase and the concomitant exponentially increasing baseline arose as the temperature was increased during an analysis. This problem was solved by E. M. Emery and W. E. Koernes of Monsanto in 1961 by using the dual column, baseline-compensation technique and dual thermal conductivity detectors. By 1962 Perkin-Elmer had introduced a commercial instrument utilizing flame ionization detectors.

Programming of the carrier gas flow rate was also originally tried by James and Martin. They used a stepwise increase in flow produced by increasing the inlet pressure, to reduce the analysis time. Although the technique became accepted, it was not widely used, even at the urging of H. Purnell in 1962. He believed the results would be equivalent to those obtained with temperature programming. Scott and others firmly established the technique in the mid-1960s, and commercial accessories became available, but this technique never gained wide acceptance.

LIQUID CHROMATOGRAPHY

Liquid-Liquid and Liquid-Solid Column Chromatography. The Russian botanist and plant physiologist Michael Tswett devised the differential migration method we know today as chromatography. Tswett was not the first scientist to use adsorbents in columns to accomplish separations. L. Reed reported, in 1893, the separation of inorganic and organic salts on a column of kaolin, and D. T. Day, in 1897, used fuller's earth to resolve petroleum. Although Day recognized the analytical

importance of his technique, he incorrectly interpreted
the separation mechanism. Even earlier, in 1850, J. T.
Way used soil columns for separations while E. Fischer
and E. Schmidmer, in 1893, utilized rolls of paper
pressed into glass tubes. These methods, like capillary
analysis on paper, involved continuous flow of the mixture into the sorptive column, which resulted in over-
lapping zones and incomplete separations of the mixture's components.

Tswett succeeded in resolving complex natural mixtures of the structurally similar yellow and green
chloroplast pigments in the leaf extracts he was studying.
His important contribution was the use of pure solvent
to develop the chromatogram after applying a narrow
initial zone of mixture to the top of the column. The
column consisted of dried precipitated chalk, and the
solvent or wash liquid was carbon disulfide; complete
separations were achieved. Tswett's first work on
chromatography appeared in 1903, and the method was
described in great detail in 1906. This latter milestone paper has been translated into English and evaluated by Strain and Sherma [*J. Chem. Educ. 44*, 235, 238
(1967)]. Tswett eventually contributed more than 50
papers and a book, published in 1910 in Russian, on
chromatography and pigments.

The colored pigments Tswett was studying formed
readily visible bands, and he coined the term chromatography for the technique although he pointed out it
could be used for separating colorless compounds. Is
it a coincidence that Tswett, in Russian, means color?
He also provided other nomenclature still in common use
today, described the physical basis of the separations
he obtained, and made extensive tests of other sorbents
and solvents. Tswett's contributions to the invention
of chromatography and the study of chloroplast pigments
have been reviewed in detail by Strain and Sherma (1972).

The liquid column adsorption chromatographic method
of Tswett was not widely used until 1931 although some
earlier use of it was made, mostly by botanists and biochemists for investigating leaf pigments. Probably the
first to grasp the importance of Tswett's method was
C. Dhéré working in Switzerland in 1911. A few others
who utilized the technique during this "dormant period"
were F. Czepak in 1913, K. H. Coward in 1926, and Th.
Lipmaa in 1926. An American agricultural scientist,
L. S. Palmer, published many papers and a book in 1914-
1922 in which chromatography was extensively applied to
research in dairy chemistry and nutrition and Tswett's
work was discussed. Palmer's book containing the method
of Tswett was an influence on E. Lederer, whose studies
in Richard Kuhn's Heidelberg laboratory in 1931 began

the wide popularity of chromatography.

Lederer "reinvented" chromatography when he demonstrated the separation of carotenes in carrots and xanthophylls in egg yolk on a column of calcium carbonate. The publication of this and other work from Kuhn's laboratory soon led to an avalanche of papers from many other laboratories throughout the world. A. Winterstein, also a member of Kuhn's group, was an active apostle of chromatography after 1931 through lectures and demonstrations. Another important factor in the widespread adoption of the method was the first accessible book on chromatography, published by L. Zechmeister and L. v. Cholnoky in 1937. Zechmeister, like Kuhn, was a student of R. Willstätter. Ironically, Willstätter, who was awarded the Nobel prize in 1915 for his studies of plant pigments, did not hold Tswett's chromatography in high esteem and probably contributed to its lack of recognition during the "dormant period." The second edition of Zechmeister's book, prepared one year after the first, was translated into English in 1941, and within a year a book by H. H. Strain, the first American pioneer in chromatography, was published. The research and writings of Hesse, Williams, Cassidy, M. Lederer, Tiselius, Claesson, Brockmann, Karrer, and Reichstein were also important in perfecting methods and in spreading the popularity and applications of chromatography.

Column partition chromatography was first described in 1941 by A. J. P. Martin and R. L. M. Synge working at the Wool Industries' Research Association laboratory in Leeds, England. They worked with systems composed of a solid carrier support and two liquid phases. This led to paper partition chromatography, which is discussed in another section.

Gel Chromatography. The earliest separations of mixtures on the basis of molecular size were made on natural and synthetic zeolites (aluminosilicates), which have a crystalline, cagelike structure with pores of uniform shape. The term "molecular sieve" was first applied to zeolites in 1926 by J. W. McBain. Since good separations could be obtained on zeolites only for low molecular weight materials, a search was made for media having pore structures also permitting separations of high molecular weight substances by molecular size. Discovery of these materials has led to the technique of gel chromatography, a term introduced by H. Determann in 1964. Gel chromatography includes the essentially identical procedures of gel permeation chromatography and gel filtration chromatography, which differ only in their fields of application. The former is used mainly to study synthetic polymers in organic solvents, while

the latter is usually applied to biological macromolecules in aqueous solution.

The first significant application of column gel
chromatography as it is practiced today dates to the
separations of amino acids by B. Lindqvist and T. Stor-
gårds, and of polysaccharides and proteins by G. H.
Lathe and C. R. Ruthven on natural and modified granu-
lated starch in 1955-56. Starch was not a very satisfactory chromatographic medium, however; thus, it was
not until the discovery of the gel filtration properties
of crosslinked dextran gels by J. Porath and P. Flodin
in Tiselius' laboratory in 1959 that gel chromatography
became practical and widespread. Porath and Flodin
synthesized these gels by reaction of the polysaccharide
dextran with epichlorohydrin, and the gels are sold
today under the trade name Sephadex. An important property of the dextran gels is their variety of pore sizes
which permits separation over a wide molecular weight
range. The same authors introduced granular cellulose
and polyvinyl alcohol, but these had less favorable
properties than crosslinked dextran. Since dextran's
discovery, many other gels for use in both aqueous and
nonaqueous solvents have become available, and modifications, such as column recycling and thin layer gel
chromatography, have been devised.

The separation of hydrophobic polymers by gel chromatography in organic solvents, which was first demonstrated by M. F. Vaughn on crosslinked polystyrene and
P. I. Brewer on vulcanized natural rubber in 1960, advanced rapidly after 1962 when J. C. Moore used improved
gels composed of hydrophobic macromolecular polymers
with a moderately rigid structure and a wide range of
permeabilities. These polystyrene gels (now marketed
as Styragel) allowed separations of components with
molecular weights from several thousand to several mil-
lion by proper choice of gel porosity. Moore also connected the gel column directly to a differential re-
fractometer detector to monitor the effluent continuously.

Rapid acceptance of gel chromatography led to development of other new sorbents in the early 1960s such
as agarose, polymethacrylate, and lipophilic Sephadex
gels and porous glass powder, which have extended applications to all areas of analytical and preparative
macromolecular chemistry. Gel chromatography is now
often combined with ion-exchange and affinity chromatography to provide an even more powerful analytical
tool.

Ion Exchange Chromatography. Ion exchange has been
recognized as a way of chemical analysis for barely 30
years. We can assign a date to its emergence: September

17, 1947. On this date a symposium was held at the
American Chemical Society's national meeting in New York
City at which reports were given of the separation of
the rare-earth elements on columns of ion-exchange
resins, research that had been done under wartime secrecy
in the Manhattan Project. The fission of uranium produced all of the rare-earth elements, and they had to
be separated; G. E. Boyd and his associates suggested
ion exchange for this purpose, and it worked.

Ion exchange in soils was observed in 1850 by H. M.
Thompson and J. T. Way, and attempts were later made to
use the technique in chemical analysis. In 1917 O. Folin
and R. D. Bell published a method for measuring ammonium
ions in urine. The urine was stirred with granules of
an insoluble sodium aluminosilicate, the so-called
"Permutit" or "Decalso." This material absorbed ammonium
ions from the urine, releasing an equivalent amount of
sodium ions. The granules were separated, washed, and
treated with sodium hydroxide solution. Ammonia was
released and measured colorimetrically by Nessler's
reagent.

As long as the only ion exchanger available was
sodium aluminosilicate, the possibilities for using ion
exchange in chemical analysis were severely limited.
This material is stable only in neutral solution; acids
and bases decompose it. Nevertheless an attempt was
made to use it in a very difficult chemical separation,
the separation of isotopes. In 1938 T. I. Taylor and
H. C. Urey took a pipe 130 ft long, mounted it in the
stairwell of the chemistry building at Columbia University, and filled it with the ion exchanger. Then they
passed a solution of lithium chloride. The rarer isotope, lithium-6, was preferentially held by the column.
Potassium isotopes were partially separated in the same
way.

A very important event in ion exchange took place
in 1935: the production of the first ion-exchange resins
by B. A. Adams and E. L. Holmes at the National Chemical Laboratory near London, England. These resins were
chemical relatives of the plastic, Bakelite, made from
phenol and formaldehyde with subsequent treatment by
sulfuric acid. They were stable towards acids and could
exchange hydrogen ions just like any other cations.
Thus, they could adsorb and desorb metal ions of all
kinds, including those that hydrolyzed in neutral solutions. This kind of resin was used in the Manhattan
Project until better resins came along, the resins based
on polystyrene that were introduced by G. F. D'Alelio
in 1944. Polystyrene-based ion-exchange resins are used
in most applications today.

Before World War II, Olof Samuelson in Sweden saw

the potential of ion-exchange resins in chemical analysis and chose this area of research for his doctoral thesis. His first publication appeared in 1939 and concerned the separation of anions and cations that interfered with one another in chemical analysis. For example, sulfate ions in aluminum sulfate could be separated from aluminum ions by passing the solution through a cation-exchange resin. The resin adsorbed aluminum and released in its place the equivalent amount of hydrogen ions, and what emerged from the column was a solution of sulfuric acid. The sulfate ions could now be precipitated quantitatively with barium chloride. Another possibility was to titrate the sulfuric acid with standard base and so find the exact concentration of the original aluminum salt solution. The ion-exchange method is a standard one used today to find the total salt concentration of solutions.

These applications are not chromatographic, that is, they do not separate ions of similar charge by differential adsorption and successive stripping from a column of resin. Isolated attempts to perform such analyses were made before atomic energy came on the scene, but, as noted, the first dramatic success of ion-exchange chromatography was the separation of the rare-earth elements in the Manhattan Project. This was the work of two groups, one at Oak Ridge under G. E. Boyd, J. Schubert, and others, the other at Ames, Iowa under F. H. Spedding. Boyd's group was concerned with isolating fission products and measuring their amounts, that is, with chemical analysis in the strict sense. Spedding's group accomplished the large-scale separation of naturally occurring rare-earth elements.

Before the rare-earth elements were separated, another and more momentous separation had been performed by ion-exchange chromatography: the separation of plutonium from uranium and of the fission products. This was done by Boyd's group in mid-1942 but was not released for open publication until much later. Boyd reasoned correctly that plutonium, which formed an ion of high charge (4+), would be held more strongly by the resin than the doubly charged uranyl ion.

The exploitation of ion exchange as a means of chemical separation and analysis is intimately related to the development of atomic energy. On the one hand, atomic energy brought a rebirth of inorganic chemistry, presenting chemists with bewildering mixtures of elements, some of which had never before been known, and posing new challenges to those who wished to separate them. On the other hand, high-energy radiation damaged living cells, and it was necessary to know more about the chemical composition of cells. Here again, ion exchange played a vital part, and historians may trace

the new molecular biology to its origins in the atomic
energy laboratories.

Let us consider first the applications of ion exchange to inorganic analysis. The key to separating the
rare earths was the use of complexing agents like citrate
ions in the eluting solution. All ion-exchange separations depend on a tug of war between the exchanger and
the surrounding solution, and nearly all separations of
metals use differences in the stability of complex ions
in the solution.

To some degree the stabilities are predictable.
Ion exchange was used extensively to separate the new,
man-made transuranium elements, and its most spectacular
success was with the isolation of element 101, mendel-
evium, by A. Ghiorso, G. T. Seaborg, and others in 1955.
Five atoms of this new element, no more, were obtained
in the first run. They emerged from an ion-exchange
column at exactly the predicted place and were identified
by their nuclear properties.

A very powerful technique for separating and con-
centrating metal ions is by anion exchange in hydrochloric acid solutions. Negatively charged chloride
complexes are formed that stick to the resin. These
vary enormously in stability from one element to another
and with the concentration of hydrochloric acid. There
are many possibilities for performing separations, and
dozens of new applications of this principle are published each year. The original development was made by
K. A. Kraus and F. Nelson at Oak Ridge National Laboratory in 1952 and was stimulated by the needs of atomic
energy research.

A new dimension was brought into inorganic ion-exchange chromatography by the discovery of J. S. Fritz
at Iowa State University in 1961 that the adsorption of
metal chloride complexes was changed drastically by
mixing the water with another solvent like acetone or
alcohol. Elution sequences could be modified and altered
completely, and often the separations were sharper than
those obtained with water alone. The idea of combining
ion exchange with solvent extraction was developed in
great detail by J. Korkisch in Vienna, Austria, and he
has applied it to the analysis of rocks, minerals, and
nuclear raw materials.

In Pretoria, South Africa, F. W. E. Strelow has
used ion exchange extensively for the analysis of minerals and mineral products. Even in this day of powerful instrumental methods, there is no substitute for
painstaking chemical separations when it comes to the
accurate, precise, and reliable analysis of really complex materials.

Applications to organic and biochemical analysis

are no less spectacular. At Oak Ridge in 1949, W. E.
Cohn adsorbed the hydrolysis products of nucleic acids
on columns of cation- and anion-exchange resins and
stripped them off, one at a time, by passing hydrochloric acid or buffer solutions. The original analyses
took many hours, even days. The same kind of analysis
is done today in minutes. At the Rockefeller Institute
for Medical Research in New York, S. Moore and W. H.
Stein in 1951 devised a way of analyzing mixtures of
amino acids by adsorbing them as cations at the inlet
of a resin column, then eluting them one by one with a
succession of buffer solutions. As the amino acids
emerged from the column their concentrations were measured continuously by the color produced with ninhydrin.
Analysis of amino acid mixtures is today the commonest
routine use of ion-exchange chromatography. It was
brought to a high level of efficiency by such people as
H. Stegemann in Germany and by P. B. Hamilton in the
United States, who prepared the way for modern high-
efficiency liquid chromatography. Moore and Stein were
awarded a Nobel prize for their research in ion exchange.

An important feature of the chromatography of organic compounds is that the compounds do not need to be
ionic to be adsorbed by an ion-exchange resin. The polymer network of the resin acts as an organic solvent in
its own right. Another factor is that in mixed solvents,
the solvent inside the resin contains a higher proportion
of water than that outside. This second effect causes
sugars and other carbohydrates to be adsorbed by resins
from water-alcohol mixtures. Chromatography of carbo-
hydrate mixtures on ion-exchange resins is therefore
possible and has been developed to a fine art in the
hands of O. Samuelson in Sweden since 1956.

The "organic solvent" character of ion-exchange
resins is being exploited actively today. A fine example
is the work of C. D. Scott on the separation and quantitative measurement of some 150 constituents of urine.
Scott works in the Biology Division of Oak Ridge National
Laboratory, bringing us back where we started to the
close connection between developments in atomic power
and developments in ion-exchange technology.

High-Speed Liquid Chromatography. In their classic
paper describing the invention of liquid-liquid partition chromatography in 1941, A. J. P. Martin and R. L.
M. Synge not only foreshadowed gas chromatography by
outlining the advantages of using a gas mobile phase in
place of a liquid, but they anticipated high-speed (or
"high-pressure" or "high-performance") liquid chromatography by stating that fast analysis would require
the use of very small particles and high-pressure

differences across the length of the column. Pioneering
work in high-speed liquid chromatography was carried out
by P. B. Hamilton in 1960 for amino acid analyses, but
probably because this work was in a specialized field,
it had little impact on liquid chromatography in general.

C. Karr et al., in 1963, were among the first to
describe successful liquid chromatographic separations
that were analogous to gas chromatographic separations.
These included long, narrow-tubing column packing that
could be used indefinitely, automatic recording of peaks,
use of a single carrier fluid, and highly reproducible
retention volumes. J. C. Giddings pointed out, in 1963,
that for the analogy between gas chromatography and
liquid chromatography to be complete, a comparison of
column efficiencies was important. He discussed methods
to improve analysis time in liquid chromatography.
Factors affecting column efficiencies had been studied
extensively in gas chromatography, and their optimization led to considerable improvement in resolution and
speed of analysis. He predicted that column parameters
could undoubtedly be found that would make column performance in liquid chromatography (LC) fully analogous
to that in gas chromatography (GC). He indicated that
the particle diameter in LC would be considerably smaller
than in GC and that large pressure drops would be required. Later, in 1965, Giddings discussed the theoretical limit of speed of separation between gas chromatography and liquid chromatography. He indicated that
the comparative speed of separation depends on the relative viscosity and diffusivity of liquids and gases.
Due to its low critical inlet pressure resulting from
low diffusivity in liquid systems, liquid chromatography,
he predicted, should be a better method than gas chromatography for extremely difficult separations. The
hypothesis of J. H. Knox, in 1961, that separation speed
is increased with larger pressure drops, was substantiated by that study.

Development of high-pressure pumping systems was
one of the factors that contributed to the blossoming
of high-speed liquid chromatography. A reciprocating
piston or bellows pump generally is utilized. The ear-
lier-designed pumps would produce pulses that would be
recorded by the detector and thus limit its sensitivity.
In 1966 R. Jentoft and T. H. Gouw designed one of the
first pulseless high-pressure pumps for use in liquid
chromatography. This pump operated at pressures up to
1000 psi and flow rates up to 100 ml/min with no dis-
cernible change in output pressure or output flow rate
during its different cycles. High-pressure air was used
to displace mercury, which was in turn used to displace
the liquid phase.

L. R. Snyder, in 1969, used a high-pressure nitrogen tank coupled with a pentane tank to achieve pulseless flow up to 5000 psi. These systems, although pulseless, were inconvenient because of their limited solvent capacity and the difficulty in changing solvent systems.

In 1969 K. J. Bombaugh et al. introduced a commercial unit that used a reciprocating pump and pulse dampener. The system noise was essentially undetectable using a refractive index detector with a sensitivity of about 10^{-7} RI units/mV.

The effect of pressure drop on column efficiency was investigated by J. F. K. Huber and J. A. R. Hulsman in 1967. Their study showed that separation time in liquid chromatography can be reduced considerably if a higher pressure drop is acceptable. This improvement was restricted by the difficulty of obtaining regular packings for very small particles. Their work substantiated Giddings' work in 1963. In 1967 J. Horvath et al. published a paper which featured a liquid chromatographic system with high inlet pressure and a sensitive UV detector. A pellicular ion-exchange column material was used to enhance the separation of a complex mixture of nanomole quantities of ribonucleoside mono-, or di- and triphosphates. This study was undertaken to investigate the feasibility of developing a liquid chromatography system which could provide speed, good resolution, and quantitative ranges similar to those obtained in gas chromatography.

The effect of column-to-particle diameter ratio on the dispersion of unsorbed solutes in chromatography was studied by J. H. Knox and J. Parcher in 1969. They concluded that "infinite" diameter columns offered some advantages in terms of efficiency over conventional columns in high-pressure, small particle liquid chromatography.

Development of efficient column packings which permit the rapid, efficient separation of complex mixtures has contributed to the improvement of high-speed liquid chromatographic methods. In 1969 J. J. Kirkland investigated the improvement of liquid chromatography column performance as a result of the development of packings made with controlled surface porosity. The following parameters in the use of controlled surface porosity were studied: liquid film thickness, support types, support surface porosity, column internal diameter, and reproducibility of column packing. It was observed that columns made with the controlled porosity supports (which are mechanically stable) can be conveniently operated at high pressures.

One of the most significant developments that helped to make high-speed liquid chromatography a viable technique was the synthesis of chemically bonded supports. Although first developed for gas chromatography, they were soon used in liquid chromatography. G. Nickless et al., in 1965, prepared a support in which the stationary phase, $n\text{-}C_{16}H_{33}$, was chemically bonded to the support phase. The resulting columns were thermally and hydrolytically stable. I. Halász and I. Sebastian, in 1969, developed what they called "brushes," in which the liquid phase was chemically bonded to the siliceous support via an ester-type linkage. Later, W. A. Aue and C. R. Hastings developed similar supports in which the organic group was bonded directly to silicon atoms in a siloxane polymer extending from the core support. In 1971 Kirkland synthesized similar stationary phases in which the organic group was an aliphatic ether or nitrile. D. C. Locke et al., in 1972, developed methods in which the organic group could be directly bonded, via a carbon-silicon bond, to the silicon atoms on the surface of the core material. These packings were thermally and solvolytically stable. Today, 5-20 μm totally porous particles are receiving major attention as efficient column packings.

Giddings continued to compare the performance and potential capability of gas chromatography with liquid chromatography. In 1964 a study concerned with the theoretical limit of separability was conducted. Having selected the best column materials and parameters for a specific separation, the degree of separation can be increased by increasing the column length. When the column gets so long that flow through it is too slow, then an increase in pressure is the most feasible alternative. Eventually a maximum pressure will be reached which the equipment can handle. The maximum pressure limit of separability can be determined by the maximum pressure limitation imposed on the system. As mentioned above, Hamilton contributed to the development of high-pressure systems as early as 1960. Ion-exchange chromatography of amino acids was performed, and the effects of pressures exceeding 600 psi and fast flow rates were investigated. Apparatus used in this study was specifically designed to tolerate fluid pressures exceeding 600 psi. Pressure as a function of column length, flow rate, and temperature was studied.

Paper Chromatography. Filter paper for chromatography was first used in the middle of the 19th century. When dyers applied a drop of a solution consisting of a mixture of dyes to a piece of fabric or paper, concentric rings were observed. This result would be analogous to what today would be termed radial frontal-development chromatography. Such phenomena were first

recorded by the German chemist F. F. Runge in 1850.
Runge, who was both poet and technologist, allowed colored substances, mostly inorganic salts, to react on
untreated or impregnated paper. Their precipitation and
diffusion produced beautiful patterns, which he attributed to the creative urge of nature and which we would
include in abstract art. A book by Runge in 1855 contains reproductions of these artistic patterns.

C. F. Schoenbein, when experimenting with ozone in
1861, immersed strips of paper into solutions of various
dyes, salts, etc., and observed that different components
ascended to different heights. This method was immediately adopted by F. Goppelsroeder as an analytical technique and called "kapillaranalyse" (capillary analysis).
Goppelsroeder worked in this field for many decades and
published a book on the technique in 1901. Capillary
analysis was also adopted by other workers in linear
(ascending) or radial arrangement. Although capillary
analysis could provide some useful analytical results,
such as characterization of certain plant extracts, it
was not very highly regarded. The separation, originally
attributed to capillary forces, was later explained by
Goppelsroeder (under the influence of W. Ostwald) as
being due to adsorption.

Michael Tswett, who originally called his column
technique "the adsorption method," laid great stress on
the distinction between his method and capillary analysis, which does not use solvent development and does
not completely resolve mixtures. Tswett at first attributed capillary analysis to the phenomena of solvent
evaporation and solute precipitation, and he only later
admitted, in 1910, that adsorption might also play a
role in the differential migration achieved. Elution
development with fresh solvent was mentioned by Goppelsroeder but was not generally used in his work. The
inorganic capillary analysis reported by H. Flood in
1937, a method based mostly on an ion-exchange mechanism,
resembled present-day paper chromatography in its use of
solvent development. Circular (radial) chromatography
with solvent development on alumina-impregnated or untreated filter paper was introduced in 1939 by W. G.
Brown.

A. J. P. Martin and R. L. M. Synge first reported
the counter-current distribution technique in 1941 and
later that year described column partition chromatography.
This was followed by the introduction of paper partition
chromatography in a paper in 1943 by Martin, Synge, and
A. H. Gordon and another in 1944 by Martin, Gordon, and
R. Consden. The originally described method used de-
scending development, and a two-dimensional modification was used to increase separation power. The happy

coincidence that a suitable paper was then readily available in England, plus the simple equipment required, caused paper chromatography to be immediately and widely accepted. The original work by Martin's group was directed toward the analysis of amino acids in protein hydrolyzates, and C. E. Dent later (1946-48) used paper chromatography in the characterization of amino acid ureas and in the discovery of many new plant amino acids. Among the first applications in other fields were those for sugars by S. M. Partridge in 1946, for antibiotics by R. R. Goodall and A. A. Levi in 1946, for radio-actively labeled substances by R. M. Fink and K. Fink in 1947 and 1948, for nucleotides by J. L. Crammer in 1948, and for purine and pyrimidine bases by E. Visher and E. Chargaff in 1948.

The use of organic stationary phases (for both "direct" and "reversed-phase" chromatography) extended the scope of paper chromatography for less polar organic compounds, such as some steroids and alkaloids. Inorganic applications soon appeared as well, e.g., work by T. V. Arden et al. and M. Lederer in 1948. There is hardly any type of compound, exept highly volatile substances and macromolecules occurring in complicated natural or synthetic mixtures, which has not been successfully analyzed by paper chromatography. Other mechanisms, in addition to liquid-liquid partition, play their role in certain systems. The additive nature of the R_M value, introduced by E. C. Bate-Smith and R. G. Westall in 1950 on the basis of Martin's theory described in 1948, has proved a useful tool for studying relationships between paper chromatographic behavior and chemical structure and, in some cases, biological activity.

The importance of paper chromatography as a research tool is illustrated by the fact that in addition to the 1952 Nobel prize to A. J. P. Martin and R. L. M. Synge for partition chromatography, the method helped the investigations for which this most coveted prize was awarded to F. Sanger (1958), V. du Vigneaud (1955), M. Calvin (1961), J. Axelrod (1970), and L. F. Leloir (1970).

When thin-layer chromatography (TLC) came to the fore, its sharpness and speed of separation were usually superior to that of paper chromatography. This has led to the relative decline of paper chromatography in recent years, its solvent systems and techniques of detection and quantitation being widely exploited in TLC. Since there are many types of foils which are difficult to classify rigidly either as paper or thin-layer media, it does not seem appropriate to drop a hard and fast line between these two types of planar or flat-bed chromatographic methods.

Thin-Layer Chromatography. Contrary to popular belief, thin-layer chromatography actually began with the experiments of the Dutch biologist M. W. Beyerinck in 1889. This predates the early work on column chromatography as reported by L. Reed but is predated by the paper chromatographic work of F. F. Runge, C. F. Schoenbein, and F. Goppelsroeder. Beyerinck allowed a drop of a mixture of hydrochloric and sulfuric acids to diffuse through a thin layer of gelatin. The hydrochloric acid traveled faster than the sulfuric acid and formed a ring around the latter. The hydrochloric acid zone was made visible with silver nitrate, and the sulfuric acid was made visible with barium chloride. Nine years later, H. P. Wijsman used the same techniques to show that there were two enzymes in malt diastase, and he also proved that only one of them split off maltose from soluble starch. Wijsman was also the first to use a fluorescent indicator to detect a chromatographic zone. He incorporated fluorescent bacteria from seawater in a gelatin layer containing starch and allowed the amylase mixture to diffuse in the layer. A fluorescent band appeared only where the β-amylase reacted with the starch. This turned out to be one of the more sensitive visualizing agents encountered in thin-layer work. It is sensitive to 1/28,000,000 mg of maltose or about 40 picograms.

N. A. Izmailov and M. S. Schraiber, in 1938 at the University of Kharkov, used a loose layer of aluminum oxide on a glass plate for circular chromatography. They placed a drop of the solution on the adsorbent and developed it into concentric zones with drops of solvent. This method has been called spread-layer chromatography. The authors pointed out the usefulness of drop chromatography for testing adsorbents and solvents for use in column chromatography.

In 1940 C. Lapp and K. Erali spread a loose layer of aluminum oxide 8 cm long on a glass slide which was supported on an inclined aluminum sheet. The latter was cooled at its upper end and heated at the lower end. The sample to be separated was placed at the top of the adsorbent and washed down with a developing solvent.

M. O'L. Crowe, in 1941, used a technique similar to that of Izmailov and Schraiber by placing the adsorbent in the cups of spot plates. After selecting the adsorbent and the solvent, a thin, wedge-shaped layer of adsorbent was formed in a petri dish by tilting the latter. A drop of the solution was flowed onto the adsorbent and was then developed dropwise.

In 1942 N. V. Békésy used an adsorbent slurry to fill a channel between two glass plates held apart by cork gaskets. This apparatus was then used in the same

manner as a chromatographic column. Békésy formed a
micro column by covering a shallow channel in a glass
plate with another glass plate. Agar was used to hold
the two plates together, and the column was formed by
filling with an adsorbent slurry.

W. G. Brown had demonstrated circular paper chromatography in 1939 by placing filter paper between two
glass plates. The upper plate contained a small hole
for sample application and addition of solvent. Because
of the mild adsorption characteristics of paper he proposed the use of a thin layer of alumina between the
sheets of paper. T. L. Williams, in 1947, eliminated
the paper and used only the adsorbent between the glass
plates.

J. E. Meinhard and N. F. Hall, in 1949, were the
first to use a binder to hold the adsorbent on the support. They bound a mixture of aluminum oxide and Celite
with starch to microscope slides. These prepared slides
were used to perform circular drop chromatography of
inorganic ions.

During the period 1945-1954 J. G. Kirchner and his
associates at the U. S. Department of Agriculture were
working on the isolation and identification of the
flavoring components present in orange and grapefruit
juice. At this time gas chromatography was in its infancy, and a microchromatographic method was needed to
help in the purification and identification of the
minute amounts of flavoring components. It was only
natural to try paper chromatography, but it was quickly
evident that paper was too limited in its adsorption
capabilities to be of any great use. Silica-impregnated
paper was then developed in 1950, but its capacity was
also limited and the preparation was rather tedious.
The work of Meinhard and Hall was published at this
time, and Kirchner conceived the idea that it would be
possible to modify the drop chromatographic technique
so as to combine the advantages of column and paper
chromatography. To achieve the desired results the following changes were made: (1) a search was made for a
starch that would permit the preparation of layers without filter aid and without cracking of the surface.
This elimination of cracking was the original purpose
of the filter aid, but it made the layers rather soft.
With its elimination a surface was obtained that could
be written on with a lead pencil; (2) many adsorbents
were checked, and silica gel was selected as the most
satisfactory and universal adsorbent; (3) the available
adsorbent was sieved so that only the finer particles
were used (finer than 149 microns); (4) gypsum was selected as an inorganic binder that could be used whenever visualizing agents were required that would react

with a starch binder; (5) more effective separations
could be achieved by using larger strips and plates;
(6) two-dimensional chromatography was introduced to
achieve greater versatility; (7) new visualizing agents
were developed to locate even very unreactive compounds
and also to indicate the types of compounds that were
being separated; and perhaps the most important was (8)
development of the layers in a closed chamber analogous
to the ascending paper chromatographic technique. The
initial work on this was published in 1951 by Kirchner
et al. Further modifications and applications of the
method followed in a series of papers during the years
1952-1957.

Although the method was used by many workers from
1951 to 1958, it attracted little attention, probably
because of its use in a specific field of interest.
This result is similar to the work of Tswett, which was
also in a specific field of interest and went relatively
unnoticed for a period of time.

In 1956 E. Stahl published his first paper on thin-
layer chromatography and asserted that he had developed
a "new method" by eliminating the difficulties of "complicated paste production with binders and the troublesome preparation of plaster strips" (i.e., gypsum).
This feat was accomplished by using an extremely fine-
grained silica gel (0.5-5 microns) which he claimed
eliminated the need for binders. It is interesting to
note that later, in 1958, Stahl returned to the uniform
gypsum bound layers of Kirchner et al. although he has
erroneously credited Gaenshirt with the development of
this binder. It was only after the standardization of
adsorbents and techniques and the development of a convenient spreader for the preparation of thin layer
plates by Stahl, and the widespread publicity of the
equipment and adsorbents given by the firms of Desaga
and Merck, that thin-layer chromatography achieved great
popularity.

Quantitative thin-layer chromatography was introduced by Kirchner et al. in 1954 with an elution method
for the determination of biphenyl in citrus fruit and
products. Since then quantitative TLC has expanded in
scope and methods and is widely used today.

ELECTROPHORESIS

When an electrical field is imposed across a fluid
suspension of charged particles, the particles migrate
toward the pole that bears the opposite charge. This
phenomenon is called electromigration. It was first
observed in 1808 by F. F. Reuss, who reported the

migration of clay particles toward the anode during a series of experiments that led to his discovery of electroosmosis. Neither he nor his colleagues recognized the importance of the observation, a fact that is hardly surprising when one recalls that the scientific community of the 19th century was inundated with discoveries of exciting and important electrical properties.

The first published application of electromigration for investigating the properties of matter was that of O. Lodge who, in 1886, used a simple apparatus to observe the movement of the boundary of a colored solution that he layered upon a clear substrate. Six years later H. Picton and S. E. Linder did similar experiments with colored colloidal suspensions. In 1899 W. B. Hardy initiated the seemingly endless series of discoveries in biological science that have been made by using electrophoresis. He investigated the influence of acid and alkali upon the migration of particles of coagulated egg white. He found that the particles moved as though positively charged when they were in an acid medium but as though negatively charged when in alkali. He noted that at some point near neutrality electromigration ceased, and he called this the isoelectric point. W. Pauli refined and extended this work to a degree that enabled L. Michaelis, in 1909, to measure the isoelectric points (as we now understand them) of proteins. The Michaelis paper was the first to use the word electrophoresis to mean the migration of charged colloidal particles in an electrical field. This work firmly established the value of moving boundary electrophoresis. During the next 50 years, under the leadership of Arne Tiselius (1902-1971), electrophoresis acquired the status of an advanced theoretical discipline. Tiselius developed the first sophisticated apparatus which used reversible electrodes, provided for temperature control to eliminate convective disturbance, and enabled its operator to observe the movement of colorless proteins by using ultraviolet light. In 1938 he improved the apparatus by incorporating the A. Toepler schlieren method for detecting small differences in refractive index. Now it was possible to follow the migration of several proteins in a mixture. His discovery that blood serum contains multiple proteins, which was an important factor in his selection as a Nobel prize recipient in 1948, was made with this apparatus.

Moving boundary apparatus is expensive, and great skill is needed both in operating it and to interpret the results obtained by its use. It has no peer as a device for measuring the electromechanical properties of colloids under conditions that are the least likely to affect those properties. It has the disadvantages that it cannot effect complete separation of the components in a mixture and that it lacks discrimination when many components are present in a wide range of concentrations.

To the extent that the charge/mass ratios of the components of a mixture of substances in a solution differ, they will move at different rates when a voltage gradient is applied across the solution. If a portion of such a mixture is placed at some point on a stabilized bed that contains an electrolyte solution, the different components will migrate at different rates so that they become separated. This process is called zone electrophoresis. P. König was the first to use paper as the stabilizing medium when he employed zone electrophoresis to separate a yellow pigment from viper venom in 1937. It seems strange that the necessary materials and knowledge were available for at least a century before someone thought of using them in this way. It is even stranger that 11 more years passed before the value of the method was recognized almost simultaneously by G. Haugaard and T. D. Kroner, and T. Wieland and F. Fischer in 1948. Suddenly in 1950 it was time for zone electrophoresis; its methodology was quickly established, and its enormous investigative value was recognized by various scientists. Even preparative electrophoresis by a method involving continuous sample flow was developed in that year. Not only was paper electrophoresis easy and inexpensive, it was useful in a clinical way for diagnostic measurements of a wide array of the substances in body fluids. The number of publications based on electrophoretic data expanded abruptly from a few each year to hundreds.

Paper is inherently inadequate for separations on the preparative scale. It is also incapable of giving the high degree of resolution that is needed in work with complex biological mixtures. The need for preparative apparatus was solved in the 1950s when paper sheet was replaced with blocks or columns of starch powder, polyvinyl chloride, cellulose powder, or some other of the many more or less inert substances. Increasing the size of the bed led to a serious loss in resolving power owing to the increased difficulty with heat management. Convection distorted the patterns, heat gradients caused uneven migrations, and evaporation caused local variations in buffer concentration, which played havoc with the voltage gradient and caused buffer to flow by capillary action into the bed, leading samples to move forward (or to regress) in response to liquid flow rather than by migration. An amazing amount of time and ingenuity have been devoted to designing apparatus for preparative electrophoresis. The best systems available even today are useful, but they are far from perfect.

The problem of improving resolution on the analytical scale has been solved much more successfully. J. Kohn introduced cellulose acetate foil in 1957, and it quickly became available from several commercial sources. It is about as easy to use as paper and gives much better resolution, particularly when immune reactions are used to detect the fractions. It has now virtually replaced paper for both clinical and research applications.

Electrophoresis on a gel (gelatin) was performed by O. Lodge in 1886 and in A. J. P. Martin's laboratory in 1946, but the superior resolving properties of this type of medium were not seriously considered until O. Smithies, in 1955, separated serum proteins into 12 well-defined components as compared with the five that are obtained with paper. Starch gel is difficult to use while agar is easy. The earliest use of agar as a stabilizing medium is attributed to C. W. Field and O. Teague in 1907; they studied the interaction of diphtheria toxin with antitoxin, thereby becoming the pioneers of immunoelectrophoresis. By 1950 agar was in common use; its sulfate-free component, agarose, which is less conducive to electroosmotic disturbances, was introduced in 1961 by S. J. Hjerten. Neither of these gels has the resolving power of starch gel because their structures do not act as molecular sieves, but they are perfectly adapted to immunoelectrophoresis, a technique that P. Grabar and C. A. Williams developed in 1955. It makes use of polyvalent anti-serum to detect and to measure antigens after they are separated electrophoretically. The serum is applied through a trough scooped in the agar bed parallel to the developed electrophoretic pattern. The antibodies diffuse to their specific antigens and react. The precipitated antigen-antibody complexes appear as multiple arcs and reveal many more components than does electrophoresis alone. This method, with its numerous variations, has been instrumental in revolutionizing immunology and has become perhaps the most important tool of the immunochemist.

The search for gels with high resolving power eventually led to the development of a special synthetic polyacrylamide which was reported by B. J. Davis and L. Ornstein at a scientific meeting in 1959. S. Raymond and Y. J. Wang described this gel in a publication the following year. Ornstein described the use of the gel for "disc electrophoresis" in a paper that was privately published and widely disseminated by Distillation Products Industries around 1961. This paper was truly revolutionary not only because it led to the immediate acceptance of acrylamide gels but because the method was consciously based upon the principles that underlie the most sophisticated methods that have been developed to this date. Polyacrylamide gels can be formed with any desired degree of crosslinking and in a wide range of concentrations; both characteristics can be adjusted to form molecular sieving gradients within a bed. Thus, molecules can be discriminated on the basis of size as well as mobility. The versatility of these gels has thus added a new dimension to zone electrophoresis. In addition to giving elegant separations, the technique provides a reliable means for measuring molecular constants, including molecular weight, Einstein-Stokes radii, and electrophoretic mobilities.

It is likely that the separation of substances on the simple basis of differential rates of electromigration will soon be obsolete. In 1923 J. Kendall and E. D. Crittenden undertook the separation of isotopes by electrical means. This approach used the fact that when a solution of heterogeneous particles with like charges but different electrophoretic mobilities is subjected to an electrical field, the particles move at different speeds until they separate into contiguous zones each of which contains a single species of particle. The interfaces between the zones are extremely sharp and are self-maintaining because any disruption causes a discontinuity in the voltage gradient which acts to restore the pattern. The concentration of material within each band is determined by the requirement for uniform conductivity. Once particles have been classified, all fractions migrate at the same rate because any differences in speed would break electrical continuity and interrupt migration until diffusion restored contact between the separated zones. L. Ornstein and B. J. Davis, in 1964, were the first to realize the value of this principle. F. M. Everaerts exploited it successfully, in 1968, in developing a method for separating ions. H. Haglund and his group, in 1970, developed this method to its present degree of sophistication and called it isotachophoresis.

In 1969 O. Vesterburg reported the synthesis of a mixture of polyaminopolycarboxylic acids (Ampholine, LKB Producter) which had a nearly continuous spectrum of dissociation constants. When a solution of these acids is subjected to an electrical field, they arrange themselves to form a continuous pH gradient in accordance with the principle just described. If the ions in the electrode chambers are correctly selected, this gradient remains stationary within the electrophoretic bed. If a mixture of amphoteric substances is introduced into this system, its components migrate to the regions corresponding to their isoelectric points, where they remain as closely packed bands. Although the polyelectrolyte pH gradient is formed by isotachophoresis, the substances that are separated on the gradient are classified on the basis of their isoelectric points rather than on their mobilities; this distinction justifies the special name isoelectric focusing that has been applied to the process.

The preceding two paragraphs are of current as well as historical interest. They mention methods and materials that are sufficiently reliable and well understood so that the empirical approach to electrophoretic separations must soon give way to a disciplined theoretical system. Examples of the kinds of developments that may be expected are found in the work of T. M. Jarvin who, in 1948, developed computer programs for planning optimum multiphasic buffer systems, and J. Lunney, A. Chrambach, and D. Rodbard who began developing, in 1971, a general theory to describe electrophoresis in polyacrylamide gels.

CHAPTER VI

INSTRUMENTATION

Many specific developments in analytical instrumentation are described elsewhere in this book. Here we take a wider view of the field as a whole, especially commenting on the impact of electronics.

The development of analytical chemistry through the years has depended largely on the availability of suitable tools, and significant advances have invariably followed the invention of new instruments. The precise balance was undoubtedly the first device worthy of the term instrument. Its importance cannot be overestimated as it enabled analysts for the first time to base their work on a truly firm foundation.

During the 19th century, the principal developments in instrumentation were in the area of spectroscopy, starting with the invention of the spectroscope by Bunsen and Kirchhoff. This device led to many exciting possibilities, including the dramatic discovery of helium in the solar atmosphere. In the early decades of the 20th century, the field of spectroscopy continued to expand with the commercial availability of large photographic spectrographs on both sides of the Atlantic.

In a number of fields basic discoveries were made during this period but were not followed up until suitable electronic measuring devices were developed much later. The Raman effect is in this category. The hydrogen-ion sensitivity of a glass membrane is another example. The whole area of nuclear chemistry is a case in point: the nature of the chief subatomic particles and their relation to bulk matter were well established, but the general analytical use of nuclear phenomena had to await convenient and reliable electronic detectors and counters.

Heyrovský's polarograph, invented in 1925, was the

first instrument to feature a built-in automatic chart
recorder. This was accomplished without the use of
electronic amplification by means of a sensitive galvanometer with a mirror to reflect a beam of light to a
sheet of photographic paper mounted on a drum rotating
in synchronism with the applied voltage ramp.

THE INTRODUCTION OF ELECTRONICS

The year 1930 marked the first significant use of
electronic techniques in analytical instrumentation.
Photoelectric devices had been tried sporadically, but
the first really successful application was the recording
spectrophotometer invented by A. C. Hardy at MIT and
subsequently manufactured by General Electric Co. This
instrument, like the polarograph, was provided with a
recording mechanism as an integral part, in this case
tied directly to the wavelength scan drive. A thyratron
was used to energize the pen motor, which also drove a
polarizer to restore the null condition in the Hüfner
type photometer.

Other manufacturers soon entered the field pioneered
by General Electric. An Eagle-mounted concave grating
spectrophotometer with a photovoltaic cell as detector
was produced by Central Scientific Co. under the name
Spectrophotelometer. In the same year (1941) the Beckman
DU spectrophotometer appeared, extending the range of
measurement into the ultraviolet. This instrument was
of great significance and was quickly adopted in many
laboratories around the world. The DU was not provided
with a recorder but depended on a manually adjusted null
circuit that rendered it nearly independent of the idio-
syncracies of vacuum tubes and other components. The
DU was followed within a few years by comparable instruments manufactured by Adam Hilger, Ltd., and others and
by the first of the line of Cary recording spectrophotometers.

In 1951 the American Optical Co. produced a unique
visible spectrophotometer that scanned the spectrum 60
times a second and displayed the results on a cathode
ray oscilloscope screen. Unfortunately the instrument
was ahead of its time. The concept was excellent, but
the electronics were not adequate to ensure useful precision of measurement. Some 20 years later several
firms manufactured comparable devices with precise digital readout.

The initial impact of electronics in electroanalytical chemistry appeared in the form of the Beckman
pH meter (1935), which so greatly simplified many laboratory procedures that it was eagerly adopted and was soon

emulated by other manufacturers. Other electronic devices of the period were largely directed at improving
the convenience and sensitivity of known methods. Thus
a number of automatic titrators were developed to free
analysts from the tedium of buret manipulations.

The servo-actuated potentiometric strip-chart recorder, as introduced by Brown Instrument Co. about
1930, was a most significant advance, utilized in many
areas of analytical instrumentation. It may be said to
have presaged the subsequent development of modular
apparatus; this recorder could be transferred from one
instrument to another as needed rather than being dedicated to a single use. It was some time, however, before this inherent capability was recognized.

At this point it is appropriate to acknowledge the
influence of Ralph Holcombe Müller on the development of
analytical instrumentation. Müller was for many years
on the faculty of New York University where he pioneered
in teaching about instruments. The first of his contributions to *Analytical Chemistry*, and its parent journal, *Industrial and Engineering Chemistry*, appeared in
a three-page 1928 paper with H. M. Partridge entitled
"Application of the Photo-Electric Cell to Automatic
Titrations." Müller's first of many lengthy tutorial
contributions was a 17-page article in 1939 on "Photoelectric Methods in Analytical Chemistry," in which he
compared in detail the principles, circuitry, and applications of both photoemissive and photovoltaic devices
in colorimetry. In October 1940, and again in 1941, an
entire issue of the *Analytical Edition of Industrial and
Engineering Chemistry*, written by Dr. Müller, was given
over to comprehensive surveys of American instrumentation
and instrumental analysis.

In 1942, together with R. L. Garman and M. E. Droz,
Müller authored the textbook "Experimental Electronics"
(Prentice-Hall) which exerted a significant influence on
analytical instrumentation. That this text reflected
the latest state of the art is indicated by inclusion of
a discussion of the multiplier phototube and even the
image orthicon. The only solid-state device mentioned
was the photovoltaic cell. Some 70 laboratory experiments are included.

Müller's continuing relations with *Analytical Chemistry* are described elsewhere in this book.

The first phase of the electronics revolution that
began in analytical chemistry in the 1930s was followed
by a second phase starting in about 1960 with the introduction of semiconductor devices. The new solid-state
units made much more efficient use of power and space
than their old vacuum-tube counterparts. Initially,
vacuum tubes were replaced by transistors with a minimum

of circuit changes, a process known as transistorization.
Before long, however, entirely new improved circuits
were devised to exploit more effectively the peculiar
properties of semiconductor devices. These advances
made it possible to expand the data-processing and control functions within the instrument, with the resulting
possibility of automation.

A number of trends can be discerned in the design
of electronic instruments with respect to their end uses.
On the one hand, dedicated instruments capable of performing only a single type of analysis with maximum efficiency were being developed--e.g., a titrator specifically intended for use with the Karl Fischer reaction
or an NMR spectrometer to be used solely for moisture
determination. On the other hand, and at the same time,
multipurpose instruments, provided with maximum flexibility, capable of being programmed to execute a variety
of analytical techniques were being developed. Still
another trend was toward modularization, with the advantage that a user needed to purchase only those portions
of an instrumental system that he required; servicing
and repair were also facilitated.

A significant development in the teaching of electronic instrumentation was the invention of a modular
system by H. V. Malmstadt and C. G. Enke at the University of Illinois in the late 1950s. Their equipment was
subsequently produced commercially by the Heath Co.,
Benton Harbor, Mich., and was described in the textbook,
"Electronics for Scientists" (Benjamin, 1962). A series
of open chassis were provided, appropriately drilled to
accomodate vacuum-tube sockets, control potentiometers,
and other major electronic components. Smaller components, such as resistors and capacitors, could be connected by convenient spring clips to the chassis-mounted
parts. Using these, students could readily synthesize
many different circuits and assemble them into complete
laboratory instruments of good quality, with which valid
analytical experiments could be performed. These out-
fits were marketed together with certain preassembled
test equipment and a combined work table and storage
cabinet. They were widely distributed in university
laboratories, where they contributed much toward the
understanding of modern electronics, not only in connection with analytical instrumentation but on a wider
basis in teaching other disciplines such as physics.

In 1969 another comparable system was announced for
the construction of digital logic circuits, with solid-
state components only. This announcement was accompanied
by the publication of a second book, "Digital Electronics
for Scientists." This important series has been continued with the appearance in 1974 of a combined and

HOWARD VINCENT MALMSTADT, 1922-

Malmstadt joined the faculty of the University of Illinois in
1951, after completion of his doctorate at the University of Wisconsin. His interests have included photometric and potentiometric titrimetry, kinetic methods, automation, and teaching equipment for electronics and analytical chemistry.

updated treatment, entitled "Electronic Measurements for Scientists," authored by H. V. Malmstadt, C. G. Enke, S. R. Crouch, and G. Horlick. The Heath Co. has also manufactured an extensive series of preassembled mechanical and optical modules for educational uses, stemming from designs by Malmstadt, Enke, and their co-workers.

SIGNAL PROCESSING

Many aspects of modern analytical chemistry find their origins in other fields, notably physics, engineering, and allied disciplines. This scheme of development is especially obvious in signal processing, which finds its roots in communications theory and radio engineering.

At the outset it is important to define what we mean by signal processing. Broadly defined, it could encompass most of chemical instrumentation as well as any other facet of chemical measurement which deals with the final development of a usable signal. For our purposes, we define signal processing as any procedure which treats a signal after it has been recorded or which is carried out during signal recording to change the signal's appearance or format to increase the yield of information. Although somewhat cumbersome, this definition excludes many aspects of chemical instrumentation which are treated elsewhere in this book.

The processing of chemical signals usually involves several steps that can include data recording, data display, and data "massaging," reduction, or improvement. For instance, in traditional procedures, analytical signals have usually involved merely a series of data points which are recorded manually. An example would be those recorded values which correspond to the weights of vessel, original sample, and final precipitate in a gravimetric determination. Simple recording of data in this way does not lend itself to convenient display, such as is required, for example, in tracing a titration curve. To appreciate properly the significance of the titration curve, the chemist must choose an appropriate display format, in this case a plot of the volume of titrant delivered against some parameter reflecting the progress of the reaction.

To improve the information yield from a given set of measurements even further, the analytical chemist msut often apply some form of data reduction or processing, sometimes referred to as "number crunching." The kind of processing first used by analytical chemists, and one still of great importance, involves statistics. By using data obtained from repeated experiments, the chemist could not only quantitate his measurements more precisely but also could attach a realistic measure of precision to the final result. Such statistical data improvement forms the basis for many of the modern signal-to-noise enhancement techniques. This fact can readily be appreciated from the definition of a signal as any quantity, usually electrical, functionally related to the quantity the chemist ultimately wishes to measure, while noise is defined as anything which obscures the signal. Clearly, random data variations constitute measurement noise, and statistics, properly applied, minimizes those variations. Finally, significance tests give the analytical chemist a means of determining and evaluating data trends.

Data formatting in the analytical laboratory began with the manual drawing of plots from prior measurements-- e.g., the titration curve cited above. It soon became apparent that formatting data differently could often increase the yield of information. Thus integration, differentiation, and least-squares fits to data plots were used not to increase the information *content* of a series of measurements but to enable the analyst more readily to appreciate the significance of the data and thereby to increase the information *yield*. For example, it was found that simple sigmoid titration curves could be differentiated to render the endpoint easier to detect.

With the first introduction of instrumentation into the analytical chemistry laboratory, many of the old methods of data display, data processing, and data formatting began to be performed by all-electronic systems. With these new devices, a continuous display of a measurement could be obtained by means of the servo-recorder or cathode ray oscilloscope. In addition, smoothing, averaging, or damping, such as could be obtained earlier only through statistical means, could conveniently be performed electronically by simple resistor-capacitor circuits. (Such smoothing or damping methods were first seen in the analytical laboratory in the magnetic device attached to a double-pan balance to reduce the amplitude and number of swings.) Although integration and differentiation could be performed electronically with these devices, entirely new methods of signal enhancement became available. For example, the repetitive, superimposed, observation of a signal waveform on an oscilloscope or chart recorder improved signal recognition capability in a way similar to that done earlier by statistics for single measurements. Such a repetitive display we now recognize as merely a form of signal or ensemble averaging, a technique in widespread use today.

An explosive growth of modern signal processing

techniques occurred during World War II, but the resulting knowledge was unavailable for use by civilian chemists until its declassification in the late 1940s. Much of this growth can be ascribed to the military emphasis on the development of radar detectors, so important to the war effort. To improve the detection and recognition of returning radar signals, highly sophisticated techniques were developed, many of which are now used widely in the chemistry laboratory. Many of the findings of this massive effort have been collected in the volumes of the MIT Radiation Laboratory series. It was during this time that the fundamentals of communication theory were established and basic limitations on the transmission, detection, and processing of signals defined. Many of these concepts were explained in an excellent article by Claude Shannon in the *Proceedings of the Institute of Radio Engineers* (1949), dealing with the information content of a signal and how that content is affected by instrument resolution, bandwidth, and accompanying noise.

The signal-to-noise enhancement techniques now considered commonplace in the laboratory had their bases in communication theory. Modulation/demodulation schemes, one outgrowth from communication theory, can now be found in a wide variety of chemical instruments. One form of modulation familiar to most analytical chemists is the simple optical or mechanical chopper which converts a light beam or an electrical signal into an ON/OFF pulsating or square-wave signal of amplitude equal to that of the original continuous level. Such modulation or chopping is done simply to enable the signal to be carried (transmitted) and measured without interference from the drift that always plagues continuous level or d.c. measurements. Modern servo-recorders, atomic absorption and infrared spectrophotometers, and many other instruments use this approach. In addition, special-purpose modulation has been found useful in some applications. An example of this latter situation occurs in a.c. polarography, where modulation (dithering) of the voltage during a polarographic scan yields significant benefits in interpretation of the detected signal.

Although the value of techniques such as lock-in amplification, signal averaging, and correlation methods, was well understood and appreciated prior to 1948, the application of such techniques was limited with respect to dynamic range, resolution, and speed. Phase-sensitive detectors were often slow electromechanical devices, and multichannel analyzers, although in routine use, were cumbersome vacuum-tube machines, limited in time-domain resolution and in amplitude dynamic range. More sophisticated techniques for signal recovery and data

processing, such as digital Fourier methods and high
resolution cross-correlation procedures, were far beyond
the reach of signal processing instrumentation in the
1940s. Signal filtering was limited to active analog
systems and, at the time, precision real-time digital
filtering was considered to be ivory-tower dreaming.
The revolution in transducers was already mature; by
1950 many different transducers were available for monitoring physicochemical phenomena.

The decade of the 1950s was not only a period of
intense development in digital circuitry, but a revolution in analog design concepts was also underway. Of
special significance to the chemist was the appearance
in 1956 of the operational amplifier. This device, a
d.c. inverting, high-gain, amplifier with high input impedance and low output impedance, serves as the heart of
a large class of circuit configurations, most of which
are basically negative-feedback control systems. With
the appearance of the operational amplifier as a circuit
element, it was no longer necessary for the chemist to
concern himself with the design and construction of individual amplifiers to conform to a given set of specifications. A standard operational amplifier configuration
could be tailored to meet the requisite specifications,
and the implementation of the circuit became not altogether unlike playing with Tinker Toys; the chemist
could focus on the selection of the signal generation
and recovery techniques and spend less effort on the
implementation of the circuit. The electrical engineers
did the work; the chemists could reap the benefits and
have the fun.

The prevalence of modulation schemes and the ability
to detect ever faster signals by new measurement devices
(transducers) provided the chemist with a host of new
signal processing tools which had been developed earlier
by electrical and communications engineers. Included in
this category are lock-in amplifiers, common in modern
chemical instrumentation, and the signal or ensemble
averagers found on NMR and ESR spectrometers and in other
laboratory instruments. The ability to detect fast signals was further enhanced with the development of stroboscopic sampling devices. In such devices, a repetitive
signal is sampled only once during each repetition. As
the signal repeats, the sampling point is progressively
delayed along the signal waveform, so that the final
observed signal appears much as did the original, except
for a substantial increase in its apparent duration.
The stroboscopic process, so called because of its similarity to the method by which the rotation speed of a
wheel is apparently reduced by a pulsing stroboscope,
finds application in the sampling oscilloscope and the

boxcar integrator, both now often used by chemists.

Most of these previously mentioned signal processing schemes find their basis in a process known as correlation. Correlation is another outgrowth of communication theory and was recognized very early by electrical engineers as a powerful signal processing operation. However, it was not until the recent availability of hardware correlators and the accessibility of digital computers that the use of correlation operations became feasible in the chemistry laboratory.

COMPUTERS

The most dramatic growth in signal processing and control over the past quarter century has occurred in digital electronics. By 1948, experiments were already progressing on stored program digital computers. By the time these first generation computers were completed in the early 1950s, they were already obsolete. The growth of discrete solid-state electronics progressed rapidly, and by the late 1950s specialization of large digital computers for scientific applications was already under way. The initial applications for such machines were for massive numerical calculations; indeed, they were of little value in signal processing. In 1959, Digital Equipment Corp. introduced the PDP-1, a relatively inexpensive ($120,000), and relatively small, online computer which was intended to be dedicated to a given laboratory task. The PDP-1 was more than a tool for manipulating data. It was designed to be connected to all types of instrumentation and equipment for online, real-time, signal monitoring and instrument control. It could also do a respectable job of signal massaging. The appearance of the PDP-1 heralded a new concept in the philosophy of digital computers, the concept that people and machines could interact on a real-time basis. By the mid 1960s chemists were becoming enthusiastic about the application of the dedicated computer (by now called the minicomputer) to the measurement of many physicochemical phenomena. The appearance of monolithic integrated circuits at the start of the decade initiated profound changes in the electronics industry, soon to be reflected in signal processing technology. Integrated circuits were truly revolutionary. Older design concepts emphasized the use of fewer active elements, which were expensive, in favor of more passive devices, which were less costly. Integrated circuits reversed this picture. Circuit isolation and component matching became insignificant problems with the use of integrated circuits. The wide acceptance of integrated

circuits in military and commercial applications, not to
mention the space program, provided tremendous impetus
to the semiconductor industry for more research and for
the development of silicon planar technology. By 1963
Digital Equipment Corp. introduced the PDP-5, predecessor of the widely accepted PDP-8 series, the first of
which appeared in 1964. By the late 1960s the price of
many computers had dropped by a factor of 10, and the
available techniques for signal manipulation and data
processing were greatly expanding for chemists.

   With the application of dedicated processors to
given laboratory operations, chemists now faced a new
type of design problem--that of the development of software to control this new tool. At first the problem
appeared more than formidable, in fact insurmountable,
for the chemist who could devote only cursory attention
to computer programming. In response to this problem,
the computer manufacturers led the way with the development of extensive software systems which could be manip-
ulated with high-level languages by the operating chemists. Algorithm development was under way at a feverish
pace. A good example was the appearance in 1968 of the
fast Fourier transform algorithm for the calculation of
discrete Fourier transforms. This algorithm could be
implemented in several seconds on 1024 data points with
a minicomputer having 8k bits of memory. The developments of operating software systems and powerful algorithms were significant achievements in signal processing
in the late 1960s; the scientist wishing to use his new
laboratory tool, the dedicated computer, could now proceed with great efficiency.

   The first half of the 1970s saw even further advances in analog signal manipulation technology and
further revolutionary advances in digital circuitry. By
the beginning of the decade, the new series-access mass
storage memories (magnetic drums and disks) and the ran-
dom-access memories (core, static, and dynamic solid-
state memories) were highly developed. Such memories
were appearing in applications other than computers--e.g.,
in signal averagers, complex function generators, trans-
ducer linearizers, and bootstrap loaders for computers--
and a great deal of attention was focusing on their
applications. Of great significance at this time was
the appearance in 1972 of TTL (transistor-transitor
logic) components. TTL devices matured as a family of
fast, low cost, large and medium scale integrated circuits which provide standard interface circuits for
solid-state memories. The TTL family soon turned into
an avalanche of components that has greatly expanded the
capabilities of the chemist attempting to control his
experiments. This effort to control solid-state memories

resulted in the development of the most revolutionary
electronic device of the century thus far, the microprocessor.

In November 1971 the Intel Corp. announced the
first commercially available microprocessor, the MCS-4.
With this device the computer was transformed from a
large, expensive, rather esoteric machine into a compact,
inexpensive device that without question will be used by
millions of individuals in the coming years. Micro-
processors offer the potential for drastically reducing
component count and design time for digital circuitry.
In January 1974 the complete central processing unit
(CPU) and all necessary data latches and interfacing
circuits were made available on a single chip. It is
estimated that the single chip Intel 8080, with a 2-μsec
cycle time (for typical operation), will drop in price
by 1977 to $30 a chip. Although such processors can
function in a limited capacity in data processing, their
main application will be for digitally programmed control and data acquisition. It has been estimated that
as of August 1975, 44,000 minicomputers and large computers were in operation in the United States; this
number is already less than one-month's production of
microprocessor chips.

Thus, the advances in digital electronics and in
monolithic analog electronics have had great implications
for practical data processing in the analytical laboratory. Obvious control applications are those such as
gas chromatography-mass spectrometry combinations and
Fourier transformation as applied to both NMR and infrared spectroscopy, which require the dedicated attention
of a minicomputer. At the time of this writing, we are
witnessing the changeover from random logic design to
fixed logic design, in which the same hardware is used
for a wide variety of applications. In the latter, only
the software code controlling the operation of the hardware is changed. An example of the application of microprocessor technology to chemistry would be the technique
of energy-dispersive x-ray fluorescence spectrometry, in
which a microprocessor controls high-speed pulse sorting,
multichannel analysis, signal averaging, signal sampling,
background correction, matrix correction, and analytical
calculations. At the 1975 Pittsburgh Conference on
Analytical Chemistry and Applied Spectroscopy, we noted
the appearance of analytical instruments which operated
completely under the control of a microprocessor. These
included an electrochemical system, a number of x-ray
fluorescence systems, a mass spectrometer, and a program-
mable graphite-furnace atomic absorption instrument. It
is difficult to overestimate the eventual impact that
the microprocessor will have on chemical instrumentation.

The decade of the 1970s will be known as the decade of the microprocessor.

Convenient access to large-scale digital computers changed the entire complexion of chemical signal processing. While earlier operations depended on alteration of the signal while it was being produced, digital processing enabled signals to be recorded, stored, and processed at a later time. Signal averaging and correlation procedures, of those mentioned previously, benefited most from digital processing. However, new, more sophisticated smoothing procedures based on digital techniques were also developed. An example of this latter type of smoothing procedure or "filter" which is familiar to most modern analytical chemists is that developed by Savitsky and Golay and published in *Analytical Chemistry* (1964) under the title, "Smoothing and Differentiation of Data by Simplified Least-squares Procedures."

Display techniques were also improved when computers were introduced into analytical chemistry. Multidimensional formatting of data and miltidimensional displays enabled the chemist to appreciate and to recognize features in his data which were otherwise impossible to perceive. Furthermore, transform techniques, such as the Fourier and Hadamard transforms, became available to permit the chemist to extract information more readily. The Fourier transform is especially important in this regard; it can transform data originally obtained in the time domain and display them as a function of their spectral or frequency content. Conversely, a recorded spectrum can be displayed in terms of its corresponding time function. Clearly, in many cases one or the other format is preferred; availability of the Fourier transform algorithm frees the chemist from the need to record data in that preferred domain.

PATTERN RECOGNITION

In recent years, the introduction of computers in the analytical laboratory has led to an enormous increase in the quantity of data that can be obtained on chemical systems. To solve a developing data analysis problem, modern analytical chemists are investigating the usefulness of advanced mathematical and statistical methods.

In 1969 P. C. Jurs, B. R. Kowalski, and T. L. Isenhour, then at the University of Washington in Seattle, together with C. N. Reilley at the University of North Carolina, published a series of pioneering in *Analytical Chemistry*, reporting the results of applying the linear learning machine to low resolution mass spectral data. The fundamental concept had been published in a book,

"Learning Machines," by N. J. Nilsson (McGraw-Hill, 1965), but no analytical applications had been made. Using an early form of artificial computer intelligence-- feedback learning--the goal of these studies was to ex- tract molecular structural information directly from spectral data. The University of Washington team soon disbanded, Jurs going to Pennsylvania State University, Kowalski going temporarily into industry, subsequently to Colorado State University, then back to Washington, and Isenhour joining Reilley at North Carolina. All of them continued to apply learning machine concepts to analytical problems. By 1972 the learning machine had been properly placed in perspective with a wide variety of multivariant data analysis methods collectively assembled under the discipline called pattern recogni- tion, and the scope of application in chemistry had broadened.

In the widest sense, pattern recognition can be used to study a collection of objects via features that char- acterize each object. For chemical applications the objects are samples, and the features are chemical mea- surements, structural details, or other data that char- acterize the samples. The goal of a typical application is to learn something new about the samples (unsuper- vised learning) or to predict a sought-for property of the samples (supervised learning). Applications include: oil spill identification, protein sequencing, forensic identification of materials, clinical measurement inter- pretation, and atmospheric pollutant identification.

Such pattern-recognition techniques now permit the nearly hands-off evaluation of recorded chemical signals or information to determine whether data patterns exist and whether data trends prevail. Also, new adaptive control schemes have been proposed and are being imple- mented, in which data can be treated or altered as they are being obtained, according to trends in previous data, to improve overall data yield, quality, or ease of recog- nition. Ideally, adaptive computer control represents the ultimate in chemical signal processing. In feed- forward and feedback control situations, data already obtained and data not yet at hand should improve those being obtained at the moment.

Pattern recognition is not the only tool of the information scientist to find important applications in chemistry. Experiment design, factor analysis, digital filtering, and optimal control methods are among the others finding increased use to obtain better informa- tion from chemical data. Kowalski has coined the word Chemometrics as a title for the new subdivision of ana- lytical chemistry using these methods of the information scientist.

NAME INDEX

SUBJECT INDEX

PICTURE CREDITS